301 LEGAL FORMS

Letters & Agreements

LAWPACK

301 Legal Forms, Letters & Agreements

First edition 1995
Second edition 1996
Third edition 1997
Fourth edition 1998
Fifth edition 1999
Sixth edition 2000
Seventh edition 2001
Eighth edition 2004
Ninth edition 2007
     Reprinted 2008

Published by

Lawpack Publishing Limited
76-89 Alscot Road
London SE1 3AW

© 2008 Lawpack Publishing

ISBN: 978-1-907765-18-6

Important facts about this Lawpack book

Legal documents need to achieve four things.:

1. They must be clear.

2. They must be complete enough to deal with all forseeable contingencies and to provide an answer to any reasonable question beginning with the words 'what if?'

3. They must contain all provisions which the law requires.

4. They must not contain anything which would bring into play a law that might make them ineffective.

Lawpack publications are designed to help you prepare legal documents by suggesting matters which you may wish to cover and by providing wording which you may be able to adapt in order to make your meaning clear and by alerting you to various relevant legal rules. However, neither this nor any other publication can take the place of a solicitor on important legal matters. There are three reasons for this. Firstly, the law can be complicated and a book like this can only provide a guide to the basics. Secondly, the particular transaction which you are undertaking may throw up complications for which an 'off the peg' form would not be appropriate. Thirdly, no book can suggest to you all of the matters that ought to be covered in your particular transaction.

This Lawpack publication is sold on the understanding that the publisher, authors and retailer are not engaged in rendering legal services. If legal advice or other expert assistance is required, the services of a competent professional should be sought.

The forms included in this Lawpack publication cover many everyday matters, but we cannot cater for all circumstances. If what you want is not included, we advise you to see a solicitor.

This Lawpack publication is designed only for use in England and Wales. It is not suitable for Scotland or Northern Ireland.

The information this book contains has been carefully compiled from reliable sources but its accuracy is not guaranteed as laws and regulations may change or be subject to differing interpretations. The law is stated as at 1st September 2007.

As with any legal matter, common sense should determine whether you need the assistance of a solicitor rather than relying solely on your own efforts, supplemented by the information and forms in this Lawpack book.

We strongly urge you to consult a solicitor whenever substantial amounts of money are involved, or where you do not understand the instructions or are uncertain how to complete and use a form correctly, or if you have any doubts about its adequacy to protect you, or if what you want to do is not precisely covered by the forms provided or if you are planning to use a form many times (e.g. as a standard form in your business).

About *301 Legal Forms...*

This book contains legal forms, letters and agreements to safeguard your legal rights and protect you… your family… your property… and your business from everyday legal problems.

With 301 essential legal documents in one book, you now have available a useful guide for simple legal matters where the inconvenience or cost of using a solicitor would not be proportionate to what is at stake.

Lawpack publications are the ideal way to 'get it in writing'. What better way is there to document your important transactions, avoid costly disputes and enforce your legal rights? In a few minutes you can draw up the legal form or agreement you need to sidestep misunderstandings, comply with legal obligations and avoid liability.

Approved by a barrister, *301 Legal Forms Letters & Agreements* has been approved for consumer use.

How to use *301 Legal Forms, Letters & Agreements...*

It is easy to use Lawpack's *301 Legal Forms, Letters and Agreements* by following these simple instructions.

1   To find the appropriate form, read the two tables of contents. The first lists each form alphabetically. The second groups them by subject.

2   You may find several forms for the same general purpose. To choose the form most appropriate for your specific needs, consult the Contents, beginning on page vii, as a guide to the purpose of each form.

3   Cut out and photocopy the form you want and keep the original so it can be used again in the future. Alternatively you can use the form as a template to prepare your own documents. Letter-type documents can be personalised by being reproduced on your own letterhead.

4   Complete each form fully. Make certain all blanks (name, address, dates, amounts) are filled in. You may need to delete or add provisions in some forms to suit your requirements. If this is necessary, make sure each deletion or insertion is initialled by all parties. If there is not enough space on the document to make your insertion, it is best to type out the entire document, including the insertion, on a new sheet of paper.

5   Some forms have footnoted instructions, which should be observed if you are to use the form properly. Some forms refer to other forms in *301 Legal Forms, Letters & Agreements*, other documents or copies of documents which will need to be attached to the form before use.

6   Some forms have 'health warnings' attached which indicate that a solicitor's advice should be sought. While you should not send forms such as these to other parties without first obtaining legal advice, you can nonetheless use the forms as a means of letting your solicitor know, quickly and economically, precisely what it is you want to achieve.

7   The pronoun 'it' within a form can refer to an individual as well as a business entity. The pronoun 'he' can refer to a woman as appropriate.

About Deeds and Agreements

Under English law a contract does not usually have to be written down to be valid and enforceable. An oral contract generally has just as much validity as a written contract. The problem associated with an oral contract is that if there is a dispute over the contract the only evidence of the terms of the contract is the evidence of each party to the contract which will be based on memory.

The reason why important contracts are written down, therefore, is so that a written record exists of what was agreed between the parties, to minimise the possibility of later disputes.

There are a few important exceptions to the rule that a contract does not have to be in writing. For example, a contract for the disposition of interests in land has to be in writing, and has to conform to the particular requirements of the Law of Property (Miscellaneous Provisions) Act 1989. Guarantees (which are a promise by one person to pay the debt of another if the other person defaults) also have requirements as to writing. Detailed requirements as to writing also affect hire purchase, loan and consumer hire agreements that are caught by the Consumer Credit Act 1974.

A contract exists where two or more parties make mutual promises to each other to take some sort of action or to make some payment to each other. An exchange of goods for money is the simplest form of contract. A simple promise by A to B, however, is not a contract if that promise is not given in exchange for an action or promise by B, because B has given no 'consideration' for A's promise. In order to turn A's promise into an enforceable contract B must also make some promise or payment in return (the 'consideration'). A contract like this involving mutual promises can be referred to as both a contract and an agreement, and both terms are used to mean the same thing in *301 Legal Forms, Letters & Agreements*.

It is sometimes the case that a simple promise by one party to another without consideration is all that the parties wish to achieve. Such an agreement can be made enforceable if, but only if, it is made in what is known as a deed. A deed is a written agreement which is given legal enforceability if it contains a description of itself as a deed and if it is executed in a particular way (see below).

You will find many of the agreements in *301 Legal Forms, Letters & Agreements* are set up as deeds to make them enforceable whether there is consideration or not.

Signature of Agreements

The part of an agreement or deed that the parties sign is known as the attestation clause. In agreements, which are not deeds, an individual signs it himself or through a person authorised to sign on his behalf. A company, being an artificial person distinct from its members or directors, cannot physically sign anything. It is, however, deemed to sign an agreement if any person, acting on the company's authority, signs on its behalf. **Important:** normally, in the case of a company contract, the directors, officers and shareholders cannot be sued if a company fails to honour its obligations under a contract. However, if a person signs for a company without including the words 'for and on behalf of X Ltd' he may be sued personally if the company does not perform its obligations.

Signature of Deeds

In deeds, the attestation clauses are different for companies and individuals. On each deed there is space for two individuals to sign, or two companies, or a combination of the two, depending on who is drawing up the deed. Each party should sign the deed and get a witness to sign and provide his or her name and address. The witness to a deed should not be a relative or cohabitant or the other party to the deed.

Use caution and common sense when using *301 Legal Forms, Letters & Agreements* – or any other do-it-yourself legal product. Whilst these forms are generally considered appropriate for self-use, you must nevertheless decide when you should seek professional legal advice instead. You should consult a solicitor if:

- You need a complex or important agreement.

- Your transaction involves substantial amounts of money or expensive property.

- You don't understand how to use a document – or question its adequacy to fully protect you.

Because we cannot be certain that the forms in this book are appropriate to your circumstances – or are being properly used – we cannot assume any liability or responsibility in connection with their use.

Contents

A

Accident Claim Notice
Notice to an insurance company of a claim following an accident   1

Acknowledgement and Acceptance of Order
Notice that a purchase order has been received and accepted   2

Acknowledgement of Alteration of Order
Letter confirming an amendment to a purchase order   3

Acknowledging a Notification of Maternity Leave
A letter informing employee of amount of maternity leave   4

Affidavit
A sworn statement of fact to be used as evidence in court   5

Affidavit of Power of Attorney
A sworn statement by an attorney that the power of attorney under which he was
appointed remains in effect and has not been revoked   6

Affidavit of Title to Goods of other Chattels
A sworn statement by a seller of goods that he has the right to transfer title to those goods   7

Agreement
An all-purpose contract between two parties   8

Agreement for the Sale of Goods
A general agreement between a seller and a buyer of goods   10

Agreement for the Sale of a Vehicle
An agreement to record the private sale of a motor vehicle   11

Agreement to Assume Debt
An agreement by which a debtor agrees to be responsible for the debt of
a customer to a creditor in return for transfer of the customer's goods   13

Agreement to Compromise Debt
An agreement by which a creditor agrees to reduce a customer's debt on certain terms   15

Agreement to Extend Debt Payment
An agreement by which a creditor agrees to extend the terms under which a
customer must repay his debt   17

Agreement to Extend Performance Date
An agreement by which two parties agree to extend the time for completion
of an existing contract   19

Agreement to Sell Personal Property
A simple agreement to record the sale of private property other than land   21

Alteration to terms of employment
A letter from an employer altering the terms of an employee's employment   22

Anti-Gazumping Agreement
An exclusivity contract between the buyer and seller of property, protecting the
buyer against being gazumped   23

Application to be accepted as Guarantor
An application to a prospective giver of credit for acceptance as a Guarantor in respect of the
debts of a person who is applying for credit   25

Applicant's Request for an Employment Reference
A letter requesting an employment reference from a previous employer   27

Application to Open a Credit Account
A form issued by a company to a potential customer wanting to open a credit account   28

Assignment of Accounts Receivable with Non-Recourse
An agreement by which a creditor sells his interest in a debt to a third party. This form
must be used in conjunction with the Notice of Assignment which the assignor
should send to the debtor   29

Assignment of Contract
An assignment by one party to an existing contract of its rights and obligations
under the contract to an outside party   30

Assignment of Insurance Policy
An assignment by an insurance policy holder of the benefit of the policy to a third party   32

Assignment of Money Due
An assignment by a creditor of the benefit of a debt owed to him to a third party in
return for a payment   33

Assignment of Option
An assignment by an option holder of the benefit of an option to a third party in
return for payment   34

Assignment of Option to Purchase Land
An assignment by an option holder of the benefit of an option to purchase land to
a third party in return for payment   35

Authorisation to Release Confidential Information
A letter giving authority to a company or individual to release confidential information   36

Authorisation to Release Employment Information
A letter giving authority to a company to release employment information   37

Authorisation to Release Medical Information
A letter giving a doctor or hospital authority to release medical information   38

Authorisation to Return Goods
A letter authorising a buyer of goods to return those goods on certain conditions   39

B

Board Resolution: Appointment of Auditors
Resolves to appoint auditors   40

Board Resolution: Approval and Registration of Transfer of Shares
Approves the transfer of shares from a shareholder to someone else and resolves
to register those shares i n that person's name   41

Board Resolution: Approval of Directors' Report and Accounts
Resolves to approve the directors' report and annual accounts   42

Board Resolution: Proposal of Alteration of Articles
Resolves to hold an extraordinary general meeting to propose changing the
articles of association   43

Board Resolution to Call Annual General Meeting
A written resolution by the directors of a company to call an annual general meeting
of the company   44

Board Resolution to Call Extraordinary General Meeting
A written resolution by the directors of the company to call an extraordinary
general meeting of the company in order to pass one or more special resolutions   45

Breach of Contract Notice
A notice sent to a party of a contract specifying the terms violated   46

Builder/Decorator Contract
An agreement between a homeowner and a builder or decorator detailing work
to be done and terms   47

Builders' Work Complaint
A letter to a builder asking that he rectify defective work   50

C
Cancellation of an Order to Stop a Cheque
A letter instructing a bank to honour a cheque which has previously been stopped   51

Certificate of Product Conformity
A certificate from a supplier certifying product conformity   52

Change of Name Deed
Document to change the name of an adult individual   53

Change in Pay or Grading Following Job Evaluation
A letter notifying an employee of a pay rise following change of job title   55

Change in Sales Representative Agreement
A letter agreement between a company and its sales representative recording a
change in the terms of engagement   56

Change of Address Notice
Letter notifying a change of address   57

Child Guardianship Consent Form
A form appointing a guardian   58

Cohabitation Agreement (for unmarried partners)
An agreement by which two people agree on the terms under which they will live
together without marrying   59

Company Let
A rental agreement to let residential property to a company for the temporary
use of its employees, officers, or visitors   62

Concession Note (Seller's where bulk goods do not conform to description or sample)
A request for non-conformity to product standards to be accepted   65

Confidentiality Agreement
An agreement between a company and an employee that the employee will keep
proprietary information secret   66

Confirmation of Agreement to Pay
A letter reminding a debtor of his agreement to pay   68

Confirmation of Verbal Order
A letter from a buyer confirming the placement of a verbal order with a seller   69

Conflict of Interest Declaration
A declaration by an employee that his personal affairs do not conflict with his
duty to his employer 70

Consent to Release of Information
A request for permission from an employee for his employer to release information
regarding the employee from a third party 71

Consent to Short Notice of an Annual General Meeting
Shareholder's written consent to an annual general meeting being held at short notice 72

Consent to Short Notice of an Extraordinary General Meeting
Shareholder's written consent to an extraordinary general meeting being
held at short notice 73

Consultant Non-Disclosure Agreement
An agreement by which a consultant agrees not to disclose his client's
confidential information 74

Contract for the Sale of Goods by Delivery
A simple commercial contract for the sale of goods delivered to the buyer under
certain terms 76

Contractor/Subcontractor Agreement
A works contract between a building contractor and his subcontractor 77

Credit Information
A response to a request for credit information from another company 79

Credit Information Request
A supplier's request for credit information from a potential customer 80

Credit Reference
A response to a request for a credit reference 81

D
Damaged Goods Acceptance with Price Reduction
A letter from a buyer to a seller accepting damaged goods subject to a price reduction 82

Debt Acknowledgement
A statement by a debtor admitting indebtedness to a creditor 83

Defect Report Memorandum
An in-house memo for recording product/service non-conformity and corrective action 84

Defective Goods Notice
A letter for a buyer to a seller rejecting defective goods and requesting a credit note 85

Demand for Delivery
A letter from a buyer to a seller demanding delivery of goods ordered and paid for 86

Demand for Explanation of Rejection of Goods
A letter from a seller to a buyer requesting an explanation for the buyer's rejection
of goods delivered 87

Demand for Payment (Final)
A demand for payment from a creditor to a debtor 88

Demand to Specify Delivery Dates
A letter from a buyer requesting a seller to confirm delivery arrangements 89

Demand to Guarantor for Payment
A creditor's demand for payment from the guarantor of a debt upon default
by the debtor 90

Demand to Pay Promissory Note
    A demand from a creditor on a debtor to repay a loan in full on default intstalments   91

Director's Resignation Reserving Rights Against the Company
    A letter from a director to his board announcing his resignation and maintaining
    his right to bring proceedings against the company   92

Dismissal, Disciplinary Rules and Procedures
    A document which sets out an employer's disciplinary rules and procedures policy   93

Dishonoured Cheque Notice
    A notice to a customer/debtor that a cheque has bounced   94

Dismissal Letter for Intoxication on the Job
    A letter of summary dismissal on the grounds of drunkenness to an employee   95

Disputed Account Settlement
    An agreement by which a debtor and a creditor agree to resolve a disputed amount   96

E
Electricity Bill Query
    A document for querying an electricity meter reading   97

Employee Agreement on Confidential Information, Inventions and Patents
    An agreement between a company and an employee that the employee keeps
    proprietory information confidential and waives rights to any inventions   98

Employee Disciplinary Report
    A company report on an employee's breach of discipline   100

Employee Dismissal for Lateness
    A notice to an employee of dismissal after verbal and written warnings   101

Employee File
    A simple resume of an employee's details and employment history   102

Employee Licence
    A rental agreement to let residential property to an employee   103

Employee Non-Competition and Confidentiality Agreement
    An agreement between a company and an employee that the employee will not
    compete with the employer's business during or after his employment   105

Employee Suspension Notice
    A notice to an employee of suspension without pay due to unsatisfactory performance   107

Employee Warning
    A notice to an employee of unsatisfactory work performance   108

Employer's Request for Reference
    A letter from an employer asking for a reference on a potential employee   109

Employment Confirmation Offer Letter
    A letter confirming a position of employment   110

Employment Contract
    A basic employment contract between an employer and an employee   112

Enquiry on Overdue Account
    A letter requesting explanation for an overdue account   116

Equal Opportunities Policy
    A policy introduced by an employer to try and address the possibility of discrimination
    occurring in the workplace   117

Exercise of Option

A letter from an option holder giving notice of the exercise of the option   118

Expenses Record

An employee's business expenses record form for claiming reimbursement   119

Extension of Option to Purchase Property

The owner of property grants an option holder further time in which to exercise
his option   120

F
Family Tree

A record of family relationships   121

Final Notice Before Legal Proceedings

A final demand from a creditor to a debtor with the threat of legal proceedings   123

Final Warning Before Dismissal

A letter to an employee giving final written warning on conduct before dismissal   124

Final Warning for Lateness

A letter to an employee giving first written warning   125

First Warning for Lateness

A letter to an employee giving first written warning   126

Form of Letter from Testator to Executor

A letter to notify an individual of their appointment as an executor to a
Last Will & Testament   127

Form of Resolution for Submission to Companies House

Written notice of a resolution passed by company shareholders for filing at
Companies House   128

Funeral Wishes

Funeral instructions of the deceased   129

Furnished House/Flat Rental Agreement

A tenancy agreement for letting furnished property on an Assured Shorthold Tenancy for
England & Wales   130

G
Garage Service Bill Complaint

A letter protesting at the unreasonable charge for repairs and requesting
reimbursement   134

Garage Service Claim

A letter protesting about faulty repair work and claiming for expenses   135

General Assignment

A basic agreement in which one party transfers its rights or title to a specific
item or contract to another   136

General Power of Attorney

A document by which one person gives another person the power to act on his
behalf (usually in the event of absence)   137

General Proxy

A notice to appoint another to vote on your behalf at a shareholders' meeting   138

General Release

An agreement by which one party releases another from any claims or demands it
may have against the other — 139

General Subordination Agreement between Creditors

An agreement by which one creditor agrees that another creditor's debt will take precedence
over his own — 140

Grievance Procedure

An employer's procedure for settling disputes and grievances of its employees — 142

Guarantee

An agreement by which a guarantor guarantees payment of a customer's debts to
induce the creditor to extend credit to that customer — 143

H

Holiday Letting Agreement

A rental agreement for letting a furnished property as a holiday let — 145

House Rules

A suggested list of rules for use in short-term bed and breakfast accommodation — 147

House/Flat Share Agreement – Non-Resident Owner

An agreement for letting a room on an Assured Shorthold Tenancy for England
& Wales — 148

Household Inventory

A record of the contents of a property to accompany a rental agreement — 152

I

Indemnity Agreement

An agreement by which one party agrees to repay to another party that other
party's costs — 154

Independent Contractor Agreement

An agreement between a property owner and a building contractor for the
performance of works to the property — 156

Insurance Claim Notice

A letter to an insurance company giving details of an insurance claim — 158

Internal Customer Complaint Memorandum

A customer services memo detailing a customer's complaint and the corrective
action taken — 159

J

Joint Venture Agreement (Non-partnership)

An agreement between partners to form a business joint venture — 160

L

Landlord's Reference Requirements

Details what references a landlord requires from a potential tenant — 162

Letter Accepting Liability

A letter to a customer from a supplier accepting liability for faulty goods — 163

Letter Accepting Return of Goods
A letter from a seller to a buyer accepting the return of goods   164

Letter Accompanying Unsolicited Goods
A letter from a supplier introducing samples to a prospective buyer   165

Letter Acknowledging Complaint
A general letter acknowledging complaint and offering to investigate   166

Letter Acknowledging Request for Trade Credit
A letter to a prospective customer requesting a credit reference   167

Letter Agreeing Appointment of an Estate Agent
A letter from a property owner to an estate agent stating the terms of appointment   168

Letter Agreeing to Trade Terms
A letter from a seller to a buyer agreeing to grant credit   169

Letter Alleging Passing Off
A letter demanding that a competitor stops using a similar product name and
threatening legal action   170

Letter Confirming Appointment of Independent Consultant
A letter from a company to a consultant setting out the terms under which the
consultant is engaged   171

Letter Confirming Reason for Instant Dismissal
A letter from a company to an employee explaining the reasons for dismissal   174

Letter Denying Liability on Complaint
A general letter denying fault and suggesting arbitration   175

Letter Expelling Partner from Continuing Partnership
A letter from remaining partners explaining the terms of one partner's
dismissal from a partnership   176

Letter from Employee Intending to Resume Work Before End of Ordinary Maternity Leave
A letter from an employee to an employer giving at least seven days' notice of her
intention to return to work before the end of her statutory Ordinary Maternity Leave   177

Letter Inviting Candidate for Interview
A letter from an employer inviting a candidate for interview   178

Letter of Claim Addressed to a Carrier
A letter from a supplier to his carrier for reimbursement of the cost of goods
damaged while in the carrier's possession   179

Letter of Redundancy
A letter from an employer to an employee giving notice of dismissal by way
of redundancy   180

Letter Offering to Purchase Leasehold Property
A letter to an owner of a leasehold property setting out the terms of an offer   181

Letter re Landlord's Agent's Authority
A letter from a landlord to a tenant regarding the appointment of an agent to act
on the landlord's behalf   182

Letter re Bills
A letter from a landlord to a utility company or authority regarding a new tenant's
responsibility for paying bills   183

Letter Refusing Return of Goods
A letter from a seller to a buyer refusing the buyer's return of goods delivered
without good reason   184

Letter Refusing Trade or Financial References
A letter refusing a request for a reference   185

Letter Refusing Trade Terms
A letter from a seller to a prospective buyer refusing a request for credit   186

Letter Rejecting Conditions of Order and Reimposing Conditions of Sale
A letter from a buyer to a seller rejecting incorrect delivery of goods   187

Letter Rejecting Incorrect Goods
A letter from a buyer to a seller rejecting incorrect delivery of goods   188

Letter Requesting Trade Terms of Payment
A letter from a prospective buyer to a seller requesting credit and offering a
bank reference   189

Letter Sending a Copy of an Agreement Regulated under the Consumer Credit Act 1974
A statutory letter from a supplier to a customer informing the customer of his right
to cancel a hire purchase agreement   190

Letter Taking Up Bank Reference
A letter from a supplier to a bank taking up the bank reference of a prospective
customer   191

Letter Taking Up Trade Reference
A letter from a supplier to a company taking up a trade reference of a prospective
customer   192

Letter Terminating Contract And Invoking Retention of Title Clause
A notice from a seller to a buyer in receivership that a supply contract is terminated
and payment is due   193

Letter to a Solicitor to Collect a Debt
A letter from a creditor to a solicitor requesting that a debt be collected   194

Letter to Credit Reference Agency for Report
A letter from a supplier requesting a credit report on a potential customer   195

Letter to Credit Reference Agency Requesting Personal Data
A letter to a credit reference agency requesting personal data under the
Data Protection Act 1984   196

Letter to Customer who has Exceeded Credit Limit
A letter from a supplier to a customer stating that credit is no longer available   197

Letter to Employee Concerning Salary Rise
A letter from an employer to an employee informing of increase in salary   198

Letter to Employee, Absent Believed Sick
A letter from an employer to an employee asking for reasons for absence   199

Letter to Former Employee who is Using Confidential Information
A letter from an employer to a former employee threatening legal action unless use of
confidential information ceases   200

Letter to Receiver or Liquidator Reclaiming Goods
A letter from a supplier to a receiver or liquidator of a customer demanding
payment for or return of goods delivered   201

Letter to Shareholders and Auditors with Resolution to be Passed
A letter from a company to shareholders enclosing a written resolution for the
signature of shareholders, together with a letter to the company's accountants   202

Letter to Unsuccessful Candidate
A letter to an unsuccessful job applicant   205

Letter Treating Breach of Contract as Repudiation and Claiming Damages
A letter from one party to a contract to another cancelling the contract, claiming that
the other party has not performed their obligation   206

Licence for Use of a Car Parking Space
A licence granted by a car-park owner to a car owner   207

Licence to Use Copyright Material
An agreement by which a copyright owner licences use of his copyright work to another   209

Limited Guarantee
An agreement by which a guarantor guarantees payment of a customer's debts
up to a certain limit to induce the creditor to extend credit to that customer   210

Limited Proxy
A notice to appoint another to vote as specified on your behalf at a shareholders'
meeting   212

Living Will
A statement of request regarding the medical treatment you want in the event that
you are unable to communicate the information yourself through incapacity   213

Loan Agreement
An agreement between a lender and a borrower setting out the terms of a loan (to be
accompanied by a Loan Note)   215

Loan Note (Long Form)
An agreement by which a borrower agrees to repay money borrowed   217

Loan Note (Short Form)
An agreement by which a borrower agrees to repay money borrowed   219

Loan Payment Record
A creditor's record of payments made on a loan by a debtor   221

Location of Important Documents and Summary of Personal Information
A record of information that an executor will need in the event of a testator's death   222

Lodger Agreement
A standard agreement for letting a room in a furnished house or flat with a
resident owner, in which common parts of the property (e.g. bathroom, lavatory,
kitchen and sitting room) are shared   224

Lodger/Bed & Breakfast Licence
A residential rental agreement for letting a room to a lodger or bed & breakfast guest   226

Lost Credit Card Notice
A letter from a cardholder to a credit card company confirming loss of a credit card   229

M

Magazine Article Commissioning Contract
An agreement between an author and a publisher for the submission of a work
to be published   230

Mailing List Name Removal Request
A letter to company requesting removal of your name from their mailing list   232

Mileage Reimbursement Report
A record of business-related mileage   233

Minutes of Annual General Meeting
Minutes of any annual general meeting   234

Minutes of Directors' Meeting Changing Objects of Company
Minutes of a meeting of directors at which it is resolved to update the company's
memorandum   235

Minutes of Extraordinary General Meeting
Minutes of an extraordinary general meeting of a company   236

Minutes of Extraordinary General Meeting Changing Objects of Company
Minutes of an extraordinary general meeting at which it is resolved to update
the company's memorandum   237

Minutes of First General Meeting of a Private Company
Minutes of First General Meeting of a Private Company   238

Mutual Termination of Contract
An agreement by which two parties agree to cancel an existing contract between them   239

Mutual Releases
An agreement by which two parties agree to discharge one another from any
claims they might have in respect of a particular contract or event   240

N

National Lottery Syndicate Agreement
An agreement for a group playing the National Lottery   241

Nominee Shareholder's Declaration of Trust
Shareholder transfers shares in trust to another party   243

Notice for Regulated Hire Purchase or Credit Sale Agreements
A statutory form informing a customer of his right to cancel a consumer credit
agreement   244

Notice of Acceptance of Goods
A letter from customer to supplier acknowledging receipt of a purchase order   245

Notice of Annual General Meeting
A notice from a company to shareholders of a forthcoming annual general meeting of the
company   246

Notice of Assignment
A letter from one party to contract to a debtor that that party has assigned his
interest in the contract to another   247

Notice of Cancellation of Purchase Order and Demand for Refund
A letter from a buyer to a seller cancelling an order for undelivered goods and
requesting a refund   248

Notice of Claim for Indemnity from Joint-Venturer (Non-Partner)
A notice from one party to another of his right to an indemnity from the other in
respect of a claim that has been made against them   249

Notice of Conditional Acceptance of Faulty Goods
A letter from a buyer to a seller accepting faulty goods subject to the seller offering a credit note   250

Notice of Conditional Acceptance of Non-Conforming Goods
A letter from a buyer to a seller accepting incorrect goods subject to the seller offering a credit note   251

Notice of Default in Payment
A notice by one party to a contract to the other that his payment under the contract is in default   252

Notice of Demand for Delivery of Goods
A letter from a buyer to a seller demanding delivery of undelivered goods or requesting a refund   253

Notice of Dismissal Letter (Capability)
An employer's letter to an employee setting out the grounds for dismissal based upon the employee's sub-standard performance   254

Notice of Dismissal Letter (Sickness)
An employer's letter to an employee setting out the grounds for dismissal based upon the employee's poor health   255

Notice of Disputed Account
A letter from a customer to a supplier explaining why an account is disputed   256

Notice of Extraordinary General Meeting
A notice from a company to shareholders of a forthcoming extraordinary general meeting of the company   257

Notice of Extraordinary General Meeting to Change Objects of Company
A notice from a company to shareholders of a forthcoming extraordinary general meeting of the company called to update the memorandum   258

Notice of Goods Sold on Approval
A letter from a supplier accompanying goods sent on approval   259

Notice of Intention to Recover Payment in Default
A letter from a finance company to a customer requesting payment of overdue amounts under a consumer credit agreement   260

Notice of Particulars of Ownership
Required by law under the Business Names Act 1985 for any trading name   261

Notice of Rejection of Non-Conforming Goods
A letter from a buyer to a seller rejecting delivery of goods for reasons stated and requesting a refund   262

Notice of Rejection of Goods
A letter from a seller to a buyer accepting the buyer's rejection of goods and giving notice of replacement   263

Notice of Replacement of Rejected Goods
A letter from a seller to a buyer accepting the buyer's rejection of goods and giving notice of replacement   264

Notice of Result of Grievance Investigation
A letter from a company to an employee replying to the employee's complaint   265

Notice of Return of Goods Sold on Approval
A letter from a customer to a supplier rejecting goods sent on approval   266

Notice of Trade Term Violations
A letter from a supplier to a customer warning the customer that they have
breached their credit terms — 267

Notice of Withheld Delivery
A letter from a seller to a buyer requesting payment of unpaid invoices before delivery — 268

Notice of Wrongful Refusal to Accept Delivery
A letter from a seller to a buyer giving notice that the seller regards the buyer's
rejection of goods to be in breach of contract — 269

Notice Requiring Possession: Assured Shorthold Tenancy Agreement
A notice from a landlord to his tenant that he requires possession of the property at
the end of the tenancy agreement — 270

Notice to Cancel Delayed Goods
A letter from a buyer to a seller cancelling order for undelivered goods — 271

Notice to Dissolve a Two-Party Partnership
A notice from one partner to another that their partnership is dissolved — 272

Notice to Employee being Laid Off and Giving Guarantee Payments
'Guarantee' payments must be made to employees with at least one month's
service, when they would normally expect to work but no work is available — 273

Notice to Employer of Intention to Take Maternity Leave
A letter from an employee to an employer giving notice of her intention to take
her entitled Ordinary Maternity Leave — 274

Notice to Stop Goods in Transit
A letter requesting shipper to return goods to the seller — 275

**Notice to Terminate Given by Owner – House/Flat Share Licence Agreement,
Resident Owner**
A notice from a resident owner to the sharer that he requires possession of a property — 276

**Notice to Terminate Given by Sharer – House/Flat Share Licence Agreement,
Resident Owner**
A notice from a house or flat sharer that they wish to terminate a rental agreement
with the resident owner — 277

Notification of Business Transfer
A notification to an employee that his employment continues although the company
has a new owner — 278

O

Offer of Employment to Avoid Redundancy
A letter from a company to an employee offering alternative employment instead of
redundancy — 279

Offer to Settle by Arbitration
A letter from one party to another offering to settle a dispute by arbitration — 280

One-Off Agency Agreement
An agreement by which a principal delivers goods to its sales agents for sale while
retaining title to the goods — 281

Option to Buy Land
An agreement by which a seller gives a potential buyer an option to purchase land — 283

Option to Purchase Goods
An agreement by which a seller gives a potential buyer an option to purchase goods 285

Order to Stop a Cheque
Request to a bank to stop a cheque 287

Organ Donation
A document in which an organ donor specifies his wishes 288

Overdue Account Reminder
A simple letter reminding a debtor that a payment is overdue 289

P

Partial Delivery Request
A letter from a seller to a buyer suggesting partial delivery of order within the terms of the buyer's credit limit 290

Partnership Agreement
An agreement between individuals wanting to establish a business partnership 291

Pay Advice
A form advising employee of salary and deductions 294

Permission to Use Photograph
Permission given by a photographer for another to use his work 295

Permission to Use Quotation or Personal Statement
Permission given by one party to another for the use and publication of spoken words and other material 296

Personal Property Rental Agreement
An agreement between an owner and a renter for the use of personal property, for example, a boat 297

Pools Syndicate Agreement Rules
An agreement for a group playing the football pools 299

Premarital Agreement
An agreement between a couple intending to marry as to the ownership of property during the marriage and in the event of divorce 302

Product Defect Notice
A letter from a customer advising manufacturer, distributor or seller of a defective product 303

Promissory Note
A promise by a borrower to repay a loan on demand 304

Promissory Note for Repayment by Instalments
A promissory note for repayment by instalments 305

Guarantee to Support a Promissory Note
An agreement by which a borrower agrees to repay money borrowed and a guarantor guarantees the repayment 306

Property Inventory
List of property owned 307

Purchase Order
A company's record of an order for goods bought in 308

Q

Quotation

A supplier's written statement of prices for specific goods — 309

R

Receipt Appropriated to a Particular Debt

General receipt payment or part payment — 310

Receipt for Company Property

Itemises company property issued to an employee — 311

Receipt in Full

Basic receipt for money paid on account — 312

Receipt Credited to a Particular Account

Basic receipt for money paid on account — 313

Receipt for Non-Cash Consideration upon Allotment of Shares

A document to record the receipt by a company of property in return for the issue of shares — 314

Redundancy with Ex Gratia Payment

A letter from an employer notifying an employee of his redundancy and redundancy payment — 315

Reference Letter on Employee

A letter in response to a request for a reference for an ex-employee — 316

Rejected Goods Notice

A letter from a buyer giving notice and reasons for the rejection of goods — 317

Reminder of Unpaid Account

A letter from a seller to a buyer requesting payment of an outstanding invoice — 318

Remittance Advice

A letter from a buyer to a seller requesting that payment be set against certain invoices — 319

Rent Review Memorandum

A record of an agreement between a landlord and a tenant on a new rent payable subsequent to a rent review — 320

Rent Statement

A record of rent payment receipts kept by a tenant or sharer — 321

Rejection of Claim for Credit Note

A letter from a seller to a buyer refusing request for a credit and giving reasons for refusal — 323

Request for Advance Payment

A letter from a seller to buyer requesting money on account — 324

Request for Bank Credit Reference

A letter requesting a reference from a bank — 325

Request for Credit Reference

A letter requesting a credit reference from another supplier — 326

Request for Guarantee

A letter from a seller to a buyer requesting a personal guarantee from the directors of the buyer's company — 327

Request for Information on Disputed Charge
A letter from a seller to a buyer requesting justification for a disputed account 328

Request for Quotation
A letter from a potential customer to a supplier seeking a price quotation 329

Request for Replacement Share Certificate
Also known as a letter of indemnity; a notice to a company secretary of the loss of a share certificate and the request for a replacement 330

Resignation
A general form of resignation from an office or job 331

Resignation of Director Relinquishing All Claims
A letter from a director to his board announcing his resignation without claim 332

Response to Employee's Complaint
A letter from an employer requesting that an employee follows a formal complaints procedure 333

Restaurant Food Poisoning Claim
A letter demanding compensation from a restaurant/wine bar after food poisoning 334

Restaurant Food Quality Complaint
A letter demanding compensation from a restaurant/wine bar after poor quality food 335

Restaurant Lost Reservation Claim
A letter demanding compensation for a reservation that was not kept 336

Revocation of Power of Attorney
A document by which a donor revokes a power of attorney previously granted by him 337

S
Sale Agreement of Moveable Property Subject to Debt
An agreement by which a buyer agrees to buy property on which a debt is payable and agrees to pay the debt 338

Sales Representative Agreement
An agreement between a company and its sales representative setting out the terms of engagement 339

Samples and Documents Receipt
An employee's receipt for samples and company documents 342

Second Notice of Overdue Account
A letter from a seller to a buyer making a second request for payment of an overdue account 343

Second Warning for Lateness
An employer's second written warning to an employee for being late for work 344

Security Agreement
An agreement between a creditor and a debtor by which the debtor offers property as a security for the debt 345

Settlement Statement
A statutory statement sent by a supplier to a customer who wishes to repay early a consumer credit agreement 347

Share Certificate
A document to record the ownership of fully paid shares in a company 348

Share Subscription/Application
An application by a prospective shareholder for shares in a company 349

Solicitor's Charges: Detailed Account Request
A letter requesting a breakdown of charges 350

Solicitor's Charges: Remuneration Certificate Request
A letter requesting a certificate with which you can obtain a judgement on
whether the solicitor's fees are too high; obtained by the solicitor on your behalf 351

Special Notice for the Removal of Auditors
A proposal for a company's annual general meeting for the removal and
replacement of auditors 352

Special Notice for the Removal of a Director
A proposal for a company's annual general meeting for the removal of a director
from the board 353

Standard Board Minutes
A standard format for recording the minutes of a company's board meeting 354

Standard Contractual Terms for Sale of Services online
Standard Contractual Terms for Sale of Services Online where the customer is a business,
services and price negotiated individually 355

Summary of Employment Terms
A potted terms and conditions of employment 358

Supplier Questionnaire
A questionnaire to a supplier issued by a company meeting the requirement of
BS5750/ISO9000 359

T

Telecoms Bill Dispute
A letter questioning an improbably large telephone bill 361

Tenant's Bank Standing Order Mandate
A form for setting up a tenant's standing order payable to his landlord 362

Trading Standards Officer Complaint
A letter asking your local officer to investigate a suspected breach of trading
standards 363

U

Unfurnished House/Flat Rental Agreement
A standard agreement for letting unfurnished property on an Assured Shorthold
Tenancy for England & Wales 364

Unsolicited Idea Acknowledgement
A letter from a company acknowledging receipt of an unsolicited idea on
certain terms 368

V

Variation of Contract
An agreement by which two parties agree to vary the terms of an existing contract 370

Variation of Employment Agreement
An agreement by which an employer and employee agree to vary the term of an existing contract 371

W
Waiver of Liability and Assumption of Risk
A document by which a customer agrees not to hold a supplier liable for any loss, damage or injury suffered by the customer 372

Warranty Increasing Statutory Rights
A supplier's promise to replace faulty goods in addition to the customer's basic statutory rights 373

Water Supply Interruption: OFWAT Investigation Request
A letter requesting the intervention of a regional Office of Water Services customer service committee in a dispute with the water company in its area. Contact OFWAT for regional addresses 374

Withheld Delivery Notice
A letter from a seller to a buyer giving reasons for the non-delivery of goods 375

Working Time Regulations Opt Out Agreement
Agreement whereby employee agrees not to be bound to the Working Time Regulations 376

Contents by Category

I. Business

Board Resolution: Appointment of Auditors 40

Board Resolution: Approval and Registration of Transfer of Shares 41

Board Resolution: Approval of Directors' Report and Accounts 42

Board Resolution: Proposal of Alteration of Articles 43

Board Resolution to Call Annual General Meeting 44

Board Resolution to Call Extraordinary General Meeting 45

Consent to Short Notice of an Annual General Meeting 72

Consent to Short Notice of an Extraordinary General Meeting 73

Director's Resignation Reserving Rights against the Company 92

Form of Resolution for Submission to Companies House 128

General Proxy 138

Joint Venture Agreement (Non-partnership) 160

Letter Expelling Partner from Continuing Partnership 176

Letter to Shareholders and Auditors with Resolution to be Passed 202

Limited Proxy 212

Minutes of Annual General Meeting 234

Minutes of Directors' Meeting Changing Objects of Company 235

Minutes of Extraordinary General Meeting 236

Minutes of Extraordinary General Meeting Changing Objects of Company 237

Minutes of First General Meeting of a Private Company 238

Nominee Shareholder's Declaration of Trust 243

Notice of Annual General Meeting 246

Notice of Extraordinary General Meeting 257

Notice of Extraordinary General Meeting to Change Objects of Company 258

Notice of Particulars of Ownership 261

Notice to Dissolve a Two-Party Partnership 272

Partnership Agreement 291

Receipt to for Non-cash Consideration upon Allotment of Shares 314

Request for Replacement Share Certificate 330

Resignation of Director Relinquishing All Claims 332

Share Certificate 348

Share Subscription/Application 349

Special Notice for the Removal of Auditors 352

Special Notice for the Removal of a Director 353

Standard Board Minutes 354

Unsolicited Idea Acknowledgement 368

II. Buying & Selling

Acknowledgement and Acceptance of Order 2

Acknowledgement of Alteration of Order 3

Agreement for the Sale of Goods 9

Agreement for the Sale of a Vehicle 10

Anti-Gazumping Agreement 23

Authorisation to Return Goods 39

Builders' Work Complaint 50

Certificate of Product Conformity 52

Concession Note (Seller's - where bulk goods do not conform to description or sample) 65

Confirmation of Verbal Order 69

Contract for Sale of Goods by Delivery 76

Damaged Goods Acceptance with Price Reduction 82

Defect Report Memorandum 84

Defective Goods Notice 85

Demand for Delivery 86

Demand for Explanation of Rejection of Goods 87

Demand to Specify Delivery Dates 88

Electricity Bill Query 97

Garage Service Bill Complaint 134

Garage Service Claim 135

Internal Customer Complaint Memorandum 159

Letter Accepting Liability 163

Letter Accepting Return of Goods 164

Letter Accompanying Unsolicited Goods 165

Letter Acknowledging Complaint 166

Letter Agreeing Appointment of an Estate Agent 168

Letter Denying Liability on Complaint 175

Letter of Claim Addressed to a Carrier 179

Letter Refusing Return of Goods 183

Letter Rejecting Conditions of Order and Reimposing Conditions of Sale 187

Letter Rejecting Incorrect Goods 188

Letter to Receiver or Liquidator Reclaiming Goods 201

Letter Treating Breach of Contract as Repudiation and Claiming Damages 206

Notice for Regulated Hire Purchase or Credit Sale Agreements 244

Notice of Acceptance of Goods 245

Notice of Cancellation of Purchase Order and Demand for Refund 248

Notice of Conditional Acceptance of Faulty Goods 250

Notice of Conditional Acceptance of Non-Conforming Goods 251

Notice of Demand for Delivery of Goods 253

Notice of Goods Sold on Approval 259

Notice of Rejection of Non-Conforming Goods 262

Notice of Rejection of Goods 263

Notice of Replacement of Rejected Goods 264

Notice of Return of Goods Sold on Approval 266

Notice of Trade Term Violations 267

Notice of Withheld Delivery 268

Notice of Wrongful Refusal to Accept Delivery 269

Notice to Cancel Delayed Goods 271

Notice to Stop Goods in Transit 275

Option to Buy Land 283

Option to Purchase Goods 285

Partial Delivery Request 290

Product Defect Notice 302

Purchase Order 308

Quotation 309

Receipt Appropriated to a Particular Debt 310

Receipt in Full 312

Rejected Goods Notice 317

Request for Quotation 329

Restaurant Food Poisoning Claim 334

Restaurant Food Quality Complaint 335

Restaurant Lost Reservation Claim 336

Sale Agreement of Moveable Property Subject to Debt 338

Solicitor's Charges: Detailed Account Request 350

Solicitor's Charges: Remuneration Certificate Request 351

Standard Contractual Terms for Sale of Services online 355

Supplier Questionnaire 358

Telecoms Bill Dispute 361

Trading Standards Officer Complaint 362

Warranty Increasing Statutory Rights 373

Water Supply Interruption: OFWAT Investigation Request 374

Withheld Delivery Notice 375

III. Credit & Debt Collection

Agreement to Assume Debt 13

Agreement to Compromise Debt 15

Agreement to Extend Debt Payment 17

Agreement to Extend Performance Date 19

Application to Open a Credit Account 28

Confirmation of Agreement to Pay 68

Credit Information 79

Credit Information Request 80

Credit Reference 81

Debt Acknowledgement 83

Demand for Payment (Final) 88

Disputed Account Settlement 96

Enquiry on Overdue Account 116

Letter Acknowledging Request for Trade Credit 167

Letter Agreeing to Trade Terms 169

Letter Alleging Passing Off 170

Letter Refusing Trade or Financial References 185

Letter Refusing Trade Terms 186

Letter Requesting Trade Terms of Payment 189

Letter Sending a Copy of an Agreement Regulated under the Consumer Credit Act 1974 190

Letter Taking Up Bank Reference 191

Letter Taking Up Trade Reference 192

Letter to a Solicitor to Collect a Debt 194

Letter to Credit Reference Agency for Report 195

Letter to Credit Reference Agency Requesting Personal Data 196

Letter to Customer who has Exceeded Credit Limit 197

Notice of Disputed Account 256

Notice of Intention to Recover Payment in Default 260

Overdue Account Reminder 289

Promissory Note 304

Promissory Note for Repayment by Instalments 305

Guarantee to Support a Promissory Note 306

Receipt Credited to a Particular Account 313

Reminder of Unpaid Account 318

Remittance Advice 319

Rejection of Claim for Credit Note 323

Request for Advance Payment 324

Request for Bank Credit Reference 325

Request for Credit Reference 326

Request for Guarantee 327

Request for Information on Disputed Charge 328

Second Notice of Overdue Account 343

Settlement Statement 347

IV. Employment

Alteration to terms of employment 22

Applicant's Request for an Employment Reference 27

Authorisation to Release Employment Information 36

Change in Pay or Grading Following Job Evaluation 55

Change in Sales Representative Agreement 56

Confidentiality Agreement 66

Conflict of Interest Declaration 70

Consent to Release of Information 71

Consultant Non-Disclosure Agreement 74

Contractor/Subcontractor Agreement 77

Dismissal, Disciplinary Rules and Procedure 93

Dismissal Letter for Intoxication on the Job 95

Employee Agreement on Inventions and Patents 98

Employee Disciplinary Report 100

Employee Dismissal for Lateness 101

Employee File 102

Employee Non-Competition and Confidentiality Agreement 105

Employee Suspension Notice 107

Employee Warning 108

Employer's Request for Reference 109

Employment Contract 112

Equal Opportunities Policy 117

Expenses Record 119

Final Warning before Dismissal 124

Final Warning for Lateness 125

First Warning for Lateness 126

Grievance Procedure 142

Independent Contractor Agreement 156

Letter Confirming Appointment of Independent Consultant 171

Letter Confirming Reason for Instant Dismissal 174

Letter from Employee Intending to Resume Work before End of
  Ordinary Maternity Leave 177

Letter Inviting Candidate for Interview 178

Letter of Redundancy 180

Letter to Employee Concerning Salary Rise 198

Letter to Employee, Absent Believed Sick 199

Letter to Former Employee who is Using Confidential Information 200

Letter to Unsuccessful Candidate 205

Mileage Reimbursement Report 233

Notice of Dismissal Letter (Capability) 254

Notice of Dismissal Letter (Sickness) — 255

Notice of Result of Grievance Investigation — 265

Notice to Employee Being Laid Off and Giving Guarantee Payments — 273

Notice to Employer of Intention to Take Maternity Leave — 274

Notification of Business Transfer — 278

Offer of Employment to Avoid Redundancy — 279

Pay Advice — 294

Receipt for Company Property — 311

Redundancy with Ex Gratia Payment — 315

Reference Letter on Employee — 316

Resignation — 331

Response to Employee's Complaint — 333

Sales Representative Agreement — 339

Samples and Documents Receipt — 342

Second Warning for Lateness — 344

Summary of Employment Terms — 358

Variation of Employment Agreement — 370

Working Time Regulations Opt Out Agreement — 376

V. Loans & Borrowing

Application to be accepted as Guarantor — 25

Demand to Guarantor for Payment — 90

Demand to Pay Promissory Note — 91

Guarantee — 143

Limited Guarantee — 210

Loan Agreement — 215

Loan Note (Long Form) — 217

Loan Note (Short Form) — 219

Loan Payment Record — 221

Notice of Default in Payment — 252

Promissory Note — 304

Promissory Note for repayment by instalments — 305

Guarantee to support promissory note — 306

Security Agreement — 345

VI. Personal & Family

Change of Address Notice — 57

Change of Name Deed — 53

Child Guardianship Consent Form — 58

Cohabitation Agreement (for Unmarried Partners) — 59

Family Tree — 121

Form of Letter from Testator to Executor 127

Funeral Wishes 129

General Power of Attorney 137

Insurance Claim Notice 158

Living Will 213

Location of Important Documents and Summary of Personal Information 222

Organ Donation 288

Personal Property Rental Agreement 297

Premarital Agreement 302

Property Inventory 307

Revocation of Power of Attorney 337

VII. Residential Tenancy

Company Let 62

Employee Licence 103

Furnished House/Flat Rental Agreement 130

Holiday Letting Agreement 145

House Rules 147

House/Flat Share Rental Agreement - Non-resident owner 148

Household Inventory 152

Landlord's Reference Requirements 162

Letter re Landlord's Agent's Authority 182

Letter re Bills 183

Lodger Agreement 224

Lodger/Bed & Breakfast Licence 226

Notice Requiring Possession: Assured Shorthold Tenancy Agreement 270

Notice to Terminate Given by Owner – House/Flat Share
   Licence Agreement, Resident Owner 276

Notice to Terminate Given by Sharer – House/Flat Share Licence
   Agreement, Resident Owner 277

Rent Review Memorandum 320

Rent Statement 321

Tenant's Bank Standing Order Mandate 362

Unfurnished House/Flat Share Agreement 364

VIII. Transfers & Assignments

Assignment of Accounts Receivable with Non-Recourse 29

Assignment of Contract 30

Assignment of Insurance Policy 32

Assignment of Money Due 33

Assignment of Option 34

Assignment of Option to Purchase Land   35

General Assignment   136

Notice of Assignment   247

IX. Other Legal Forms

Accident Claim Notice   1

Affidavit   5

Affidavit of Power of Attorney   6

Affidavit of Title to Goods and other Chattels   7

Agreement   8

Agreement to Sell Personal Property   21

Authorisation to Release Confidential Information   36

Authorisation to Release Medical Information   38

Breach of Contract Notice   46

Builder/Decorator Contract   47

Cancellation of an Order to Stop a Cheque   51

Dishonoured Cheque Notice   94

Exercise of Option   118

Extension of Option to Purchase Property   120

Final Notice before Legal Proceedings   123

General Release   139

General Subordination Agreement between creditors   140

Indemnity Agreement   154

Letter Offering to Purchase Leasehold Property   181

Letter Terminating Contract and Invoking Retention of Title Clause   193

Licence for Use of a Car Parking Space   207

Licence to Use Copyright Material   209

Lost Credit Card Notice   229

Magazine Article Commissioning Contract   230

Mailing List Name Removal Request   232

Mutual Termination of Contract   239

Mutual Releases   240

National Lottery Syndicate Agreement   241

Notice of Claim for Indemnity from Joint-Venturer (Non-Partner)   249

Offer to Settle by Arbitration   280

One-Off Agency Agreement   281

Order to Stop a Cheque   287

Permission to Use Photograph   295

Permission to Use Quotation or Personal Statement   296

Pools Syndicate Agreement Rules   299

Variation of Contract   370

Waiver of Liability and Assumption of Risk   372

Accident Claim Notice

Form OLF01

Date _____

To _____

_____

_____

Dear _____

You are hereby notified of a claim against you for damages arising from the following accident or injury, to which I believe you and/or your agents are liable.

Description of Accident[1] _____

_____

_____

_____

_____

Date _____

Time _____

Location _____

_____

Please ask your insurance company or solicitor to contact me as soon as possible.

Yours sincerely

Signature _____

Name _____

Address _____

_____

Health warning: A form of this nature will usually precede a court case, in which you may need the help of a solicitor. You should only use this form if the loss of property or injury to yourself is minor and you are willing to act for yourself in any court case, if it is not possible to agree a settlement with the defendant or his insurers. If you do not wish to represent yourself you should leave all correspondence, including an initial letter such as this one, to your solicitor.

[1] Enter a description of the accident. For example 'whilst I was [driving] / [sitting as a passenger in] motor car registration number [____] that car was struck by a motor car, registration number [____] driven by [you] / [your agent]. [As a result, I suffered bodily injury.] or 'During the course of my employment with you I fell from a platform and suffered bodily injury'.

Acknowledgement and Acceptance of Order   Form BS01

Date   _____

To   _____

_____

_____

Dear   _____

Re: Your Order No. _____

We acknowledge receipt of your order no. _____

and confirm our acceptance, which, as advised, is subject to our terms and conditions of business.

Yours sincerely

_____

Note: Only use this form if you have already shown your terms and conditions to the customer, or at the least if you have already alerted your customer to the fact that you have a set of standard terms and conditions. Ideally, you should have a copy of the standard terms and conditions, receipted by the customer before he placed the order, or a copy of those terms, signed by the customer as agreed to by him.

Acknowledgement of Alteration of Order Form BS02

Date _____

To _____

_____

_____

Dear _____

I refer to your order number dated _____

This letter acknowledges that the order is altered and superseded by the following agreed change in terms

_____

_____

_____

All other terms shall remain as stated.

Please indicate your agreement to the alteration by signing below and signing the enclosed copy of this letter which we should be grateful if you would return to us for our file.

Yours sincerely

_____

The above alteration is acknowledged.

_____

Acknowledgement of Alteration of Order Form BS02

Acknowledging a Notification of Maternity Leave   Form E67

Dear   _____

Thank you for informing me of your pregnancy and the date that your baby is due. I am writing to you about your maternity leave and pay.

You are eligible for _____.

You have told me that you would like to begin your maternity leave on _____.
If you want to change this date, you must notify me 28 days before the new intended start date or, if that is not reasonably practicable, as soon as you can. Your maternity leave period will end on _____.[1]
If you want to come back to work before this date, **you must notify me eight weeks before your new intended return date or, if that is not reasonably practicable, as soon as you can.** This is a legal requirement, but obviously it helps with planning. If you don't give notice, the Company has the right to postpone your return for eight weeks from the date you informed me that you would like to return early or the end of your maternity leave period if this is earlier.

If you decide that you do not want to return to work, you will be required to give four weeks' written notice in accordance with your contract of employment.

You are eligible for _____.[2]

The Company will pay you for six weeks at 90 per cent of your average weekly earnings, calculated based on a legal formula, which I have calculated as _____. The Company will then pay you the standard rate of statutory maternity pay of _____ for the remaining 33 weeks.[3]

During your period of maternity leave, we will make reasonable contact with you to discuss and plan for your return. If you have any questions, please contact me to discuss any aspects of your maternity entitlements.

Yours sincerely

_____

Personnel Manager

---

[1] i.e. 52 weeks after the start of maternity leave.

[2] If the employee is not eligible, state 'not eligible for statutory maternity pay'.

[3] If the employee is not entitled to statutory maternity pay, replace with 'I have given you form SMP1, which explains why you do not qualify for statutory maternity pay. You may, however, be entitled to maternity allowance. If you take this form to a Benefits Agency, it will discuss your entitlements with you'.

Affidavit   Form OLF02

I, _____(name)

of _____(address)

_____(occupation)

MAKE OATH and say as follows:_____

_____

_____

_____

_____

_____

_____

_____

_____

_____

_____

_____

_____

_____

_____

_____

Signature

SWORN AT _____(address)

this _____ day of _____ year _____

before me,

_____

(A Solicitor or Commissioner for Oaths)

Affidavit of Power of Attorney Form OLF03

I _____ ,

of _____ ,

MAKE OATH and say as follows:

1. The Power of Attorney granted to me by _____ ,

    on _____ , a true copy of which is annexed hereto, is in full force and effect.

2. At the time of the execution of _____ [1],

    on _____ I had no knowledge of or actual notice of the revocation or

    termination of the Power of Attorney by death or otherwise.

3. I make this affidavit for the purpose of inducing _____

    to accept the above described instrument as executed by me as attorney knowing that in accepting

    the aforesaid instrument they will rely upon this affidavit.

SWORN AT _____

the ____ day of _____ year ___

Before me

_____

(A Solicitor or Commissioner for Oaths)

Health warning: Unless the Power of Attorney is an Enduring Power of Attorney made in the form prescribed under the Enduring Power of Attorney Act 1985, it will be automatically revoked if the person who gives the power becomes mentally incapacitated. Therefore, if the Power of Attorney is not an Enduring Power of Attorney and if the person giving the power has become of unsound mind, you must not use this form. If the Power of Attorney is an Enduring Power of Attorney it must be registered once the person giving it has become mentally incapacitated, and no further use must be made of it until registration. Note that when it comes into force (1 October 2007) the Mental Capacity Act 2005 will require new Powers of Attorney to be in the form of 'Lasting Powers of Attorney' instead of in the form of Enduring Powers of Attorney, if they are to remain valid after the maker of the power becomes mentally incapacitated. Please check with the Public Guardianship Office that you are using the right form when you next create a Power of Attorney.

[1] Describe the document that has been executed under the Power of Attorney.

Affidavit of Title to Goods or other Chattels   Form OLF04

I, _____ (name)

of _____ (address)

_____ (occupation)

MAKE OATH and say as follows:

1.   I certify that I am now in possession of and am the absolute owner of the following property:

     _____

     _____

2.   I also state that its possession has been undisputed and that I know of no fact or reason that may prevent transfer of this property to the buyer.

3.   I also state that no liens, contracts, debts, or lawsuits exist regarding this property, except the following:

     _____

     _____

4.   [I finally state that I have full power to transfer title to this property to the buyer with [full]/[limited] title guarantee.][1]

_____

Signature

SWORN AT _____ (address)

this _____ day of _____ year _____ .

before me,

_____

(A Solicitor or Commissioner for Oaths)

[1]   Do not insert this paragraph without the advice of a solicitor or a licensed conveyancer.

Agreement

THIS AGREEMENT is made the _____ day of _____ year _____

BETWEEN:

(1) _____ of _____ (the 'First Party');and

(2) _____ of _____ (the 'Second Party').

NOW IT IS HEREBY AGREED as follows:

1. That in consideration of the promises made herein by the Second Party the First Party hereby promises and agrees that it shall: _____

    _____

    _____

    _____

    _____

    _____

    _____

    _____

2. That in consideration of the promises made herein by the First Party the Second Party hereby promises that it shall: _____

    _____

    _____

    _____

    _____

    _____

    _____

    _____

3. In consideration of the aforementioned promises, the Parties hereto agree that the following terms shall have effect: _____

    _____

    _____

    _____

    _____

    _____

    _____

Continued on next page

Agreement (continued)   Form OLF06

4.   This agreement shall be binding upon the parties, their successors and assigns. This is the entire
      agreement.

5.   [Nothing in this Agreement is intended to confer any benefit on a third party whether under the
      Contracts (Rights of Third Parties) Act or otherwise].[1]

IN WITNESS OF WHICH the parties have signed this agreement the day and year first above written.

_____

Signed by or on behalf of the first party

_____

Signed by or on behalf of the second party

---

[1]   This should be omitted if the parties desire the agreement to benefit a non-party and if they wish that the non-party should be
      entitled to sue in respect of it.

Agreement for the Sale of Goods   Form BS03

THIS AGREEMENT is made the _____ day of _____ year _____

BETWEEN:

(1) _____ of _____(the 'Buyer'); and

(2) _____ of_____(the 'Seller').

NOW IT IS HEREBY AGREED as follows:

1.   In consideration for the sum of £ _____, receipt of which the Seller hereby acknowledges, the Seller hereby sells and transfers to the Buyer and his/her successors and assigns absolutely, the following goods (the 'Goods'):

_____

_____

_____

[2.   Although this sale is not made in the course of any business of the Seller, it is nonetheless agreed that the statutory terms as to satisfactory quality set out in the Sale of Goods Act Section 14 shall have effect and it is further agreed that the Goods sold under this agreement shall be fit for their purpose, that is to say: _____

_____

_____

_____]¹

IN WITNESS OF WHICH the parties have signed this agreement the day and year first above written

_____   _____

Signed by or on behalf of the Buyer   Signed by or on behalf of the Seller

_____   _____

in the presence of (witness)   in the presence of (witness)

Name _____   Name _____

Address _____   Address _____

_____   _____

Occupation _____   Occupation _____

¹ Insert the purpose for which the buyer has stated that he intends to use the goods. Under statute, in a sale of goods between private individuals that is not made in the course of the seller's business, there is no automatic promise by the seller to the effect that the goods will be of satisfactory quality or fit for any particular purpose, even where the seller knows of the buyer's purpose for the goods. Paragraph two on this form inserts promises as to quality and fitness for purpose. They can be removed if that is what the parties agree. If the sale is made in the course of the seller's business, the sale is automatically made subject to statutory terms as to quality and fitness for purpose, and there is no power to remove these from the agreement except where the buyer has bought them in the course of the buyer's business and either the buyer buys goods of this type frequently or else if the goods are not of a kind which is normally bought for private use.

Under statute, all sales of goods are subject to a promise by the seller that he has title to the goods that he is selling. The only exception is where he makes it clear that he is selling them with such title as he may have. If he does this, he must add a term revealing anything known to him which makes his title open to question. The statutory promises as to title apply, whether or not the seller is selling in the course of a business. It cannot be excluded from the agreement save where the seller is only selling such title as he has.

Agreement for the Sale of a Vehicle   Form BS04

THIS AGREEMENT is made the _____ day of _____ year _____

BETWEEN:

(1) _____ of _____ (the 'Buyer'); and

(2) _____ of _____ (the 'Seller').

NOW it is HEREBY agreed as follows:

1. In consideration of the sum of £ _____, receipt of which the Seller acknowledges, the Seller sells and transfers to the Buyer the vehicle (the 'Vehicle'):

    Make: _____   Model: _____

    Registration Number: _____   Chassis Number: _____

    Year of Manufacture: _____   Mileage: _____

    Colour: _____   Extras: _____

2. The Seller hereby warrants:

    _____

3. The Seller warrants that while the Vehicle was in the Seller's possession, the odometer was not altered or disconnected and that to the best of the Seller's knowledge the odometer reading above:

    ( ) reflects the actual mileage.

    ( ) reflects the actual mileage in excess of 99,999 miles.

4. The Buyer agrees to despatch the Vehicle's Registration Document to DVLA as soon as practicable after signature of this Agreement, informing DVLA of the Buyer's ownership of the Vehicle.

[5. Save as aforesaid the Seller gives no warranty that the vehicle is of satisfactory quality or that it is fit for any particular purpose].

or

[5. Although his sale is not made in the course of any business of the Seller, it is nonetheless agreed that the statutory terms as to satisfactory quality set out in the Sale of Goods Act Section 14 shall have effect and it is further agreed that the car shall be fit for its purpose, that is to say:

    _____]

[6. In part payment of the purchase price, the Buyer has paid to the Seller the sum of £_____. The remainder of the purchase price, being the sum of £_____ shall be paid to the Seller on or before

    _____]

[7. The Seller remains the owner of the car until the entire purchase price is paid].

Continued on next page

Agreement for the Sale of a Vehicle (continued)　　　　Form BS04

[8.　　The Buyer shall be entitled to remove the car from the Seller's premises when the entire purchase price is paid, at which time ownership of the car, the risk of loss or damage to it, and the responsibility to insure it will pass to the Buyer. For the avoidance of doubt, if the price is paid by cheque, the price will not be deemed to have been paid until the cheque has cleared].

[9.　　This is the entire agreement between the parties. Further, the Buyer accepts that he has not relied upon any statement which the Seller may have made].

10.　　The applicable law of this Agreement is English law.

The parties hereto have signed this Agreement the day and year first written above.

SIGNED_____　　SIGNED　_____

Signed by or on behalf of the Buyer　　　　　　Signed by or behalf of the Seller

Note: This form is not appropriate where a seller is selling the car in the course of a business to a person who is buying as a consumer, because it allows the parties, if they agree, to exclude any warranty of satisfactory quality or fitness for purpose. The law does not allow this where goods (including cars) are sold in the course of a business to a person who is buying as a consumer.

The seller must take care to ensure that the car is roadworthy, as otherwise he could be guilty of a criminal offence, even if the car is not sold in the course of a business.

A check through HPI Ltd should be undertaken by the buyer in order to ensure that the car is not subject to an earlier hire purchase agreement. Although the law gives some protection to private purchasers who innocently buy a car that turns out to be subject to a hire purchase agreement, this protection is by no means foolproof.

Agreement to Assume Debt   Form CDC01

THIS AGREEMENT IS MADE the _____ day of _____ year ____

BETWEEN:

(1) _____ of _____(the 'Creditor');

(2) _____ of _____(the 'Debtor'); and

(3) _____ of _____ (the 'Customer').

1.   The Customer acknowledges that the Customer at present owes the Creditor the sum of
      £_____ (the 'Debt') and that the Customer is currently in the possession of certain assets or
      goods which are the property of the Creditor (the 'Goods').

2.   In consideration of the Creditor transferring ownership of the Goods to the Customer, the Debtor
      unconditionally and irrevocably agrees to assume and pay the Debt, as a principal debtor.

3.   The Debt shall be due and payable on the following terms[1]:_____
      _____
      _____

4.   Nothing in this agreement shall constitute a release or discharge of the obligations of the Customer to
      the Creditor for the payment of the Debt, provided that so long as the Debtor shall promptly pay the
      Debt in the manner above described, the Creditor shall forebear in commencing any action against the
      Customer. In the event of any default, the Creditor shall have full rights, jointly and severally, against
      both the Customer and/or the Debtor for any balance then owing.

5.   This agreement shall be binding upon and inure to the benefit of the parties, their successors and assigns.

Continued on next page

Agreement to Assume Debt (continued)   Form CDC01

IN WITNESS OF WHICH the parties have signed this agreement the day and year first above written

_____   _____
Signed by or on behalf of the Creditor   Signed by or on behalf of the Debtor

_____   _____
in the presence of (witness)   in the presence of (witness)

Name _____   Name _____

Address _____   Address _____

_____   _____

Occupation _____   Occupation _____

_____
Signed by or on behalf of the Customer

_____
in the presence of (witness)

Name _____

Address _____

_____

Occupation _____

Health warning: This form should not be used if the original agreement is one which is regulated under the Consumer Credit Act 1974. Broadly speaking the Act, at the time of writing, applies to any loan, hire or hire purchase agreement for £25,000 or less. This is unless one of a limited number of exceptions applies (for example, a non-cash loan, no more than four instalments are to be paid and they are all to be paid within a year, or if a loan is a low cost loan as defined in the Act). If the Act does regulate the original agreement, it will also regulate any variation to the agreement (such as this one). In those circumstances, this form will not comply with the requirements of the Act and the agreement may therefore be unenforceable. Note also that by the time you use this form, the law may have changed so as to bring within the scope of the Act loans of more than £25,000, save for those which are entered into for the borrower's business, where the borrower's business is a firm with more than three partners. However, you may use this form in all circumstances if the debtor and the customer are both limited companies.

¹ No more than four payments should be provided for, and the debt must be stated to be repayable within one year. Otherwise, the Consumer Credit Act 1974 may apply.

Agreement to Compromise Debt   Form CDC02

THIS DEED is made the _____ day of _____ year _____

BETWEEN:

(1) _____ of _____(the 'Customer'); and

(2) _____ of _____(the 'Creditor').

WHEREAS:

(A)   The Customer and the Creditor acknowledge that the Customer is indebted to the Creditor in the sum

of £ _____ (the 'Debt'), which sum is now due and payable.

(B)   The Creditor agrees to forgo payment of part of the Debt.

[(C)   A dispute has arisen between the Customer and the Creditor which they have agreed to compromise

on the terms of this Deed.]

NOW THIS DEED WITNESSES as follows:

1.   [In pursuance of the agreement to compromise the said dispute] the parties agree that the Creditor

shall accept £ _____ (the 'Sum') in full and final settlement of the Debt and in complete

discharge and satisfaction of all monies due, provided the Sum is punctually paid as follows: _____

_____

_____

2.   Should the Customer fail to pay the Sum on the terms set out in paragraph 1 the entire Sum shall fall

due and the Creditor shall have full rights to prosecute its claim for the full total of the Debt, less any

payments made.

3.   Upon default, the Customer agrees to pay all reasonable solicitors' fees and costs of collection.

4.   This agreement shall be binding upon and inure to the benefit of the parties, their successors and

assigns.

Agreement to Compromise Debt   Form CDC02

Continued on next page

Agreement to Compromise Debt (continued)   Form CDC02

IN WITNESS OF WHICH the parties have executed this deed the day and year first above written

(Individual)   (Company)

_____   Signed for and on behalf of:

Signed by the Customer   _____Ltd

_____   _____

in the presence of (witness)   Director

Name _____

Address _____   _____

_____   Director/Secretary

Occupation _____

                                                         Signed for and on behalf of:

                                                         _____Ltd

_____   _____

Signed by the creditor   Director

_____   _____

in the presence of (witness)   Director/Secretary

Name _____

Address _____

_____

Occupation _____

Health warning: This form should not be used if the original agreement is one which is regulated under the Consumer Credit Act 1974. Broadly speaking the Act, at the time of writing, applies to any loan, hire or hire purchase agreement for £25,000 or less. This is unless one of a limited number of exceptions applies (for example, a non-cash loan, if no more than four instalments are to be paid and they are all to be paid within a year, or if a loan is a low cost loan). If the Act does regulate the original agreement, it will also regulate any variation to the agreement (such as this one). In those circumstances, this form will not comply with the requirements of the Act and the agreement may therefore be unenforceable. Note also that by the time you use this form, the law may have changed so as to bring within the scope of the Act loans of more than £25,000, save for those which are entered into for the borrower's business, where the borrower's business is a firm with more than three partners. However, you may use this form in all circumstances if the debtor and the Customer are both limited companies.

Unless the agreement takes the form of a Deed, the Customer may not be able to rely upon it, because a promise by a Creditor to accept a lesser sum in full satisfaction of his debt will often fail if there is no consideration. In order to overcome this problem, the parties can either use the form of a Deed (such as appears above) or they can agree that the customer will make an additional promise to the Creditor going beyond a mere promise to pay the reduced sum. Just about anything will do. Paying a peppercorn in addition to the new sum will do. Most commonly, a debt is compromised because a disagreement has arisen as to how much is owing or as to whether anything is owing at all. The compromise of such an agreement will be sufficient consideration. If that is what you are doing, mention in a paragraph under 'whereas' the fact that a disagreement has arisen and that it is being compromised on the terms set out in this document.

Agreement to Extend Debt Payment   Form CDC03

THIS DEED is made the _____ day of _____ year _____

BETWEEN:

(1) _____ of _____ (the 'Customer'); and

(2) _____ of _____ (the 'Creditor').

WHEREAS:

(A) The Customer and the Creditor acknowledge that the Customer is indebted to the Creditor in the sum of £ _____ (the 'Debt'), which sum is now due and payable.

(B) The Creditor agrees to extend the term for payment of the Debt.

NOW THIS DEED WITNESSES as follows:

1.   The Creditor agrees to the payment of the Debt on extended terms, together with interest on the unpaid balance payable in the following manner: _____

_____

_____

2.   The Customer agrees to pay the Debt to the Creditor together with interest thereon under the terms set out in paragraph 1.

3.   In the event that the Customer shall fail to make any payment on the due date, the Creditor shall have full rights to collect the entire balance then remaining which amount shall be immediately due and payable and the Creditor shall be entitled to interest, both before and after any judgment, at the rate of _____% per annum on the said balance until judgment or sooner payment.

4.   In the event of default, the Customer agrees to pay all reasonable solicitors' fees and costs of collection.

5.   At the election of the Creditor, the Customer agrees to execute note(s) evidencing the balance then due on terms consistent with this agreement.

6.   This agreement shall be binding upon and inure to the benefit of the parties, their successors and assigns.

Continued on next page

Agreement to Extend Debt Payment (continued)   Form CDC03

IN WITNESS OF WHICH the parties have executed this deed the day and year first above written

(Individual)   (Company)

_____   Signed for and on behalf of:
Signed by the Customer   _____Ltd

_____   _____
in the presence of (witness)   Director
Name _____
Address _____   _____
_____   Director/Secretary
Occupation _____

_____   Signed for and on behalf of:
Signed by the creditor   _____Ltd

_____   _____
in the presence of (witness)   Director
Name _____
Address _____   _____
_____   Director/Secretary
Occupation _____

Health warning: This form should not be used if the original agreement is one which is regulated under the Consumer Credit Act 1974. Broadly speaking the Act, at the time of writing, applies to any loan, hire or hire purchase agreement for £25,000 or less. This is unless one of a limited number of exceptions applies (for example, a non-cash loan, no more than four instalments are to be paid and they are all to be paid within a year, or if a loan is a low cost loan). If the Act does regulate the original agreement, it will also regulate any variation to the agreement (such as this one). In those circumstances, this form will not comply with the requirements of the Act and the agreement may therefore be unenforceable. Note also that by the time you use this form, the law may have changed so as to bring loans of more than £25,000, save for those which are entered into for the borrower's business, within the scope of the Act loans of more than £25,000, save for those which are entered into for the borrower's business, where the borrower's business is a firm with more than three partners. However, you may use this form in all circumstances if the debtor and the Customer are both limited companies.

It is important that the document is signed and witnessed as provided for, because otherwise the promise to give time to pay may not be effective.

Agreement to Extend Performance Date   Form CDC04

THIS DEED is made the _____ day of _____ year _____

BETWEEN:

(1) _____ of _____ (the 'First Party'); and

(2) _____ of _____ (the 'Second Party').

WHEREAS:

(A)   The parties entered into an agreement dated _____ year _____ (the 'Agreement') which provides that full performance of the Agreement shall be completed by both parties on or before _____ year _____, (the 'Completion Date').

(B)   The parties acknowledge that the Agreement cannot be performed and completed by both parties by the Completion Date and therefore wish to extend the date for mutual performance of the Agreement.

NOW THIS DEED WITNESSES as follows:

1.   The parties hereby agree that the date for performance of the Agreement be continued and extended to _____ o'clock on _____day_____month_____year _____, [time being of the essence][1].

2.   No other variation of the terms of the Agreement, nor any extension of time for its performance is to be implied. The parties' rights in respect of any breach of the Agreement including, for the avoidance of doubt, any rights to claim damages for delayed completion, are hereby reserved.

3.   This agreement shall be binding upon and inure to the benefit of the parties, their successors and assigns.

Continued on next page

Agreement to Extend Performance Date (continued)   Form CDC04

IN WITNESS OF WHICH the parties have executed this deed the day and year first above written

(Individual)   (Company)

_____   Signed for and on behalf of:

Signed by the First Party   _____Ltd

_____   _____

in the presence of (witness)   Director
Name _____
Address _____   _____

_____   Director/Secretary
Occupation _____

                                                     Signed for and on behalf of:

_____   _____Ltd

Signed by the Second Party

_____   _____

in the presence of (witness)   Director
Name _____
Address _____   _____

_____   Director/Secretary
Occupation _____

---

[1] If you include these words it will mean that if one party is late in performing an obligation under the contract, the other party is free to terminate it, even if the delay is entirely trivial.

Agreement to Sell Personal Property (not land)   Form OLF07

THIS AGREEMENT is made the _____ day of _____ year _____

BETWEEN:

(1) _____ of _____ (the 'Buyer'); and

(2) _____ of _____ (the 'Seller').

NOW IT IS HEREBY AGREED as follows:

1.   The Seller agrees to sell, and the Buyer agrees to buy the following property (the 'Property'):

     _____

2.   The Buyer agrees to pay to the Seller and the Seller agrees to accept as total purchase price, inclusive

     of Value Added Tax if any, the sum of £ _____, payable as follows:

     £ _____ deposit herewith paid; and

     £ _____ the balance payable on delivery by cash, or cheque supported by bankers card.

3.   The Seller warrants it has good and legal title to the Property, full authority to sell the Property, and

     that the Property shall be sold free of all liens, charges, encumbrances, liabilities and adverse claims of

     every nature and description whatsoever.

[4. The Property is sold as seen, and the Seller disclaims any warranty of working order or condition of the

     Property except that it shall be sold in its present condition, reasonable wear and tear excepted.][1]

5.   The parties hereto agree to transfer title on _____ year _____, at the address of the

     Seller.

6.   This agreement shall be binding upon and inure to the benefit of the parties, their successors and assigns.

IN WITNESS OF WHICH the parties have signed this agreement the day and year first above.[1]

_____   _____

Signed by the Buyer   Signed by the Seller

_____   _____

in the presence of (witness)   in the presence of (witness)

Name _____   Name _____

Address _____   Address _____

_____   _____

Occupation _____   Occupation _____

---

[1] Delete unless either (1) the seller is not selling in the course of a business or (2) the buyer is buying in the course of a business and
     either he buys property of this type frequently or the property is not of a type which is normally acquired for private use.

Alteration to Terms of Employment   Form E68

Date _____ [1]

To   _____

_____

_____

This letter is to let you know that the terms and conditions of your contract have been amended as set out below.

If you wish to discuss any of these changes or require any further information, please let me know.

Date changes effective: _____

New wages/salary: _____

New hours of work: _____

New location: _____

Changes to duties and responsibilities: _____

Please acknowledge receipt of this letter and your agreement to the terms set out in it by signing the attached copy of this letter and returning it to _____. You should retain the top copy with your contract of employment.

_____

Signed

for

_____

I, _____, acknowledge that I have received a statement of alteration to the particulars of my employment as required by section 1 of the Employment Rights Act 1996 and agree to the terms set out in that statement.

_____

Signed

_____

Dated

Alteration to Terms of Employment   Form E68

---
[1] This must be no later than one month after the change to the terms of employment.

Anti-Gazumping Agreement   Form BS05

(AN EXCLUSIVITY CONTRACT BETWEEN THE BUYER & SELLER OF PROPERTY)

THIS AGREEMENT is made the _____ day of _____ year _____

BETWEEN

(1) _____ of _____(the 'Seller');

and

(2) _____ of _____(the 'Buyer').

BACKGROUND

A   The parties have, subject to contract, agreed to a transaction ('the Sale') in which the Seller will sell and the Buyer will buy the property described in the First Schedule ('the Property') at the price of (£ _____).

B   The solicitors specified in the Second Schedule ('the Seller's Solicitors') will act for the Seller on the Sale.

C   The solicitors specified in the Third Schedule ('the Buyer's Solicitors') will act for the Buyer on the Sale.

NOW IT IS HEREBY AGREED as follows:

1.   Exclusivity Period

     1.1   The Exclusivity Period shall begin on the exchange of this Agreement and shall end (subject to Clause 5.1 below) at 5 pm on the _____ day after the Buyer's Solicitors receive the draft contract from the Seller's Solicitors pursuant to Clause 2(b) below or on _____, whichever shall be the earlier.

     1.2   If and for as long as the Buyer complies with his obligations under this Agreement, the Seller agrees that during the Exclusivity Period neither the Seller nor anyone acting on the Seller's behalf will:

           (a)   seek purchasers for the Property;

           (b)   allow any prospective purchaser or mortgagee or any surveyor, valuer or other person acting on his or their behalf to enter the Property (other than under clause 4.3 below);

           (c)   provide a draft contract or property information concerning the Property to anyone other than the Buyer's Solicitors;

           (d)   negotiate or agree with anyone other than the Buyer or the Buyer's Solicitors any terms for the sale of the Property;

           (e)   enter into any commitment, whether or not legally binding, to proceed with any other potential purchaser following the expiry of the Exclusivity Period.

2.   Seller's instructions to solicitors

     The Seller will immediately:

     (a)   appoint the Seller's Solicitors to act for him on the Sale; and

     (b)   instruct them to send to the Buyer's Solicitors as soon as practicable a draft contract for the Sale and such information about the Property as accords with good conveyancing practice and to deal promptly and reasonably with any enquiries asked by the Buyer's Solicitors and with any amendments to the draft contract proposed by the Buyer's Solicitors.

3.   Buyer's instructions to solicitors

     The Buyer will immediately:

     (a)   appoint the Buyer's Solicitors to act for him on the Sale; and

     (b)   instruct them to make all necessary searches and enquiries as soon as practicable and to deal promptly and in accordance with good conveyancing practice with the draft contract for the Sale and such title and other information about the Property as they receive from the Seller's Solicitors and to negotiate with the Seller's Solicitors promptly and reasonably any amendments to the draft contract which the Buyer's Solicitors propose.

4.   Surveys, mortgages, etc.

     4.1   If the Buyer requires a mortgage loan in connection with the purchase of the Property, the Buyer

Continued on next page

Anti-Gazumping Agreement (continued)   Form BS05

shall within [one week] from the date of this Agreement apply to such building society, bank or other prospective lender ('the Mortgagee') as may reasonably be expected to lend the required amount to the Buyer and the Buyer shall complete such application forms and pay such fees as the Mortgagee shall require in order to process the Buyer's application as quickly as possible.

4.2   If the Buyer or the Mortgagee require the Property to be surveyed and/or valued, the Buyer will use all reasonable endeavours to arrange for the survey and/or valuation inspection to take place within _____ days of the date of this Agreement.

4.3   The Seller will give such access to the Property as is reasonably required by any surveyor or valuer appointed by the Buyer or the Mortgagee for the purpose of surveying and/or valuing the Property.

5.   Good faith and withdrawal

5.1   During the Exclusivity Period the Seller and the Buyer will deal with each other in good faith and in particular (but without limiting the above):

(a)   if during the Exclusivity Period the Buyer decides not to buy the Property or becomes unable to buy the Property, he will immediately give written notice to that effect to the Seller and the Exclusivity Period will then cease;

(b)   if during the Exclusivity Period the Seller decides not to proceed with the Sale or becomes unable to sell the Property, he will immediately give written notice to that effect to the Buyer and the Buyer's obligations under this Agreement will cease but the restrictions imposed on the Seller by Clause 1.2 above shall continue until the expiry of the Exclusivity Period.

(c)   The Buyer shall promptly furnish to the Seller any information which the Seller may reasonably require with regard to the Buyer's performance of his obligations under this Agreement and will not assert any claim of legal professional privilege in answer to such a request.

5.2   Nothing in Clause 5.1 above or elsewhere in this Agreement will impose on the Seller any greater duty to disclose matters affecting the Property than are imposed by statute or common law.

5.3   If the Buyer shall fail to comply with his obligations under this Agreement in any material respect or if the Buyer shall indicate to the Buyer that he is unwilling or unable to proceed save upon terms that the purchase price shall be reduced, the Seller shall be entitled to terminate the Exclusivity Period forthwith, and thereafter all obligations of the Seller under this Agreement will cease.

6.   Miscellaneous

6.1   This Agreement does not form part of any other contract.

6.2   In this Agreement the expression 'property information' includes title details and any other information about the Property which a prudent prospective buyer or his solicitors would require the seller or his solicitors to provide.

6.3   The headings shall not affect the interpretation of this Agreement.

THE FIRST SCHEDULE   THE SECOND SCHEDULE   THE THIRD SCHEDULE

The Property   The Seller's Solicitors   The Buyer's Solicitors

_____   _____   _____

_____   _____   _____

_____   _____   _____

SIGNED_____   SIGNED_____

by or on behalf of the Seller   by or on behalf of the Buyer

Health warning: It is important to know what this agreement can and what it cannot achieve. It can create an enforceable obligation in the seller, during a defined period, not to take any steps to sell the property to somebody else. The practical effect of such an obligation is that the seller will be more likely than not to keep to his promise that he would sell the property to the buyer on certain terms. Moreover, the various promises that are made about how the negotiations are conducted will, if they are not observed, tend to expose the true intentions of a buyer or seller who is just a time-waster. The Agreement cannot, however, create a legal obligation on the seller to negotiate in any particular way or actually to sell the property. Until everything is agreed there would be merely an 'agreement to agree' which would be too vague to be enforceable.

If you want to impose an obligation on a seller to sell the property to you at a given price and upon given terms, but you are not yet in a position to commit yourself the only way in which you can do it is by getting the seller to agree to grant you an option. For that, however, you will need a solicitor or licensed conveyancer to help you.

Application to be Accepted as a Guarantor   Form LB12

_____ Ltd.

Name of Company for which you wish to be a guarantor _____

Company's Registration No. _____

Company's address _____

_____

Your name _____

Your address _____

_____

How long have you been at this address? _____ years ____ months

(If less than one year, please give previous address _____

_____)

Your date of birth _____

Your home telephone number _____

Your work telephone number _____

Your mobile phone number _____

Your email address _____

Do you

☐   Own your home?

    If yes:

    Current value £ _____

    What percentage of the equity do you own? _____

    Is it mortgaged? If yes, name each mortgagee and state the amount of the mortgage debt.

    _____

☐   Rent your home?

    If yes, please give name and address of landlord?

    _____

☐   Other (please give details) _____

    _____

Your bank _____

Address of Branch _____

Account number _____

Application to be Accepted as a Guarantor   Form LB12

Continued on next page

Application to be Accepted as a Guarantor (continued)   Form LB12

Employer's name   _____

Employer's address_____

_____

Employer's telephone number _____

Employer's email address _____

Your current monthly salary £ _____

Are you self-employed? _____

If yes:

Please give name and address of your accountants:

_____

_____

What profits from that business did you declare as your income on your most recent tax return

£ _____

Date of return _____

If applicable, please state the maximum amount which you are prepared to guarantee:

£ _____

Is there any other matter which you regard as relevant to your application which you would like to tell us

about? _____

_____

I hereby apply for approval to be a guarantor for the above-mentioned company.

I authorise you _____ [1] in connection with this application to make enquires of and

to receive information about me from any bank, accountant, landlord, mortgagee, employer or credit

reference agency which you consider appropriate.

_____

(signed)

_____

(dated)

---

[1] Insert name of company giving credit.

Applicant's Request for an Employment Reference — Form E03

Date _____

To _____
_____
_____

Dear _____

The above named has applied to us for the position of _____ and has given us your name as a referee. We understand that _____ was employed by you from _____ to _____ as a _____. We should be grateful if you would confirm that this is the case and let us know whether, in your opinion, she performed her tasks competently and conscientiously.

We should also be grateful if you would let us know whether you would consider _____ a reliable and responsible employee. Could you also let us know the reasons why she left your employment?

We assure you that any reply you may give will be treated in the strictest confidence.

A stamped addressed envelope is enclosed.

Yours sincerely

_____

Application to Open a Credit Account   Form CDC05

with _____ Ltd

Company Name	
Address	Invoice Address (if different)
Tel No.	Fax No.
Name of Buyer	

VAT Registration No. Company Reg. No.	Value of Initial Order £	Requested Credit Limit £
Trade Reference (1)	Trade Reference (2)	Bank Reference

Parent Company (if applicable)

I hereby agree to the terms and conditions of sale accompanying this application.

NAME _____

POSITION _____

SIGNED _____ DATE _____

OFFICE USE ONLY					
	Date	Agency Rating	Credit Limit	Authorised	Date
Application Rec'd		Accounts Rec'd			
Refs Applied For					
Account Opened					

Account No. [_____]   Credit Limit [_____]

Health warning: Use this form only where the customer is a limited liability company or where for some other reason the Consumer Credit Act 1974 does not apply.

Assignment of Accounts Receivable with Non-Recourse   Form TA01

THIS AGREEMENT is made the _____ day of _____ year _____

BETWEEN:

(1) _____ of _____(the 'Assignor'); and

(2) _____ of _____(the 'Assignee').

NOW IT IS HEREBY AGREED as follows:

1.   In consideration for the payment of the sum of £ _____ (receipt of which the Assignor hereby acknowledges) the Assignor hereby assigns and transfers to the Assignee all rights, title and interest in and to the account(s) receivable described as follows (the 'Accounts'):

     _____

     _____

     _____

2.   The Assignor warrants that the Account(s) are due and the Assignor has not received payment for the same or any part thereof.

3.   The Assignor further warrants that it has full title to the Accounts, full authority to sell and transfer the Accounts and that the Accounts are sold free and clear of all liens, encumbrances and any known claims.

4.   This Agreement shall be binding upon and inure to the benefit of the parties, their successors and assigns.

5.   Upon being required by the Assignee so to do the Assignor shall forthwith instruct each person indebted under the Accounts herein assigned, that payment should be made direct to the Assignee.

IN WITNESS OF WHICH the parties have signed this Agreement the day and year first above written

_____   _____

Signed by or on behalf of the Assignor   Signed by or on behalf of the Assignee

_____   _____

in the presence of (witness)   in the presence of (witness)

Name _____   Name _____

Address _____   Address _____

_____   _____

Occupation _____   Occupation _____

Note: Non-recourse means that the risk of the debtor not paying is on the assignee and that if the parties wish to place the risk on the assignor they should add a term stating 'if the indebtedness due under any Account shall not be paid by _____, the Assignee shall be entitled to require the Assignor to repurchase the Account for the sum that was paid by the Assignee to the Assignor in respect of the same plus interest at _____% per annum from that date.

Assignment of Contract

Form TA02

THIS DEED is made the _____ day of _____ year _____

BETWEEN:

(1) _____ of _____(the 'Assignor');

(2) _____ of _____(the 'Assignee'); and

(3) _____ of _____(the 'Third Party').

WHEREAS:

(A)   The Assignor and the Third Party have entered into an agreement dated_____ _____

year _____ (the 'Agreement').

(B)   With the consent of the Third Party the Assignor wishes to assign all its rights and obligations under the Agreement to the Assignee.

NOW THIS DEED WITNESSES as follows:

1.   The Assignor warrants and represents that the Agreement is in full force and effect and is fully assignable.

2.   In consideration of £_____ paid by the [Assignee to the Assignor], [Assignor to the Assignee] The Assignor hereby assigns its rights under the Agreement to the Assignee and the Assignee hereby assumes and agrees to perform all the remaining and executory obligations of the Assignor under the Agreement and agrees to indemnify and hold the Assignor harmless from any claim or demand resulting from non-performance or defective performance by the Assignee.

[3.   The Assignee shall be entitled to all monies remaining to be paid under the Agreement, which rights are also assigned hereunder.]

4.   The Assignor warrants that the Agreement has not been modified and that the terms contained therein remain in force. [The Assignor further agrees to indemnify the Assignee and hold the Assignee harmless from any claim or demand resulting from non-performance or defective performance by the Assignor prior to the date hereof.]

5.   The Assignor further warrants that it has full right and authority to transfer the Agreement and that the Agreement rights herein transferred are free of lien, encumbrance or adverse claim.

[6.   The Third Party agrees to the assignment of the Agreement upon the terms stated herein, [and agrees further that as regards any future non-performance or defective performance he shall have recourse only against the Assignee] or [but without prejudice to his right of recourse against the Assignor in respect of any non-performance or defective performance, whenever the same may occur.]]

IN WITNESS OF WHICH the parties have executed this deed the day and year first above written

Continued on next page

Assignment of Contract (continued)   Form TA02

(Individual)   (Company)

_____   Signed for and on behalf of _____

Signed by the Assignor   _____Ltd

_____   _____

in the presence of (witness)   Director

Name _____

Address _____   _____

_____   Director/Secretary

Occupation _____

_____   Signed for and on behalf of:_____

Signed by the Assignee   _____Ltd

_____   _____

in the presence of (witness)   Director

Name _____

Address _____   _____

_____   Director/Secretary

Occupation _____

Note: In law, it is possible to assign the benefit of a contract without the consent of the other party to the contract. However, care needs to be taken to ensure that the other party knows about the assignment. It is also possible for one party to delegate performance of the contract to somebody else without such consent, unless personal performance is part of what is expected, say in a contract to paint a portrait.

However, if one party has duties under the contract, it is not possible to assign the legal responsibility to perform those duties without the consent of the other party to the contract. For example, if I contract to deliver a tonne of coal, I can perform that contract by getting somebody else to deliver it, but I remain responsible to ensure that it is delivered and that it is of the correct grade. Therefore, if the contract is not properly performed, I can be sued, although I may have delegated its performance.

The effect of this form is to provide for one person to take over the benefits and the performance of the duties under a contract which arise in the future, and to be indemnified for any breaches of contract which the assignor may have committed before the assignment. Sometimes, a contract is profitable, and a person will pay for the privilege of taking it over. Sometimes, a contract is unprofitable, and a person will pay for the privilege of having someone else take it on. In this form you will find wording in square brackets to cover either possibility. Make sure that you strike out the one which does not apply.

There are also square brackets to cover the question of whether the third party is to continue to have a remedy against the Assignor after the assignment. Again make sure that you strike out the one which does not apply, and that it is altered, if necessary, in such a way as to reflect your intentions.

Assignment of Insurance Policy

Form TA04

THIS DEED is made the _____ day of _____ year _____

BETWEEN:

(1) _____ of _____ (the 'Assignor'); and

(2) _____ of _____ (the 'Assignee').

WHEREAS:

(A)   The Assignor is the holder of a Policy of Insurance number _____ issued by the

_____ Insurance Company (the 'Policy').

(B)   The Assignor wishes to assign the benefit of the Policy to the Assignee.

NOW THIS DEED WITNESSES as follows:

1.   The Assignor warrants that the Policy is in full force and effect and all premiums thereon have been paid in

full to date.

2.   The Assignor further warrants that he/she has full authority to transfer the Policy, and shall execute all

further documents as may be required by the Insurance Company or broker to effect this Assignment.

3.   The Assignor hereby assigns to the Assignee and the Assignee hereby accepts the assignment of the

Policy and all the obligations and benefits attaching thereto.

4.   This assignment shall by binding upon and inure to the benefit of the parties, their successors and assigns.

IN WITNESS OF WHICH the parties have executed this deed the day and year first above written

(Individual)

_____

Signed by the Assignor

_____

in the presence of (witness)

Name _____

Address _____

_____

Occupation _____

_____

Signed by the Assignee

_____

in the presence of (witness)

Name _____

Address _____

_____

Occupation _____

(Company)

Signed for and on behalf of _____

_____Ltd

Director

_____

Director/Secretary

Signed for and on behalf of:

_____Ltd

Director

_____

Director/Secretary

Note: This form is suitable for a case where property is being sold along with the benefit of an insurance policy. It is not suitable where an insurance policy is being assigned as security for a debt owed by the Assignor to the Assignee. **Above all, remember that it is absolutely essential** for the insurance company to be informed about the sale and to agree to the assignment of the property before the sale takes place, as otherwise the policy could be made void. If you only want to assign your entitlement to monies which you are expecting to receive under a claim that has already been made, as opposed to the right to be insured against future mishaps, then you only need to use a form for the assignment of a debt, modified slightly so as to specify the payment the name of the insurance company and the nature of the claim. In that case, too, it is wise to discuss the matter with the insurance company in advance.

Assignment of Money Due

THIS agreement is made the _____ day of _____ year _____

BETWEEN:

(1) _____ of _____ (the 'Assignor'); and

(2) _____ of _____ (the 'Assignee').

WHEREAS:

(A)   The Assignor is entitled to the payment of certain monies under a contract dated

_____ year _____ ('the Contract') and made between the Assignor

and_____ _____ (the 'the Third Party').

(B)   The Assignor wishes to assign the benefit of the Contract to the Assignee.

NOW IT IS HEREBY AGREED as follows:

1.   In consideration for the sum of £_____, receipt of which the Assignor hereby acknowledges, the Assignor assigns and transfers to the Assignee all monies now due and payable to the Assignor and to become due and payable to the Assignor under the terms of the Contract to the Assignee.

2.   The Assignor hereby warrants that there has been no breach of the Contract by any party, and that the Assignor is in full compliance with all the terms and conditions of the Contract, and that he has not assigned or encumbered all or any rights under said contract.

3.   The Assignor authorises and directs the Third Party to deliver any and all cheques, drafts, or payments to be issued pursuant to Contract to the Assignee; and further authorises the Assignee to receive such cheques, drafts, or payments from, and to collect any and all funds due or to become due pursuant thereto.

4.   The Assignee will at the Assignor's request, immediately serve notice in writing upon the Third Party informing him of the assignment to the Assignee of the Assignor's rights under and in respect of the Contract and requiring him to forward to the Assignee a copy of the notice, signed by the Third Party.

IN WITNESS OF WHICH the parties have signed this agreement the day and year first above written

_____   _____

Signed by or on behalf of the Assignor   Signed by or on behalf of the Assignee

_____   _____

in the presence of (witness)   in the presence of (witness)

Name _____   Name _____

Address _____   Address _____

_____   _____

Occupation _____   Occupation _____

Note: It is essential to inform the Third Party of the assignment as soon as possible, because it is only after notice that the third party will be obliged to pay the Assignee instead of the Assignor. Until the third party is informed, the Assignee will have no remedy against him if he pays the debt to the Assignor, and although the Assignee would have a remedy against the Assignor, that remedy will not necessarily be worth anything against an Assignor who has accepted a payment to which he is no longer entitled.

The assignment is complete as soon as the third party knows of it, no matter who informs him. As a practical matter, however, it is best if the Assignor informs him, because otherwise the third party will be left in doubt as to whether the debt has really been assigned, and he will probably not act upon the assignment without the Assignor's confirmation. If the Assignor refuses to confirm the assignment, the third party will be entitled not to pay until a court decides the matter.

Assignment of Option
Form TA06

THIS AGREEMENT is made the _____ day of _____ year _____

BETWEEN:

(1) _____ of _____(the 'Assignor'); and

(2) _____ of _____(the 'Assignee').

WHEREAS:

(A)   The Assignor has been granted the following option (the 'Option')[1]: _____

_____

_____

_____

(B)   The Assignor wishes to sell the Option to the Assignee.

NOW IT IS HEREBY AGREED as follows:

1.   In consideration for the payment of £ _____, receipt of which the Assignor hereby acknowledges, the Assignor hereby assigns to the Assignee his/her entire interest in the Option and all his/her right thereunder to the Assignee with [Full]/[Limited]/Title Guarantee.

2.   The Assignee, by accepting the transfer of this Option, agrees to exercise the Option, if at all, according to its terms.

3.   This agreement shall be binding upon and inure to the benefit of the parties, their successors and assigns.

IN WITNESS OF WHICH the parties have signed this agreement as a deed the day and year first above written

_____   _____

Signed by or on behalf of the Assignor   Signed by or on behalf of the Assignee

_____   _____

in the presence of (witness)   in the presence of (witness)

Name _____   Name _____

Address _____   Address _____

_____   _____

Occupation _____   Occupation _____

Note: This form is not appropriate for an assignment of an interest in land. For such an assignment use the form TA07.

The words 'Full Title Guarantee' and 'Limited Title Guarantee' incorporate different promises into the assignment. It is best to refer to a solicitor about these. For present purposes these promises relate to the absence of charges and incumbrances. If the Title Guarantee is full, the Assignor promises that the Option is free of any such charges etc except those which he could not reasonably be expected to know about. If the Title Guarantee is Limited, the Assignor promises merely that the Assignor has not charged the Option and that he is not aware of anyone else having done so since the time it was created or last sold. As a rough guide, Limited Title Guarantee is appropriate where the Assignor has inherited the Option, whereas Full Title Guarantee is appropriate where the Assignor has paid for it. If the Option has been created I enwriting, then set out a full description of all of the documents which have created the Option. Better still, state that the documents are attached to the Option and then attach them.

Note that an Option cannot be assigned if it is personal to the Assignor. The Option should be examined carefully in order to determine whether there is a potential problem here.

[1]   Enter Option details, in particular the price paid for the Option, the items which the Assignor has the right to purchase and the deadline for exercising the Option. An Option is personal if it is intended by the person granting it and the person to whom it is granted that it should be exercisable only by the grantee and not by anyone to whom he might assign the Option.

Assignment of Option to Purchase Land — Form TA07

THIS AGREEMENT is made the _____ day of _____ year _____

BETWEEN:

(1) _____ of _____(the 'Assignor'); and

(2) _____ of _____(the 'Assignee').

WHEREAS:

(A) The Assignor is the holder of an option granted on _____ to purchase property located at
_____ which expires on _____ year _____ (the 'Option'), a copy of which is annexed.

(B) The Assignor wishes to sell the Option to the Assignee.

NOW IT IS HEREBY AGREED as follows:

1. In consideration for the payment of £ _____, receipt of which the Assignee hereby acknowledges, the Assignor hereby transfers his/her entire interest in the Option and all his/her rights thereunder with [Full]/[Limited] Title Guarantee to the Assignee absolutely.

2. The Assignor warrants that the Option is fully assignable.

3. The Assignee, by accepting the transfer of the Option, agrees to exercise the Option, if at all, according to its terms.

4. This agreement shall be binding upon and inure to the benefit of the parties, their successors and assigns.

IN WITNESS OF WHICH the parties have signed this agreement as a Deed the day and year first above written.

_____   _____

Signed by or on behalf or the Assignor   Signed by or on behalf of the Assignee

_____   _____

in the presence of (witness)   in the presence of (witness)

Name _____   Name _____

Address _____   Address _____

_____   _____

Occupation _____   Occupation _____

Note: The words 'Full Title Guarantee' and 'Limited Title Guarantee' incorporate different promises into the Assignment. It is best to refer to a solicitor about these. For present purposes, these promises relate to the absence of charges and incumbrances. If the Title Guarantee is Full, the Assignor promises that the Option is free of any such charges etc except those which he could not reasonably be expected to know about. If the Title Guarantee is Limited, the Assignor promises merely that the Assignor has not charged the Option and that he is not aware of anyone else having done so since the time it was created or last sold. As a rough guide, Limited Title Guarantee is appropriate where the Assignor has inherited the Option, whereas Full Title Guarantee is appropriate where the Assignor has paid for it.

An Option cannot be assigned if it is personal to the Assignor. The Option should be examined carefully in order to determine whether there is a potential problem here.

An Option is the right to enter into a binding contract. Contracts for the sale of land usually involve large sums of money and are often complicated. Make certain that you fully understand the obligations which you are taking on and the rights which you are acquiring under the contract to which the Option refers. If you have any doubts at all, see your solicitor.

It is very important to register a Notice of the Option and of the Assignee's entitlement under this Option at H.M. Land Registry, as otherwise the interest created by this Option will be defeated if the land is sold to somebody else and if the sale is registered.

It is important to remember that the grant or assignment of an Option for the purchase of an interest in land may be subject to Stamp Duty Land Tax and must be declared to the Stamp Duty Land Tax Office by the Grantee or Assignee on a form SDLT1 even if no tax is payable. There are strict time limits which must be observed, otherwise you may be liable for a fine. The helpline for the Office is 0845 6030135. It is especially important to note that an Option to acquire any interest in land must be granted in writing and observe the requirements set out in the Law of Property (Miscellaneous Provisions) Act 1989. See a solicitor to make sure that the Option is valid.

Authorisation to Release Confidential Information   Form OLF08

Date _____

To _____

_____

_____

Dear _____

I hereby authorise and request you to send copies of the following documents which I believe to be in your possession and which contain confidential information concerning me to:

Name _____

Address _____

_____

_____

Documents:_____

_____

_____

_____

_____

[I shall of course reimburse you for any reasonable costs incurred by you in providing the requested information.]

Yours sincerely

Signature _____

Name _____

Address _____

_____

Authorisation to Release Employment Information Form E04

Date _____

To _____
_____
_____

Dear _____

I hereby authorise and request you to send the information ticked below to:

☐ the following party: _____
☐ any third party _____

The information to be released includes: (tick)
☐ Salary
☐ Position/department/section
☐ Date employment commenced
☐ Part-time/full-time or hours worked
☐ Garnishee orders or wage attachments, if any
☐ Reason for redundancy
☐ Medical/accident/illness reports
☐ Work performance rating
☐ Other:_____

Yours sincerely

Employee Signature _____
Print Name_____
Position or Title _____
Department _____

Authorisation to Release Medical Information   Form OLF09

Date _____

To _____

_____

_____

Dear _____

I hereby authorise and request that you release and deliver to: _____

_____

_____

_____

_____

all my medical records, files, charts, x-rays, laboratory reports, clinical records, and such other information concerning me that is in your possession. I would also request that you do not disclose any information concerning my past or present medical condition to any other person without my express written permission.

Yours sincerely

Signature _____

Printed Name _____

In the presence of

Witness's address _____

_____

Authorisation to Return Goods   Form BS06

Date _____

To _____

_____

_____

Dear _____

This letter is to confirm that we shall accept the return of certain goods we have supplied to you and credit your account. The terms for return are:

1.   The value of the goods returned shall not exceed £ _____.

2.   We shall deduct _____ % of the invoice value as a handling charge and credit your account with the balance.

3.   All return goods shall be in a re-saleable condition and must be goods we either currently stock or can return to our supplier for credit. We reserve the right to refuse the return of goods that do not correspond with this description.

4.   You shall be responsible for the costs of shipment and the risk of loss or damage in transit. Goods shall not be accepted for return until we have received, inspected and approved the goods at our place of business.

5.   Our agreement to accept returns for credit is expressly conditional upon your agreement to settle any remaining balance due on the following terms: _____

_____

_____

Yours sincerely

_____

Health warning: Do not use this form if your customer has suggested that the goods are defective, or if he has purchased the goods in a consumer sale as to which see the notes to form BS03 above. This is to avoid you committing a breach of the Consumer Transactions (Restrictions on Statements) Order 1976 (as amended).

Board Resolution: Appointment of Auditors Form C07

THE COMPANIES ACT 1985
PRIVATE COMPANY LIMITED BY SHARES
WRITTEN RESOLUTION OF THE BOARD OF DIRECTORS

Company Number: _____

_____ LIMITED

Pursuant to the Articles of Association of the Company, the undersigned, being all the directors of the company, hereby resolve:

THAT _____

of _____ be the auditors

of the Company with effect from _____ at a fee to be agreed.[1]

Directors' signatures: Date of each signature:

_____   _____

_____   _____

_____   _____

---

[1] Generally, the directors may appoint only the first auditors of the company who may hold office until the conclusion of the first general meeting at which accounts are presented to the members. The auditors must then be reappointed at this general meeting or, subject to the giving of special notice, an alternative auditor can be appointed by a resolution of the shareholders. The directors may also, however, fill any casual vacancy in the office of auditor – such appointment is only effective until the conclusion of the next general meeting at which accounts are presented to the shareholders. It should be noted that, in the case of private companies only, an elective resolution may be passed which removes the requirement for auditors to be reappointed annually. A copy of such a resolution must be reported to Companies House within 15 days of its being passed.

Many small private companies are exempt from having to appoint auditors.

Details of the exemptions and the requirements as to filing documents can be found on the Companies House website at www.companieshouse.gov.uk.

Board Resolution:
Approval and Registration of Transfer of Shares

Form C27

THE COMPANIES ACT 1985
PRIVATE COMPANY LIMITED BY SHARES
WRITTEN RESOLUTION OF THE BOARD OF DIRECTORS

Company Number: _____
_____ LIMITED

Pursuant to the Articles of Association of the Company, the undersigned, being all the directors of the Company, hereby resolve:

THAT in accordance with the Company's Articles of Association and subject to its being presented with a duly stamped share transfer form the directors approve the transfer of _____ shares of _____ each from _____

to _____ on _____,

THAT the name of _____be entered in the register of members in respect of the shares transferred to him/her and THAT the Secretary be instructed to prepare a share certificate in respect of the shares transferred and to deliver it to _____

_____.[1]

Directors' signatures: Date of each signature:

_____   _____

_____   _____

_____   _____

---

[1] Check the articles - they may have a restriction on the transfer of shares. Table A places no restrictions on transfers of fully-paid shares. They may also allow the directors to refuse to register a transfer, although again Table A does not allow them to refuse to register the transfer of fully-paid shares. However, it does entitle the directors to require proof that the transferor is entitled to make the transfer (e.g. by requiring presentation of the share certificate).

Board Resolution:
Approval of Directors' Report and Accounts

Form C14

THE COMPANIES ACT 1985
PRIVATE COMPANY LIMITED BY SHARES
WRITTEN RESOLUTION OF THE BOARD OF DIRECTORS

Company Number: _____

_____ LIMITED

Pursuant to the Articles of Association of the Company, the undersigned, being all the directors of the Company, hereby resolve:

THAT the directors' report and accounts for the year ended _____

have been prepared in accordance with the Companies Act 1985[1] and are hereby approved, and _____

_____

be authorised to sign the report and the balance sheet on behalf of the Company.

Directors' signatures: Date of each signature:

_____   _____

_____   _____

_____   _____

Note: A director or two directors must sign the balance sheet. The directors' report must be signed by either a director or by the company secretary. Where different individuals sign, the resolution should be amended to reflect this. Any copy of the balance sheet and of the report which is laid before the general meeting of the company must state the name of the person who signed it on behalf of the company. Note that there are penalties for late filing of these documents. If yours is a 'small company' you may wish to check whether various possible exemptions for filing directors' reports and for abbreviating the company's accounts apply to your company.

[1]   From 1 October 2007 the provisions of the Companies Act 2006 relating to accounts will be in force from which time you should refer to the provisions of the Companies Act 2006. You should check with Companies House to see to what extent any legislative requirements may be altered in the future with regard to the company's accounts and the filing of them.

Board Resolution: Proposal of Alteration of Articles

THE COMPANIES ACT 1985
PRIVATE COMPANY LIMITED BY SHARES
WRITTEN RESOLUTION OF THE BOARD OF DIRECTORS

Company Number: _____

_____ LIMITED

Pursuant to the Articles of Association of the Company the undersigned, being all the directors of the Company, hereby resolve:

THAT an [extraordinary general]/[A] meeting of the Company be convened[1] to authorise the alteration of the Articles as set out below

(1)   By deletion of Articles _____

       and   _____

       and altering the subsequent numbering accordingly.

(2)   By the addition of the new Articles as set out in the attached document to be

       numbered _____

       and   _____ .

Directors' signatures: Date of each signature:

_____   _____

_____   _____

_____   _____

---

[1] At present 21 clear days' notice must be given (i.e. not counting the day when notice is received or when the meeting is held); although in the case of a private company, the holders of 95 per cent of the shares which entitle the holder to attend the meeting may if they agree specify a shorter period of notice.

From 1 October 2007 only 14 days' notice will be required of any meeting of a private company unless it is proposed to pass a resolution requiring special notice, in which case 28 days' notice will be required. Although a 'special resolution' is required to alter the articles, 'special notice' is not required. Therefore, 14 days' notice will suffice for this purpose. Also, the holders of 90 percent of the voting shares will be able to consent to short notice of the meeting except where a resolution requiring special notice is to be considered. A special resolution requires a majority of 75 percent. The company is required by law to keep copies of all board resolutions and all minutes of general meetings for 10 years.

Board Resolution to Call [Annual] General Meeting   Form B04

_____ Limited

We, being all the directors of _____Limited

who are entitled to receive notice of a meeting of the directors, RESOLVE that an annual general meeting of

the Company shall be convened on the _____ day of _____ year _____ for the

following purposes: _____

_____

_____

_____

_____

_____

_____

_____

_____

and that the secretary be instructed to give notice of the meeting to all shareholders [and obtain the

consent of all members to the meeting being held on short notice].[1]

Dated this _____ day of _____ year _____

_____

Director's Signature

_____

Director's Signature

_____

Director's Signature

[1] 21 clear days' notice must be given (i.e. not counting the day when notice is received or when the meeting is held). If the meeting is
    to be held on short notice, add the wording in square brackets.

From 1 October 2007 private companies are no longer obliged to hold an annual general meeting. Whenever a meeting is to be held
only 14 days' notice will be required unless it is proposed to pass a resolution requiring special notice, in which case 28 days' notice will
be required. The form is retained because many companies will find it convenient to hold AGMs. Also, the holders of 90 percent of the
voting shares will be able to consent to short notice of the meeting except where a resolution requiring special notice is to be
considered. A special resolution requires a majority of 75 percent. The company is required by law to keep copies of all board
resolutions and all minutes of general meetings for 10 years.

Board Resolution to Call Extraordinary General Meeting

_____ Limited

We, being all the directors of _____Limited
who are entitled to receive notice of a meeting of directors, RESOLVE that an extraordinary general meeting
of the company be convened forthwith for the purpose of considering and, if thought fit, passing the
following resolution(s) as (a) special resolution(s) or (an) ordinary resolution(s) as appropriate[1]: _____

_____
_____
_____
_____
_____
_____

[The Company Secretary be instructed to arrange to obtain the consent of the requisite majority of
members to the meeting being held on short notice.]

Dated this _____ day of _____ year _____

_____

Director's Signature

_____

Director's Signature

_____

Director's Signature

[1] 21 clear days' notice must be given (i.e. not counting the day when notice is received or when the meeting is held). If the meeting is
    to be held on short notice then add the words in square brackets. The requisite majority is 95 per cent of the shareholders. Certain
    types of resolution, for example to remove a director before the end of the term or to remove auditors, require 'special notice' of 28
    days. Note that forms for these types of resolution are found elsewhere in this book.

From 1 October 2007 the distinction between annual general meetings and extraordinary general meetings will be abolished in the
case of private companies. For resolutions made after that date use form B04 instead of this form.

Breach of Contract Notice   Form OLF10

Date _____

To _____

_____

_____

Dear _____

We refer to the agreement between us dated _____, which provides that:

_____

_____

_____

PLEASE TAKE NOTE that you are in breach of your obligations under the agreement as follows: _____

_____

_____

_____

We invite you to remedy the breach by immediately taking steps to do the following: _____

_____

_____

_____

If you fail to remedy the breach as requested within 14 days of the date of this letter, such period being provided in clause _____ of the agreement, we shall have no alternative but to commence legal proceedings to claim damages from you as a result of the breach. We will also hold you liable for the costs of those proceedings.

Yours sincerely

Name _____

Address _____

_____

Note: Use this form if , but only if, you do not wish to put an end to the contract altogether. If you think it would be best to refuse to perform any more of your obligations under it, and to refuse to accept any further performance of it by the other party, you could deprive yourself of this option if you use this form. Remember, however that putting an end to a contract because of the other party's breach can be very risky, because if you are not entitled to end the contract, the other party will be able to claim against you for breach. Therefore, if you want to put an end to the contract, it is essential that you to consult a solicitor.

Builder/Decorator Contract Form OLF11

DATED_____

BETWEEN

(1) _____ of _____

_____ (the 'Employer');

and

(2) _____ of _____

_____(the 'Contractor').

NOW IT IS HEREBY AGREED :

1. The Contractor shall carry out the Works as defined below ('the Works').

2. The Works shall be[1] _____

_____

_____

_____

_____

_____

_____

Any plans or specifications that form part of the description of the Works are attached, have been signed by both parties and form part of this Contract.

3. The Works shall be carried out at_____('the Site') under the direction of _____(['the Foreman']/ ['the Architect'] / ['the Surveyor'])*.

4. The Employer shall pay to the Contractor for the Works £ _____ payable as follows:

_____.

or [The Contractor shall every ____ weeks during the course of this Contract submit to [the Foreman]/[the Architect]/[the Surveyor]* a claim for payment for the works thus far done and shall provide all documents which may be necessary to support the claim whereupon the Employer shall pay to the Contractor the amount certified by [the Foreman]/[the Architect]/[the Surveyor]* as being the value of the works done during the period to which the certificate relates. [_____ per cent of the said sum shall be retained for a period of 6 months following practical completion (as defined below) at which time the Employer shall pay the same to the Contractor subject to such deductions in respect of unremedied defects, not evident at the time of practical completion, as the Contractor and Employer may agree or as may be determined by a court or arbitrator]. For the purposes of this Contract 'Practical Completion' shall mean the apparent completion of the works (as amended in accordance with Clause 11 hereof)) without the presence of any evident omission or defect.]

Continued on next page

Builder/Decorator Contract (continued)   Form OLF11

5.   The Contractor shall begin the Works on or before _____ and shall complete the Works on or

before _____ (the 'Completion Date') or such later date as may be determined under Clause 12

hereof. If the Works have not been completed by the Completion Date or later as aforesaid the

Contractor shall pay or allow to the Employer £_____ for every_____ or part_____ between

the Completion Date and the date of actual completion as liquidated damages which sum the parties

agree is a reasonable pre-estimate of losses arising from such delay. The Contractor shall not, however,

be responsible for delays outside his control and not reasonably foreseeable by him.

6.   The_____ shall obtain every licence, permission or authority required for the exercise

of the Works and the _____ shall pay all the fees or charges in respect of them.

7.   In carrying out the Works, the Contractor shall use all reasonable skill, care and diligence, suitable good

quality materials and comply with any higher specifications of materials or workmanship contained in

the description of the Works and shall further comply with all applicable building regulations and

other statutory provisions and shall at its own expense procure all appropriate certifications that such

regulations have been complied with.

8.   The Contractor shall take all reasonable precautions to minimise disruption and the risk of any loss or

damage at the Site arising out of the execution of the Works. On completion of the Works the

Contractor shall leave the Site clean and tidy to the reasonable satisfaction of the Employer and shall

make good at his own cost all damage caused by execution of the Works.

9.   The Contractor shall promptly make good any defects or faults which appear within six months of the

date of actual completion and are due to materials or workmanship not being in accordance with this

Contract entirely at his own expense insofar as the cost of such remedy may exceed the sum retained

in accordance with Clause 4 hereof.

10. The Contractor shall be responsible for any loss or damage to the Site and any death or personal injury

or damage to property arising out of the execution of the Works. The Contractor confirms that he has

or will obtain adequate insurance (being not less than £_____) against any liability and will

produce evidence of it to the Employer on request. The Works shall be at the Contractor's risk until

completion. The [Employer]/[Contractor]*shall obtain and maintain throughout the period prior to

Practical Completion, a policy of insurance in the joint names of the Contractor and the Employer

against any damage to the Site as may be caused by fire, lightning, aircraft, explosion, earthquake,

storm, flood, escape of water or oil, riot, malicious damage, theft or attempted theft (including theft of

materials not fixed), falling trees and branches and aerials, subsidence, heave, landslip, collision, and

accidental damage to underground services (such cover to include professional fees, demolition and

site clearance costs). The nature of the Works and the periods during which the Site is likely to be

unoccupied shall be disclosed in the proposal for the policy. Such policy shall require that sums paid

Continued on next page

Builder/Decorator Contract (continued)   Form OLF11

out thereunder shall be paid to the Employer.

11.   The Employer shall be entitled to vary, delete or add to the Works. In the case of any such variation or addition the price of the Works shall be increased or decreased by a reasonable amount, taking into account the rates for which work is charged under this Contract.

12.   If there shall be any variation of the Works under Clause 11 hereof or if there shall be any delay to the Works by reason of the occurrence of matters, which were not caused by any act or omission of the Contractor, or which the occurrence of which was not reasonably foreseeable by the Contractor, the date for practical completion of the Works shall be extended by such reasonable period as [the Foreman]/[the Architect]/[the Surveyor]* _____ shall determine.

IN WITNESS OF WHICH the parties hereto have signed this Agreement the day and year first above written.

SIGNED   _____   _____

              Signed by or on behalf of the Contractor   in the presence of (witness)

                                                              Name   _____

                                                              Address _____

                                                              _____

              Dated _____   Occupation _____

SIGNED   _____   _____

              Signed by the Employer _____   in the presence of (witness)

                                                              Name   _____

                                                              Address _____

                                                              _____

              Dated _____   Occupation _____

Note that this contract should only be used where the contractor has engaged the builder to work on his residence.

¹   It may be desirable to price each item separately.

*Delete as appropriate.

Builders' Work Complaint   Form GS03

Date   _____

To   _____

_____

_____

Ref Estimate No. _____

Dear   _____

You carried out building work at the following address: _____

_____

as per the above estimate finishing on: _____.

I am writing to inform you that the work has proved to be defective in the following manner: _____

_____

_____

_____

[The terms of our Contract] or [The Supply of Goods and Services Act 1982 and the common law]* requires that you should have completed the work with reasonable skill and care using appropriate materials of suitable quality. The defects described above clearly indicate that you have not fulfilled your legal obligations and that you are in breach of contract.

While reserving my rights, I am giving you the opportunity to carry out remedial repairs free of charge. Failing that I will obtain quotations from other builders and will have them carry out the work, claiming any expenses incurred from you as I am entitled to do by law.

I look forward to hearing from you within seven days.

Yours sincerely

Signature   _____

Name   _____

Address   _____

_____

Tel.   _____

* Delete as appropriate

Cancellation of an Order to Stop a Cheque   Form OLF12

Date   _____

To   _____

_____

_____

Dear   _____

On   _____,

we requested you to stop payment on the following cheque that we issued:

Cheque No: _____

Dated: _____

Amount: _____

Payable to: _____

Account No: _____

We have now advised the payee to re-present the cheque for payment, and we should be grateful if you would now honour the cheque on re-presentation.

Yours sincerely

Signature   _____

Account   _____

Account No.   _____

Certificate of Product Conformity   Form BS07

_____ Ltd

To:				Order No:	
				Ref No:	
FAO:				Date:	
Product ID	Qty	Description	Spec no.	Model no	Test reports

This certifies that all of the above goods have been inspected, tested and unless otherwise stated conform in all respects to the order requirements.

Signed _____

Customer Services Manager

Change of Name Deed   Form PF19

THIS DEED (which is intended to be enrolled at the Central Office of the Supreme Court) is made by me

[formerly] [now] called _____ [1] of _____ this_____day

of_____20__

WITNESSES AND IT IS HEREBY DECLARED

1   I am a [Commonwealth citizen]/[British citizen]/[British Overseas Territories Citizen]/[British Overseas

    Citizen [under section ____ of the British Nationality Act 1981][2]

2   I absolutely renounce and abandon the use of my former name of _____ and assume

    adopt and determine to take and use the name of _____ [3]

3   I authorise and require all persons at all times to refer to describe and address me as

    _____

4   I declare that I am [single]/[married]/[divorced]/[a widow[er]/[a civil partner]/[[a former civil partner

    under a civil partnership which has ended by [death][dissolution]]

[5 [I confirm that the forenames which I am renouncing and the use of which I am abandoning in this Deed

    have not been conferred upon me in a ceremony of baptism] [Although the change of name herein

    effected involves the change of forenames, which were conferred upon me in a ceremony of baptism, I

    confirm that I have decided to use my new forenames in place of my former forenames, notwithstanding

    the decision of. Mr. Justice Vaisey in *re Parrott*]][4]

SIGNED AS A DEED AND DELIVERED:

By the above-named:

Formerly known as:

In the presence of

Name :_____

Address:_____

Name:_____

Address;_____

Continued on next page

Change of Name Deed (continued)   Form PF19

[I, _____ of _____address hereby certify that I am the [husband]/[wife]/[civil partner] of the

above-mentioned _____ [5] and that I hereby consent to the Change of Name effected by this Deed

from _____ [6] to _____ [7] and to the enrolment of this Deed in the Central Office of

the Supreme Court.

Signed _____

In the presence of:

Name _____

Address _____

Name _____

Address_____] [8]

Note: As long as you do not use a name for a dishonest purpose, you may use any name that you wish and you do not need to execute any document in order to do so. There is no magic in a Deed Poll. A Deed Poll, however, can provide evidence of your change of name which may be useful if you wish to have dealings in a name other than the one on your birth certificate, and it may be essential for certain official purposes. The most persuasive evidence of change of name is a Deed Poll which has been registered in the Central Office of the High Court in London. In order for such a Deed to be capable of registration, it will need to contain the details in this form. When you apply to register your Deed Poll, you will also need to submit various other documents, as set out in the Enrolment of Deeds (Change of Name) Regulations 1994 (SI 1994/604) as amended by The Enrolment of Deeds (Change of Name) (Amendment) Regulations 2005 (SI 2005/2056). These are available on the government website www.opsi.gov.uk.

You will be very unlikely to need a Deed Poll at all if the only reason why you are changing your name is that you are a woman and are changing your surname to that of your husband. Your marriage certificate will suffice.

If you are married or in a civil partnership, you will need the consent of your spouse or civil partner in order for your Deed Poll to be registered.

If you are registering a change of name for a child you should certainly consult a solicitor.

[1] Insert name you are changing from.

[2] Omit the reference to the British Nationality Act if you are a Commonwealth Citizen, and are not a British Citizen, British Overseas Territories Citizen or British Overseas Citizen. If you were born before 1st January 1983 and were a Citizen of the United Kingdom and Colonies and had the right to live in the UK as of that date without any restriction of the time you could remain there, insert 'Section 11'. Insert 'Section 1' if you were born on or after 1st January 1983 and were born in the UK and your father or mother was a British citizen or ordinarily resident in the UK without any restriction on the period he or she could remain there. If none of the foregoing applies to you, or if you are uncertain about it, consult a solicitor.

[3] Insert new name.

[4] Omit this clause if you are changing only your surname.

[5] Insert old name.

[6] Insert old name.

[7] Insert new name.

[8] Delete this section if you are not married or in a civil partnership.

.

Change in Pay or Grading Following Job Evaluation   Form E05

Date   _____

To   _____

_____

_____

Dear   _____

Following our job evaluation review it has been decided to upgrade your job title to   _____

_____with effect from

_____

From that date your salary will be increased to £ _____ per _____.

All other terms and conditions of your employment remain unchanged.

We offer our congratulations on your promotion, and hope that you enjoy your new position.

Yours sincerely

_____

Change in Sales Representative Agreement   Form E06

Date _____

To _____

_____

_____

Dear _____

I refer to the sales representative agreement between us dated _____,
a copy of which is attached.

This letter acknowledges that the agreement is modified and superseded by the following agreed change in
terms: _____

_____

_____

_____

All other terms shall remain as stated.

Please sign below to indicate your acceptance of the modified terms.

Yours sincerely

_____

_____

Company

I agree to the above modification:

_____

Sales Representative

Note: Changes in the terms of the engagement of a commercial agent should be by true consent and should not be imposed, in case the
agent is able to say that the change amounted to a repudiation of the agency agreement, therefore entitling him to compensation under
the Commercial Agents (Council Directive) Regulations 1993. The principal should therefore be careful to preserve correspondence
evidencing such consent, and should keep a memorandum detailing how the change was for the benefit of both parties.

Change of Address Notice   Form PF01

Date _____

To _____

_____

_____

Dear _____

Please note that as from _____, our address will change from:

_____

_____

_____

to

_____

_____

_____

Our new telephone number will be _____

and fax number _____

Please make note of the above information and direct all future correspondence to us at our new address. Thank you.

Yours sincerely

_____

Child Guardianship Consent Form   Form PF02

I _____,

of _____,

hereby appoint _____,

of _____, _____,

as the legal guardian of my child(ren). The guardian shall have the following powers:_____

_____

_____

_____

_____

_____

_____

_____

_____

_____

_____

_____

_____

_____

Signed this _____ day of _____, year _____.

_____

_____

Heath warning: You should take legal advice when appointing a guardian for your children and this form will enable you to give instructions to your solicitor more efficiently.

Cohabitation Agreement (for Unmarried Partners)   Form PF03

THIS DEED OF AGREEMENT is made the _____ day of _____ year _____

BETWEEN:

(1) _____ of _____ ('the First Party'); and

(2)_____ of _____ ('the Second Party').

WHEREAS:

(a)   The Parties live together and wish to enter this Agreement to set out their rights and responsibilities towards each other.

(b)   The Parties intend that this Agreement will be legally binding on them.

1.   OWNERSHIP OF THE HOME

The Parties [live]/[are about to live] at the address given above ('the Home') which is a property [about to be] purchased in their joint names/in the sole name of the First/Second Party*.

2.   DIVISION OF PROCEEDS OF SALE OF THE HOME

Where the Home is owned in joint names:

Option 1:   The rights and interests of the Parties in the Home and its net proceeds of sale are set out in a Declaration of Trust dated _____ and are not in any way varied or affected by this Deed.

Option 2:   The Parties agree that they shall hold the beneficial interest in the Home:

as tenants in common in equal shares.

[Before any division of the proceeds is made the parties shall each receive out of the said proceeds the sums which they have respectively contributed out of their own resources (such sums not to bear interest) and if the net proceeds of sale shall be insufficient to enable the parties to recover the entirety of their said contributions they shall each receive such proportion of the same as their respective contributions bear to the totality of the contributions made until the net proceeds shall have been exhausted.]

OR

as to _____ % for the First Party and as to _____ % for the Second Party.

OR

in the proportions in which they contribute to the purchase of the Home whether by contribution to the purchase price, payment of mortgage instalments and mortgage-linked endowment premiums, or by way of improvements which add to the value of the Home (and if the Parties cannot agree the value of any such improvements the value shall be determined by a valuer appointed by the President of the Royal Institution of Chartered Surveyors).

Where the Home is owned in the sole name of one Party:

Option 3:   The Parties agree that they shall hold the beneficial interest in the Home:

as tenants in common in equal shares

[Before any division of the proceeds is made the parties shall each receive out of the said proceeds the sums which they have respectively contributed out of their own resources

(*delete as appropriate)

Continued on next page

Cohabitation Agreement (for Unmarried Partners) (cont)   Form PF03

(such sums not to bear interest) and if the net proceeds of sale shall be insufficient to enable the parties to recover the entirety of their said contributions they shall each receive such proportion of the same as their respective contributions bear to the totality of the contributions made until the net proceeds shall have been exhausted].

OR

as to _____ % for the First Party and as to _____ % for the Second Party.

OR

in the proportions in which they contribute to the purchase of the Home whether by contribution to the purchase price, payment of mortgage instalments and mortgage-linked endowment premiums, or by way of improvements which add to the value of the Home (and if the Parties cannot agree the value of any such improvements the value shall be determined by a valuer appointed by the President of the Royal Institution of Chartered Surveyors).

Option 4:   The Parties agree that the First/Second* Party is the sole beneficial owner of the Home and that regardless of contributions to the purchase maintenance or improvement of the Home the other Party is not and will not acquire any beneficial interest in the Home or in its proceeds of sale.

3.   CONTENTS AND PERSONAL BELONGINGS

Any household and personal item shall be owned:

Option 1:   Entirely by the Party who acquired it (whether by inheritance, gift, purchase or otherwise).

Option 2:   By both Parties equally (regardless of when or by whom it was acquired) unless the Parties expressly agree otherwise in writing provided however that any items used exclusively by one of the parties shall belong entirely to that party. Unless the Parties shall agree otherwise within one month of the date of termination of this Agreement all jointly owned items shall be sold and the net proceeds of sale divided equally between them.

4.   BANK OR BUILDING SOCIETY ACCOUNTS

It is agreed that:

Option 1:   The Parties do not intend to open a joint account. Each Party shall maintain separate bank or building society accounts and the money in each account will remain his or her separate property.

Option 2:   The Parties shall maintain a joint bank or building society account ('The Joint Account').

The Parties shall pay into the Joint Account sums sufficient to meet their agreed share of common expenses (referred to in clause 5). The money in the Joint Account shall belong to the Parties in equal shares regardless of the actual sums which either of them may have paid into or withdrawn from the Joint Account. Any money in any bank or building society account maintained separately by either Party shall belong to that Party alone. Any investments purchased with monies in the joint account shall belong to the parties in equal shares.

(*delete as appropriate)

Continued on next page

Cohabitation Agreement (for Unmarried Partners) (cont) Form PF03

5. COMMON EXPENSES

Common household expenditure including mortgage repayments, mortgage-linked endowment premiums, ground rent, service charges, rental payments, buildings and household insurance premiums, council or other local taxes, charges for water rates, gas, electricity, telephone, television licence and rental, food, decoration and repairs shall be:

Option 1:   paid by the First/Second* Party alone.

Option 2:   shared equally by the Parties.

Option 3:   paid as to _____ % by the first Party and as to _____ % by the Second Party.

Unless otherwise agreed in writing, the rights of the parties shall not be affected by any excess or shortfall which may occur in respect of such payments whilst the parties are cohabiting. If they should cease to cohabit and if either party shall pay more than his or her share of the above, he or she shall be entitled to be credited in respect of the excess and the other party shall be debited for the same, but such credit or debit shall not attract interest. Any entitlement to such credit is without prejudice to any entitlement which a party who has left the Home might have for the payment of an occupation rent by the party who remains in residence.

6. VARIATION/TERMINATION

This Agreement shall be varied only by written agreement of the Parties. This Agreement shall terminate by written agreement of the Parties or upon the death or marriage of either one of them or upon the Party's separation for a period exceeding three months following which [the Home] [and any property owned jointly or in common by the parties] shall be valued and either sold and the proceeds divided, either Party being at liberty to buy the Home.

SIGNED AS A DEED

by the said _____

Name _____

in the presence of

Signature _____

Name _____

Address_____

SIGNED AS A DEED

by the said _____

Name _____

in the presence of

Signature _____

Name _____

Address _____

Health Warning: This form should only be used in order to enable you to put down your thoughts so that you can instruct a solicitor or licensed conveyancer more quickly and cheaply. On no account should anyone make a cohabitation agreement without the assistance of a solicitor or licensed conveyancer. This is because any court which is later asked to enforce such an agreement will need to be satisfied that the agreement was not obtained by the misuse of the trust and confidence which one party placed in the other; or (worse still) that the agreement was gained through the use of pressure. Taking independent advice from a solicitor or licensed conveyancer will help to ensure that the agreement is fair, that the often complicated circumstances of the parties are taken properly into account and that it is less open to legal challenge. It will also ensure that various possible complications (e.g. who is to live at the property prior to its being sold and for how long) can be thought through and provided for.

The form of ownership provided for in these forms does not allow for one party's share to be inherited by the other party upon death. **It is essential that you make a Will disposing of your property, especially your interest in the home. Note there is no automatic transfer upon death of your property to a partner to whom you are not married or in a civil partnership with, no matter how long you may have lived together.**

Note: Clauses in square brackets should be deleted as appropriate and both Parties should initial the deletion.

Company Let
(For a Furnished or Unfurnished House or Flat)

Form RT01

The PROPERTY _____
_____

The LANDLORD _____
_____
_____

The TENANT _____LIMITED/PLC

whose Registered Office is at _____
_____
_____
_____(Company Registration No._____)

The TERM _____ months beginning on
_____

> Subject to the right for either party at any time during the Term to end this
> Agreement earlier by giving to the other written notice of _____
> week(s)/month(s)*

The RENT £ _____ per week/month* payable in advance on the _____ of each
week/month*

The DEPOSIT £ _____

The INVENTORY means the list of the Landlord's possessions at the Property which has been signed by
the Landlord and the Tenant

(delete if unfurnished)

DATED _____   _____

SIGNED _____   _____

_____   _____

(The Landlord)   (Director/Secretary for and on
behalf of The Tenant)

THIS AGREEMENT comprises the particulars detailed above and the terms and conditions printed overleaf
whereby the Property is hereby let by the Landlord and taken by the Tenant for the Term at the Rent.

Terms and Conditions on next page

(*delete as appropriate)

Company Let Terms & Conditions

1. The Tenant will:
   1.1 pay the Rent at the times and in the manner aforesaid without any deduction abatement or set-off whatsoever
   1.2 pay all charges in respect of any electric, gas, water and telephonic or televisual services used at or supplied to the Property and Council Tax or any similar property tax that might be charged in addition to or replacement of it
   1.3 keep the interior of the Property in a good, clean and tenantable state and condition and not damage or injure the Property or any part of it
   1.4 yield up the Property at the end of the Term in the same clean state and condition it was in at the beginning of the Term and if any item listed on the Inventory requires repair, replacing, cleaning or laundering pay for the same (fair wear and tear and damage by fire or similar catastrophes not caused by the Tenant excepted).
   1.5 maintain at the Property and keep in a good and clean condition all of the items listed in the Inventory
   1.6 not make any alteration or addition to the Property nor without the Landlord's prior written consent to do any redecoration or painting of the Property
   1.7 not do or omit to do anything on or at the Property which may be or become a nuisance or annoyance to any other occupiers of the property or owners or occupiers of adjoining or nearby premises or which may in any way prejudice the insurance of the Property or cause an increase in the premium payable therefore
   1.8 not without the Landlord's prior written consent allow or keep any pet or any kind of animal at the Property
   1.9 not use or occupy the Property in any way whatsoever other than as a private residence
   1.10 not assign, sublet, charge or part with or share possession or occupation of the Property or any part thereof provided however that the Tenant may permit the residential occupation of the Property as a whole by the Tenant's officers and employees, so long as the Tenant continues to be responsible for the Rent and all other outgoings and does not make any charge whatsoever in respect of the same to the occupier and no relationship of landlord and tenant is created or allowed to arise between the tenant and the occupier and provided further that the Landlord's prior written consent (not to be unreasonably withheld) is obtained to each such occupier
   1.11 allow the Landlord or anyone with the Landlord's written permission to enter the Property at reasonable times of the day to inspect its condition and state of repair, carry out any necessary repairs and gas inspections, or during the last month of the term, show the Property to prospective new tenants, provided the Landlord has given reasonable prior notice (except in emergency)
   1.12 pay interest at the rate of 4% above the Base Lending Rate for the time being of the Landlord's bankers upon any Rent or other money due from the Tenant under this Agreement which is more than 3 days in arrears in respect of the period from when it became due to the date of payment

2. Subject to the Tenant paying the rent and performing his/her obligations under this Agreement the Tenant may peaceably hold and enjoy the Property during the term without interruption from the Landlord or any person rightfully claiming under or in trust for the Landlord

3. The Landlord will:
   3.1 keep in repair the structure and exterior of the Property (including drains gutters and external pipes)
   3.2 keep in repair and proper working order the installations at the property for the supply of water, gas and electricity and for sanitation (including basins, sinks, baths and sanitary conveniences)
   3.3 keep in repair and proper working order the installations at the Property for space heating and heating water

But the Landlord will not be required to:
   3.4 carry out works for which the Tenant is responsible by virtue of his/her duty to use the Property in a tenant-like manner
   3.5 rebuild or reinstate the Property in the case of destruction or damage by fire or by tempest flood or other inevitable accident

4. In the event of the Rent being unpaid for more than 10 days after it is due (whether demanded

Continued on next page

Company Let Terms & Conditions (continued)   Form RT01

or not) or there being a breach of any other of the Tenant's obligations under this Agreement or the Tenant entering into liquidation or having a receiver or administrative receiver appointed then the Landlord may re-enter the Property and this Agreement shall thereupon determine absolutely but without prejudice to any of the Landlord's other rights and remedies in respect of any outstanding obligations on the part of the Tenant. Note: The Landlord cannot recover possession under this clause without a court order while anyone is living at the property

5.   The Deposit

   5.1   The Deposit will be held by the Landlord and will be refunded to the Tenant at the end of the Term (however it ends) at the forwarding address provided to the Landlord but less any reasonable deductions properly made by the Landlord to cover any reasonable costs incurred or losses caused to him by any breaches of the obligations in his Agreement by the Tenant. No interest will be payable to the Tenant in respect of the Deposit money

   5.2   The Deposit shall be re-payable to the Tenant as soon as reasonably practicable, however the Landlord shall not be bound to return the Deposit until after he has had a reasonable opportunity to assess the reasonable cost of any repairs required as a result of any breaches of his obligations by the Tenant or other sums properly due to the Landlord under clause 5.1 However, the Landlord shall not, save in exceptional circumstances, retain the Deposit for more than one month after the end of the tenancy

   5.3   If at any time during the Term the Landlord is obliged to deduct from the Deposit to satisfy the reasonable costs occasioned by any breaches of the obligations of the Tenant the Tenant shall make such additional payments as are necessary to restore the full amount of the Deposit

6.   The Landlord hereby notifies the Tenant under Section 48 of the Landlord & Tenant Act 1987 that any notices (including notices in proceedings) should be served upon the Landlord at the address stated with the name of the Landlord overleaf

7.   In the event of damage to or destruction of the Property by fire or any other catastrophe not caused by the Tenant the Tenant shall be relieved from payment of the Rent to the extent that the Tenant's use and enjoyment of the Property is thereby prevented and from performance of its obligations as to the state and condition of the Property to the extent of and so long as there prevails such damage or destruction.

8.   So long as the reference to a right of early termination in the definition of the 'TERM' overleaf (the 'early termination right') has not been deleted then either party may at any time during the Term terminate this Agreement by giving to the other prior written notice to that effect, the length of such notice to be that stated in the early termination right, and upon the expiry of said notice this Agreement shall end with no further liability of either party save for any antecedent breach

9.   Where the context so admits:

   9.1   The 'Landlord' includes the persons for the time being entitled to the reversion expectant upon this Tenancy

   9.2   The 'Tenant' includes any persons deriving title under the Tenant

   9.3   The 'Property' includes all of the Landlord's fixtures and fittings at or upon the Property

   9.4   The 'Term' shall mean the period stated in the particulars overleaf or any shorter or longer period in the event of an earlier termination or an extension or holding over respectively

10. All references to the singular shall include the plural and vice versa and any obligations or liabilities of more than one person shall be joint and several and an obligation on the part of a party shall include an obligation not to allow or permit the breach of that obligation

Concession Note (Seller's - Where Bulk Goods do not Conform to Description or Sample)   Form E05

_____Ltd

To   _____Ltd   Concession Note No _____

    _____

    _____   Customer Order No _____

Please indicate whether or not you accept the concession for material/product non-conformity described below by completing this form and returning it to us as soon as possible. We will only despatch goods upon receipt of your approval. PLEASE NOTE THAT A REFUSAL TO APPROVE DOES NOT AFFECT YOUR STATUTORY RIGHTS.

Product Code   Product Description

Details of [alleged] non-conformity   _____

Description of goods now proposed
 to be supplied   _____

Details of Concession offered   _____

                                        _____

                                        _____

Customer Service Officer

In consideration of the concession, we are prepared to accept goods of the description appearing above in substitution for those originally ordered and in full satisfaction of any claims which we may have in respect of the order.

Name _____   Position _____

Signed _____   Date _____

Confidentiality Agreement   Form E08

THIS AGREEMENT is made the _____ day of _____ year _____

BETWEEN:

(1) _____ (the 'Company'); and

(2) _____ (the 'Employee').

WHEREAS:

(A)   The Company agrees to give the Employee access to certain confidential information relating to the affairs of the Company solely for purposes of: _____

_____

_____

_____

_____

_____

(B)   The Employee agrees to obtain, inspect and use such information only for the purposes described above, and otherwise to hold such information confidential and secret pursuant to the terms of this agreement.

[(C)   The Employee and the Company are in discussions with a view to the possible future employment of the Employee by the Company, and in consideration of the Company entering into such discussions and in further consideration of the payment to the Employee by the Company of the sum of one pound, the Employee has agreed to give the undertakings hereinafter contained.]

NOW IT IS HEREBY AGREED as follows:

1.   The Company has or shall furnish to the Employee confidential information ('Information'), described on the attached list, and may further allow suppliers, customers, employees or representatives of the Company to furnish such information to the Employee. Such Information includes but is not limited to the information described on the attached list attached hereto. It also includes any confidential or proprietory information, trade secrets and Information about the Company's customers, suppliers and employees which may be furnished to the Employee.
     The Employee agrees to hold all such Information in trust and confidence and agrees that the Information shall be used only for the contemplated purpose, and not for any other.

2.   No copies may be made or retained of the Information without the Company's written consent.

3.   [If the discussions between the Employee and the Company shall conclude without the Employee being employed by the Company or] upon demand by the Company, all Information, including written notes, photographs, or memoranda containing the same shall be promptly returned to the Company. The Employee shall retain no copies or written documentation relating thereto.

4.   This Information shall not be disclosed to any third party, whether or not an employee of the Company, unless the third party agrees to execute and be bound by the terms of this agreement, and disclosure is first approved by the Company in writing.

Continued on next page

Confidentiality Agreement (continued)   Form E08

5.   The Employee shall have no obligation with respect to any information known by the Employee, or generally known within the industry prior to date of this agreement, or that shall become common knowledge within the industry thereafter, or which the Employee is entitled to disclose pursuant to the Public Interest Disclosure Act 1998.

6.   The Employee acknowledges the Information disclosed herein contains proprietary or trade secrets and in the event of any breach, the Company shall be entitled to apply for injunctive relief and to claim for damages of breach.

7.   This agreement shall be binding upon and inure to the benefit of the parties, their successors and assigns.

8.   This constitutes the entire agreement between the parties. Any amendments to this agreement shall only be valid if both parties confirm such amendments in writing.

IN WITNESS OF WHICH the parties have signed this agreement the day and year first above written

Signed for and on behalf of the Company by

_____

Director

_____

Director/Secretary

_____

Signed by or on behalf of the Employee

_____

in the presence of (witness)

Name _____

Address _____

_____

Occupation_____

Note: The matters arising in respect of an employee or an independent consultant with regard to confidentiality are often very similar. It is suggested that you examine Form E12 to see if any of the clauses in that form may usefully be added or substituted for those in this form.

Confirmation of Agreement to Pay   Form CDC06

Date _____

To _____

_____

_____

Dear _____

We send you this letter to confirm our agreement, made on _____,
that you will pay your overdue balance of £ _____ according to the following terms:

_____

_____

_____

If this letter does not conform to our agreement, please inform us immediately.

We understand your financial difficulties and, to accommodate you, will accept payments on these extended terms provided each payment is punctually made when due. If any of the payments now agreed to be made by you are not met in full on or before the date specified above (time being of the essence) the entire sums outstanding shall immediately be due and payable.

Whilst this balance remains outstanding we shall supply you on a cash on delivery basis.

We are pleased this matter could be resolved on terms satisfactory to us both, and we look forward to your payments and continued business.

Please indicate your agreement to the above by signing and returning to us a copy of this letter.

Yours sincerely

_____

Confirmation of Agreement to Pay   **Form CDC06**

Note: Do not use this form where the original agreement is regulated by the Consumer Credit Act 1974.

Confirmation of Verbal Order   Form BS09

Date   _____

To   _____

_____

_____

Dear   _____

This letter confirms our verbal order of   _____ .

A copy of our confirmatory purchase order containing the stated terms is enclosed as order

no.:   _____

Please confirm in writing by return that the confirmatory purchase order accurately records our agreement.

Thank you for your cooperation.

Yours sincerely

_____

Conflict of Interest Declaration   Form E09

Employee _____

Company _____

_____

I acknowledge that I have read the Company policy statement concerning conflicts of interest and I hereby declare that neither I, nor any other person to which I may be connected as set out in the Companies Act 2006 section 252 to 254, has any conflict of interest with the Company as would constitute a violation of that Company policy. Furthermore, I declare that during my employment, I shall continue to maintain my affairs in accordance with the requirements of the Company policy and to disclose any conflict of interest which may arise between the Company and any person with whom or with which I may be connected.

_____

Employee's Signature

_____

Date

Consent to Release of Information Form E11

To _____

From Personnel Office

A request for certain employment information concerning you has been received from: _____

_____

_____

_____

_____

Please tick below those items of information that you permit us to disclose.

- ☐ Salary
- ☐ Position
- ☐ Department
- ☐ Supervisor
- ☐ Health records
- ☐ Dates of employment
- ☐ Hours worked
- ☐ Wage attachments
- ☐ Reason for redundancy
- ☐ Other:

_____

_____

_____

Employee Signature _____ Date _____

Please return this form to the Personnel Office as soon as possible. Your consent on this occasion will not constitute a consent to release information on future occasions.

Consent to Short Notice of an Annual General Meeting   Form B01

_____ Limited

We, the undersigned, being all members for the time being of the company having the right to attend and vote at the Annual General Meeting of such company convened to be held at _____

_____

_____ on the _____ day of _____ year ___
(the attached notice being the notice convening the meeting), hereby agree:

[a)][1]   in accordance with section [369(3) of the Companies Act 1985][2] [307 of the Companies Act 2006] of the Companies Act 1985 to the holding of such meeting notwithstanding that less than the statutory period of notice thereof has been given; [and

b)   to accept service of documents in accordance with section 238(1) of the Companies Act 1985 notwithstanding that the documents were sent less than 21 days before the meeting.][3]

Dated this _____ day of _____ year ___.

_____

Member's signature

_____

Member's signature

_____

Member's signature

_____

Member's signature

Note: From 1 October 2007 private companies are no longer obliged to hold an annual general meeting. Whenever a meeting is to be held only 14 days' notice will be required unless it is proposed to pass a resolution requiring special notice, in which case 28 days' notice will be required. The form is retained because many companies will find it convenient to hold AGMs. Also, the holders of 90 percent of the voting shares will be able to consent to short notice of the meeting except where a resolution requiring special notice is to be considered. A special resolution requires a majority of 75 percent. The company is required by law to keep copies of all board resolutions and all minutes of general meetings for 10 years.

[1] Delete from 1 October 2007.

[2] Delete from 1 October 2007.

[3] Delete from 1 October 2007.

Consent to Short Notice of an Extraordinary General Meeting

Form B02

_____ Limited

We, the undersigned, being a majority in number of the members of the company holding not less than [95 per cent] [90 per cent][1] of the issued share capital having a right to attend and vote at the Extraordinary General Meeting of the said company convened by a Notice of Meeting dated _____ year _____ and to be held on _____ year _____, hereby agree to the holding of such meeting and to the proposing and passing of the special resolutions on the day and at the time and place set out in such Notice, notwithstanding that less than the statutory period of the Notice thereof has been given to us.

Dated this _____ day of _____ year ____.

_____

Member's signature

_____

Member's signature

_____

Member's signature

_____

Member's signature

Note: From 1 October 2007 the distinction between AGMs and EGMs for private companies will be abolished. This form may be retained because companies may find it convenient to hold AGMs and to distinguish between those meetings and other meetings. Also, the holders of 90 percent of the voting shares will be able to consent to short notice of the meeting except where a resolution requiring special notice is to be considered.

[1] Delete '95 per cent' from 1 October 2007.

Consultant Non-Disclosure Agreement   Form E12

THIS AGREEMENT is made the _____ day of _____ year _____
BETWEEN:
(1) _____ of _____ (the 'Client'); and
(2) _____ of _____ (the 'Consultant').

WHEREAS the Client and the Consultant are in negotiations with a view to the Client retaining the Consultant as an outside Consultant and in the course of such negotiations the Client may furnish the Consultant with certain information that is confidential as hereinafter defined AND WHEREAS the Consultant in consideration of the Client taking part in such negotiations and in the further consideration of the payment to the Consultant by the Client of the sum of one pound (receipt of which the Consultant hereby acknowledges) the Consultant has agreed to make the warranties, representations, agreements and to enter into the covenants hereinafter set out.

NOW the Consultant hereby warrants, represents, covenants, and agrees as follows:

1. **Engagement.** The Consultant, prior to and in the course of engagement by the Client, may or will have access to or learn certain information belonging to the Client that is proprietary and confidential (Confidential Information).

2. **Definition of Confidential Information.** Confidential Information as used throughout this agreement means any secret or proprietary information relating directly to the Client's business and that of the Client's affiliated companies and subsidiaries, including, but not limited to, products, customer lists, pricing policies, employment records and policies, operational methods, marketing plans and strategies, product development techniques or plans, business acquisition plans, new personnel acquisition plans, methods of manufacture, technical processes, designs and design projects, inventions and research programs, trade 'know-how,' trade secrets, specific software, algorithms, computer processing systems, object and source codes, user manuals, systems documentation, and other business affairs of the Client and its affiliated companies and subsidiaries.

3. **Non-disclosure.** The Consultant agrees to keep strictly confidential all Confidential Information and will not, without the Client's express written authorisation, signed by one of the Client's authorised officers, use, sell, market, or disclose any Confidential Information to any third person, firm, corporation, or association for any purpose, other than to the Consultants employees and advisors for the purpose of the conduct of negotiations with the Client or the discharge of its duties to the Client. The Consultant further agrees not to make any copies of any documents (whether in written or machine readable form) containing the Confidential Information except upon the Client's written authorisation, signed by one of the Client's authorised officers, namely _____ and will not remove any copy or sample of Confidential Information from the premises of the Client without such authorisation, save for the purpose of communicating the same to its employees or advisors for the purposes aforesaid. The Consultant will not disclose any information or provide any copies of documents as aforesaid to such persons without first having procured the signature of such person to a copy of this agreement and without having delivered the same to the Client. The Consultant shall be liable to the Client for any

Continued on next page

Consultant Non-Disclosure Agreement (cont)   Form E12

loss or damage caused by any use made of the information by any person to whom the Consultant may have disclosed information or provided copies as aforesaid.

4. **Return of Material.** Upon receipt of a written request from the Client, the Consultant will return to the Client all copies of documents and all samples or other items from which confidential information can be acquired that, at the time of the receipt of the notice, are in the Consultant's possession.

5. **Obligations Continue Past Term.** The obligations imposed on the Consultant shall continue with respect to each item of the Confidential Information following the termination of the business relationship between the Consultant and the Client, and such obligations shall not terminate until such item shall cease to be secret and confidential and shall be in the public domain, unless such event shall have occurred as a result of wrongful conduct by the Consultant or the Consultant's advisers agents, servants, officers, or employees or a breach of the covenants set forth in this agreement.

6. **Equitable Relief.** The Consultant acknowledges and agrees that a breach of the provisions of Paragraph 3 or 4 of this Agreement would cause the Client to suffer irreparable damage that could not be adequately remedied by an action at law. Accordingly, the Consultant agrees that the Client shall have the right to seek specific performance of the provisions of Paragraph 3 to enjoin a breach or attempted breach of the provision thereof, such right being in addition to all other rights and remedies that are available to the Client at law, in equity, or otherwise.

7. **Invalidity.** If any provision of this agreement or its application is held to be invalid, illegal, or unenforceable in any respect, the validity, legality, or enforceability of any of the other provisions and applications therein shall not in any way be affected or impaired.

IN WITNESS OF WHICH the parties have signed this agreement the day and year first above written

_____

Signed by or on behalf of the Client   Signed by or on behalf of the Consultant

_____

in the presence of (witness)   in the presence of (witness)

Name _____   Name _____

Address _____   Address _____

_____

Occupation _____   Occupation _____

Note: The matters arising in respect of an independent consultant and of an employee with regard to confidentiality are often very similar. It is suggested that you examine form E08 to see if any of the clauses in that form may usefully be added or substituted for those in this form.

Contract for the Sale of Goods by Delivery — Form BS10

THIS AGREEMENT is made the _____ day of _____ year _____

BETWEEN:

(1) _____(the 'Seller'); and

(2) _____(the 'Buyer').

NOW IT IS HEREBY AGREED as follows:

1. In consideration for the payment of £ _____ (the 'Purchase Price'), on the terms set out below, the Seller agrees to sell and the Buyer agrees to buy the following goods (the 'Goods'):

    _____

    _____

2. The Buyer agrees to pay the Purchase Price and the Seller agrees to accept such payment on the following terms:_____

    _____

    _____

3. The Seller agrees that the Goods will be delivered to the Buyer's place of business by _____ . The shipping costs are estimated at £ _____ and will be paid by the _____.

4. The Buyer will have competent persons available to take delivery of the Goods at such time as the Seller or the Seller's carrier shall indicate that the goods are to be delivered.

5. The risk in the Goods shall pass from the Seller to the Buyer upon delivery.

6. The Seller represents that it has legal title to the Goods and full authority to sell the goods. The Seller also represents that the Goods are sold free and clear of all liens, mortgages, indebtedness, or liabilities.

7. No variation of this Contract will be effective unless it is in writing and is signed by both parties. [Time is of the essence for the purposes of this Contract].[1] This Contract binds and benefits both the Buyer and Seller and any successors. This Contract, including any attachments, is the entire agreement between the Buyer and Seller.

IN WITNESS OF WHICH the parties have signed this agreement the day and year first above written.

_____   _____
Signed by or on behalf of the Seller   Signed by or on behalf of the Buyer

_____   _____
in the presence of (witness)   in the presence of (witness)

Name _____   Name _____

Address _____   Address _____

_____   _____

Occupation _____   Occupation _____

Contractor/Subcontractor Agreement   Form E13

THIS AGREEMENT is made the _____ day of _____ year _____

BETWEEN:

(1) _____.of _____ (the 'Contractor'); and

(2) _____ of _____(the 'Subcontractor').

WHEREAS:

(A)   The Contractor has entered into an agreement ('the Main Contract') dated _____

 year _____, with _____ (the 'Company') for the performance of certain

 works (the 'Works'),

(B)   The Contractor wishes to subcontract certain portions of the Works to the Subcontractor.

NOW IT IS HEREBY AGREED as follows:

1.   The Subcontractor, as an independent contractor, agrees to furnish all of the labour and materials as

 may reasonably be required to complete the following portions of the Works: _____

 _____

 _____

 _____

 _____

 _____

 Any plans or specifications attached hereto shall form part of this Agreement.

2.   The Subcontractor agrees that the following portions of the Works will be completed by the dates

 specified:

 Work _____ Date _____

 _____   _____

 _____   _____

 _____   _____

 _____   _____

 _____   _____

 _____   _____

 _____   _____

 Or

 [The Subcontractor agrees that it will undertake any part or parts of the works under this Agreement

 within [three] working days of being directed by the Contractor to begin the same, and will complete

 them promptly so as to enable the Contractor to perform his obligations in respect of the Main

 Contract.]

3.   The Subcontractor agrees to perform this work in a workmanlike manner and with proper materials so

 as to achieve compliance with the Contractor's obligations under the Main Contract according to

 standard practices.

Continued on next page

Contractor/Subcontractor Agreement (continued)   Form E13

The Contractor agrees to pay the Subcontractor £ _____ as payment for the full performance of its obligations hereunder. This sum will be paid to the Subcontractor in instalments upon satisfactory completion of stages of the work as follows:

_____

4.   The Contractor and Subcontractor may agree to extra services and work, but any such extras must be set out and agreed to in writing by both the Contractor and the Subcontractor.

5.   The Subcontractor agrees to indemnify and hold the Contractor harmless from any claims or liability arising from the Subcontractor's work under this Contract but shall not be liable for losses caused by circumstances beyond the control or reasonably foreseeable by the Subcontractor.

6.   No modification of this agreement will be effective unless it is in writing and is signed by both parties. This agreement binds and benefits both parties and any successors. This document, including any attachments is the entire agreement between the parties.

[7.   For the purposes of the Contracts (Rights of Third Parties) Act 1999 this agreement does not confer any right of action in respect of it upon any person who is not a party to it.]

8.   This Agreement shall not constitute or give rise to a partnership or joint venture.

IN WITNESS OF WHICH the parties have signed this agreement the day and year first above written

_____

Signed by or on behalf of the Contractor

_____

in the presence of (witness)

Name _____

Address _____

_____

Occupation _____

_____

Signed by or on behalf of the Subcontractor

_____

in the presence of (witness)

Name _____

Address _____

_____

Occupation _____

Credit Information   Form CDC07

Date   _____

To   _____

_____

_____

Dear   _____

Re   _____

This letter is in reply to your request for credit information on the above account. Accordingly, we submit the following information:

1.   The account was opened with us on _____ year _____

2.   The account's present balance is:

                   Under 30 days   £_____

                   30-60 days   £_____

                   60-90 days   £_____

                   Over 90 days   £_____

                   Total owed   £_____

3.   The credit limit is:

_____

4.   Other credit information:

_____

_____

_____

We are pleased to be of service to you and trust this information will be held in strict confidence.

Yours sincerely

_____

Please note that this information is given without responsibility on the part of this Company or any of its officers or employees for the accuracy or completeness of such information.

Health warning: Do not provide information without first having obtained permission from the person to whom the data relates.

Credit Information Request   Form CDC08

Date   _____

To   _____

        _____

        _____

Dear   _____

Thank you for your recent order dated   _____

We would be pleased to offer you credit under our standard terms and conditions. In order to enable us to do so, we should be grateful if you would supply us with the following references and information regarding your financial status[1]:

_____

_____

_____

_____

_____

The referees you name will not provide any information about you to us, unless you authorise them to do so. Please therefore include in your reply, letters signed by you on your headed notepaper, addressed to the referees and giving them authority to provide credit information about you to us.

Pending receipt of this information we suggest C.O.D. terms or a deposit of £ _____ to enable us to deliver your order. Upon receipt of your confirmation we shall immediately deliver your order.

Of course, all credit information submitted shall be held in strict confidence.

Yours sincerely

_____

---

[1] Enter reference/information details which you require.

Credit Reference   Form CDC09

Date _____

To _____
_____
_____

Dear _____

Re _____

In response to your letter dated _____, the above mentioned has been known to us for _____ years. Over that period they have satisfactorily and promptly discharged all their obligations to us.

We have extended them credit and they have never abused our trust nor delayed payment of due accounts. We would, without hesitation, extend credit to them in the amount you have indicated.

We are giving this reference in an endeavour to be helpful to you. We must, however, make it clear that in doing so we accept no responsibility to you for the accuracy or completeness of this information.

Yours sincerely

_____

Credit Reference   Form CDC09

Note: Do not provide any credit reference unless you are authorised to do so by the person to whom it relates.

Damaged Goods Acceptance With Price Reduction   Form BS11

Date   _____

To   _____

_____

_____

Dear   _____

In fulfilment of our order dated _____, we have received goods from you which are defective in the following manner:

_____

_____

_____

_____

By reason of the presence of these defects the goods are not of satisfactory quality. We are therefore entitled to and do reject the goods.

We accordingly request that you collect the goods immediately. Although we will take reasonable care for the safekeeping of the goods for a maximum of 14 days from the date of this letter, the goods are henceforth at your risk.

[Notwithstanding the matters stated above, we would be prepared to retain the goods provided that we are accorded a price reduction of £_____. Please advise us as to whether your propose to accord this reduction or to remove the goods.]

Yours sincerely

_____

Note: Unless the sale is a consumer sale this form should not be used if the defects are minor and easily remediable, as in such circumstances it would be open to the seller to say that the rejection of the goods was improper, in which case the seller might be able both to recover the goods and to sue for the value of the profits lost on the sale.

Debt Acknowledgement   Form CDC10

The undersigned hereby confirms and acknowledges to _____ ('the Creditor')
that the undersigned is indebted to the Creditor in the amount of £ _____ as of the date hereof, which
amount is due and owing and includes all accrued interest and other permitted charges to date. The
undersigned further acknowledges that there are no credits or rights of set off against the balance owing.

Signed this _____ day of _____ year _____.

In the presence of

Witness _____   Debtor_____

Note: From the point of view of the Debtor, there is no point to signing an acknowledgment such as this unless something is given in
return, such as an agreement by the Creditor that the sum stated is all that is owing, or an undertaking by the Creditor to give more
time to pay.

Defect Report Memorandum   Form BS12

_____ Ltd

Date:	Report No:	
Product code:	Description:	Batch:

Defect:

Non-conformity details:

Non-conformity cause:

Corrective action to be taken:

Signed _____
Customer Services Officer

Result of corrective action:

Signed _____ Date: _____
Customer Services Officer

Defect Report Memorandum   Form BS12

Defective Goods Notice   Form BS13

Date _____

To   _____

      _____

      _____

Dear _____

This is to inform you that we have received goods delivered by you as per your invoice or order no. _____, dated _____.

Certain goods as listed on the attached sheet are defective or do not comply with our order for the following reasons:

_____

_____

_____

_____

_____

Accordingly, we wish to return these goods in exchange for a credit note in the amount of £_____. We also intend to return the goods to you at your cost unless you collect them. Please confirm the credit and also issue instructions for the return of the goods.

You are advised by this notice that we reserve our legal rights.

We look forward to your prompt reply.

Yours sincerely

_____

Demand for Delivery   Form BS14

Date _____

To _____

_____

_____

Dear _____

We have made full payment to you in the sum of £ _____ for the delivery of certain goods pursuant to our accepted order dated _____. [Despite the fact that our agreement specified that the goods should be delivered to us by _____ or [Despite the fact that delivery later than _____ was unreasonable in all the circumstances], the goods have still not been delivered. We demand delivery of the goods in accordance with our order.

Unless the goods are received by us on or before _____, which gives you an entirely reasonable period within which to comply with this notice, we shall consider you to be in repudiatory breach of contract and we shall thereupon expect a full refund. We reserve such further rights as we have under the law arising out of any loss or damages sustained.

We would appreciate immediate notification of your intentions in this matter.

Yours sincerely

_____

Note: This notice should only be served if there has been unreasonable delay, or if the contract specifies a date for delivery and that date has passed. Once there has been unreasonable delay or the date for delivery has passed, the notice may be served, but then the time specified for delivery should be a reasonable time in the light of the circumstances prevailing at the time when the notice is served. If a new promise has been made by the seller for delivery by a given date, such a date could be used. Otherwise, it is a matter of what, in common sense, is fair to both parties. Remember that if the notice is served prematurely, or if it specifies an unreasonably early date for compliance, the service of the notice could itself amount to a breach of contract and give rise to a claim against you.

The issues arising in connection with this form are very similar to those arising in connection with form BS16. It is suggested that you examine form BS16 to see if any of the clauses in that form may usefully be added or substituted for those in this form.

Demand for Explanation of Rejection of Goods   Form BS15

Date   _____

To   _____

_____

_____

Dear   _____

Re   _____

On _____, we shipped the following goods to you pursuant to your order no. _____, dated _____:

_____

_____

_____

On _____, we received notice that you had rejected delivery of these goods without satisfactory explanation. We therefore request that you provide us with an adequate explanation for this rejection. Unless we are provided with such explanation within 10 days, we will have no option but to enforce payment for these goods.

Please be advised that we reserve all our rights under the law.

Thank you for your immediate attention to this matter.

Yours sincerely

_____

Demand for Payment (Final)   Form CDC11

Date   _____

To   _____

_____

_____

Dear   _____

We have tried on several occasions to secure payment of your overdue account but it remains unpaid. Your account is overdue in the amount of £ _____.

This is your final notice. Unless we receive your cheque for _____ pounds (£ _____) within ten (10) days, we shall have to consider referring your account to our solicitors for collection.

Please note that immediate payment is in your own best interests as it will save you further interest and costs, and help preserve your credit rating.

Yours sincerely

_____

Demand to Specify Delivery Dates   Form BS16

Date _____

To _____

_____

_____

Dear _____

We request that you confirm and specify delivery arrangements in respect of our order dated

_____, and further confirm that you will abide by those arrangements.

Failure to provide this confirmation shall constitute a breach of contract and we shall no longer consider

ourselves bound by this contract. Further, we shall hold you responsible for all resultant damages

recoverable at law.

Please confirm delivery dates, in writing, no later than _____.

Yours sincerely

_____

Note: This notice should only be served if there has been unreasonable delay in providing details for delivery, or if the contract
specifies a date for such details to be provided and if that date has passed. Once there has been unreasonable delay or the date for
providing details has passed, the notice may be served, but then the time specified for providing details of delivery should be a
reasonable time in the light of the circumstances prevailing at the time when the notice is served. If a new promise has been made by
the seller for details to be produced by a given date, such a date could be used. Otherwise, it is a matter of what, in common sense, is
fair to both parties. Remember that if the notice is served prematurely, or if it specifies an unreasonably early date for compliance, the
service of the notice could itself amount to a breach of contract and give rise to a claim against you.

The issues arising in connection with this form are very similar to those arising in connection with the Demand for Delivery form BS14. It is
suggested that you examine that form to see if any of the clauses in that form may usefully by added or substituted for those in this form.

Demand to Guarantor for Payment   Form CDC43

Date _____

To _____

_____

_____

Dear _____

As you are aware, we hold your guarantee dated _____, wherein you guaranteed the debt owed to us by _____

_____

You are advised that this debt is now in default. Accordingly, demand is made upon you as guarantor for full payment on the outstanding debt due us in the amount of £ _____.

In the event payment is not made within _____ (_____) days, we shall be compelled to enforce our rights against you under the guarantee by referring this matter to our solicitors.

Yours sincerely

_____

Note: If the debt has arisen under an agreement which is Regulated under the Consumer Credit Act 1974, the Debtor or Hirer must have been served with an appropriate notice of termination in accordance with that Act and the Consumer Credit (Enforcement Default and Termination Notices) Regulations 1983. It would be advisable to enclose a copy of that notice with this form. If you are not familiar with claims under Regulated agreements, you should consult your solicitor.

Demand to Pay Promissory Note — Form LB02

Date _____

To _____

_____

_____

Dear _____

I refer to a promissory note dated _____ , in the original principal amount of £ _____ and of which I am the holder.

You are in default under the note in that the following payment(s) have not been made:

Payment Date	Amount Due
_____	_____
_____	_____
_____	_____

Accordingly, demand is hereby made for full payment of the entire balance of £ _____ due under the note. In the event payment is not received within _____ days, this note shall be forwarded to our solicitors for collection.

Yours sincerely

_____

Note: If the debt which is the subject of the Promissory Note has arisen under an agreement which is Regulated under the Consumer Credit Act 1974, the Debtor must have been served with an appropriate notice of termination in accordance with that Act and the Consumer Credit (Enforcement Default and Termination Notices) Regulations 1983. It would be advisable to enclose a copy of that notice with this form. If you are not familiar with claims under Regulated agreements, you should consult your solicitor.

Director's Resignation Reserving Rights Against the Company	Form B03

Date _____

To: Board of Directors

_____Limited

_____

_____

Dear Sirs

I resign my office of director of the company with immediate effect and I hereby reserve my right to take all proceedings which may be available to me to recover any fees, expenses, compensation and damages to which I am entitled.

Yours faithfully

_____

Dismissal and Disciplinary Rules and Procedure   Form E14

at _____Limited

1. The Company's aim is to encourage improvement in individual performance and conduct. Employees are required to treat members of the public and other employees equally in accordance with the Equal Opportunities Policy. This procedure sets out the action which will be taken when disciplinary rules are breached.

2. Principles:
   (i) The list of rules is not to be regarded as an exhaustive list.
   (ii) The procedure is designed to establish the facts quickly and to deal consistently with disciplinary issues. No disciplinary action will be taken until the matter has been fully investigated.
   (iii) At every stage employees will have the opportunity to state their case and be accompanied by a fellow employee of their choice at the hearings.
   (iv) When the Company is contemplating dismissal for disciplinary or non-disciplinary grounds, statutory dispute resolution procedures will be adopted. Where the Company is contemplating taking disciplinary action (other than a warning) statutory dispute resolution procedures will also be adopted.
   (v) Only a Director has the right to suspend or dismiss. An employee may, however, be given a verbal or written warning by their immediate superior.
   (vi) An employee has the right to appeal against any disciplinary decision.

3. The Rules:
   Breaches of the Company's disciplinary rules which can lead to disciplinary action are:
   - failure to observe a reasonable order or instruction;
   - failure to observe a health and safety requirement;
   - inadequate time keeping;
   - absence from work without proper cause (including taking parental leave dishonestly);
   - theft or removal of the Company's property;
   - loss, damage to or misuse of the Company's property through negligence or carelessness;
   - conduct detrimental to the interests of the Company;
   - incapacity for work due to being under the influence of alcohol or illegal drugs;
   - physical assault or gross insubordination;
   - committing an act outside work or being convicted for a criminal offence which is liable adversely to affect the performance of the contract of employment and/or the relationship between the employee and the Company;
   - failure to comply with the Company's Equal Opportunities Policy.

4. The Procedure:
   (a) Oral warning
       If conduct or performance is unsatisfactory, the employee will be given a formal oral warning, which will be recorded. The warning will be disregarded after six months satisfactory service.
   (b) Written warning
       If the offence is serious, if there is no improvement in standards, or if a further offence occurs, a written warning will be given which will include the reason for the warning and a notice that, if there is no improvement after twelve months, a final written warning will be given.
   (c) Final written warning:
       If conduct or performance is still unsatisfactory, or if a further serious offence occurs within the 12-month period, a final warning will be given making it clear that any recurrence of the offence or other serious misconduct within a period of one month will result in dismissal.
   (d) Dismissal
       If there is no satisfactory improvement or if further serious misconduct occurs, the employee will be dismissed.
   (e) Gross misconduct
       If, after investigation, it is confirmed that an employee has committed an offence of the following nature (the list is not exhaustive) the normal consequence will be dismissal:
           theft or damage to the Company's property, incapacity for work due to being under the influence of alcohol or illegal drugs, physical assault and gross insubordination, discrimination or harassment contrary to the Company's Equal Opportunities Policy.
       While the alleged gross misconduct is being investigated the employee may be suspended, during which time he or she will be paid the normal hourly rate. Any decision to dismiss will be taken by the employer only after a full investigation.
   (f) Appeals
       An employee who wishes to appeal against any disciplinary decision must do so
       to:_____ within two working days. The employer will hear the appeal and decide the case as impartially as possible.

Dishonoured Cheque Notice Form OLF13

Date _____

To _____

_____

_____

Dear _____

Payment of your cheque no. _____ in the sum of £ _____ , dated _____ payable to us has been dishonoured by your bank.

Please therefore ensure sufficient funds are put into your account to enable us to re-present the cheque immediately, or remit your payment in cash to our address by hand.

Yours sincerely

_____

Dismissal Letter for Intoxication on the Job   Form E15

Date   _____

To   _____

          _____

          _____

Dear   _____

Further to the disciplinary meeting with you on _____. This letter is to inform you that we are terminating your employment with immediate effect from _____. This decision is based on an incident reported to me on _____ by your supervisor, _____ and on your explanation given at the disciplinary meeting. The report recommended your dismissal because of your repeated intoxication during working hours.

As you are aware, the first reported incident of your intoxication on the job was on _____. That report was placed on your personnel file, and you were informed at that time that another incident would result in a disciplinary action or possible dismissal.

This second incident of intoxication adversely affected the operational efficiency and effectiveness of your department and threatened the safety of other employees and this amounts to an act of gross misconduct. Your final pay cheque, including all forms of compensation due to you, can be picked up in the personnel office when you leave. If you wish to appeal against the decision to dismiss you, please notify me within _____ days.

Yours sincerely

_____

Personnel Manager

Before any decision to dismiss is made the statutory dismissal and disciplinary procedure and any contractual procedures may be followed to avoid legal repercussions.

Disputed Account Settlement   Form CDC12

THIS AGREEMENT IS MADE the _____ day of _____ year _____

BETWEEN:

(1) _____ (the 'Creditor'); and

(2) _____ (the 'Debtor').

WHEREAS:

(A)   The Creditor asserts a claim (the 'Claim') against the Debtor in the amount of

  £ _____ arising from the following transaction:

  _____

  _____

  _____

(B)   The Debtor disputes the Claim, and denies the said debt is due.

(C)   The parties have agreed to settle the Claim on the terms hereinafter appearing.

NOW IT IS HEREBY AGREED as follows:

1.   The Debtor agrees to pay the Creditor and the Creditor agrees to accept from the Debtor the sum of

  _____ Pounds (£ _____) in full payment, settlement, satisfaction,

  discharge and release of the Claim.

2.   The Debtor and the Creditor agree that each of them is hereby released from further obligations

  arising out of the transaction and from any liability relating hereto.

IN WITNESS OF WHICH the parties have executed this agreement the day and year first above written

(Individual)   (Company)

_____   Signed for and on behalf of

Signed by the Creditor   _____Ltd

_____

               _____

               Director

_____   _____

Signed by the Debtor   Director/Secretary

_____

               Signed for and on behalf of:

               _____Ltd

               _____

               Director

               _____

               Director/Secretary

Electricity Bill Query   Form GS06

Date _____

To _____

_____

_____

Ref _____

Dear _____

I have received my bill reference number _____ dated _____ regarding the above account.

I am writing to question the accuracy of the meter reading, as the units of electricity consumed appear to be far above my normal usage for this time of year. I have tested the meter with all electrical appliances in the property turned off and observed the meter still running.

Please therefore arrange for an engineer to test the meter so we can determine its accuracy and settle the matter. Please advise me of any charge for doing this and confirm that costs for meter testing are refundable should the meter indeed prove faulty and that in addition I may be entitled to compensation.

I look forward to hearing from you with a proposed appointment date.

Yours sincerely

_____

Name _____

Address _____

_____

Tel. _____

Employee Agreement on Confidential Information, Inventions and Patents

Form E16

THIS AGREEMENT is made the _____ day of _____ year _____

BETWEEN:

(1) _____ (the 'Employee'); and

(2) _____ (the 'Company').

NOW IT IS HEREBY AGREED as follows:

In consideration of the employment of the Employee by the Company, the parties agree as follows:

1. The Employee agrees that he will not use any information or material for himself or others, and not take any such material or reproductions thereof from the Company, being apparatus, equipment, drawings, systems, formulae, reports, manuals, invention records, customer lists, computer programmes, or other material embodying trade secrets or confidential technical or business information of the Company or its Affiliates at any time during or after employment by the Company except in the performance of the Employee's duties to the Company.

2. In this Agreement, the Company's 'Affiliates' shall comprise any subsidiary, holding company or subsidiary of any holding company of which the Company is a subsidiary as well as any person which may be a client, customer or partner of the Company or any other person to who or to which the Company owes any obligation of confidence.

3. The Employee agrees immediately to return all such material and reproductions thereof in his possession to the Company upon request and in any event upon termination of employment.

4. Except with prior written authorisation by the Company, the Employee agrees not to disclose or publish any trade secret or confidential technical or business information or material of the Company or its Affiliates.

5. The Employee shall keep a complete and updated record of any and all inventions, patents and improvements, whether patentable or not, which he, solely or jointly, may conceive, make, or first disclose during the period of his employment by the Company and will furnish that record to the Company immediately upon being required to do so.

6. The Employee confirms that he has no entitlement to any rights relating to any invention which he may make in the course of his employment with the Company save insofar as is provided by the Patents Act 1977 section 39.

7. The Employee agrees that he will aid the Company or its nominee in the acquisition of any United Kingdom or other Patents which it may wish to acquire in respect of any invention the rights to which belong to the Company or its nominee, by virtue of the same having been made in the course of the employee's employment, and that he will do all lawful acts and execute any documents in relation to such acquisition as may reasonably be requested at any time before and after his employment by the Company, without additional compensation but at the Company's expense.

8. The Employee agrees that if he accepts employment with any firm or engages in any type of activity on his own behalf or on behalf of any organisation following termination of his employment within the Company, the Employee shall notify the Company in writing within thirty days of the name and

Continued on next page

Employee Agreement on Confidential Information, Inventions and Patents (continued)

address of such organisation and the nature of such activity.

9. The Employee agrees to give the Company timely written notice of any prior employment agreements or patent rights that might conflict with the entitlement of the Company or its Affiliates to benefit from the work undertaken or the inventions made by the Employee.

10. No waiver by either party of any breach by the other party of any provision of this agreement shall be deemed or construed to be a waiver of any succeeding breach of such provision or as a waiver of the provision itself.

11. This agreement shall be binding upon and pass to the benefit of the successors and assigns of the Company and, insofar as the same may be applied thereto, the heirs, legal representatives, and assigns of the Employee.

12. This agreement shall supersede the terms of any prior employment agreement or understanding between the Employee and the Company. This agreement may be modified or amended only in writing signed by an executive officer of the Company and by the Employee.

13. Should any portion of this agreement be held to be invalid, unenforceable or void, such holding shall not have the effect of invalidating the remainder of this agreement or any other part thereof, the parties hereby agreeing that the portion so held to be invalid, unenforceable, or void shall, if possible, be deemed amended or reduced in scope.

14. The Employee acknowledges reading, understanding and receiving a signed copy of this agreement.

IN WITNESS OF WHICH the parties have signed this agreement the day and year first above written

_____

Signed by the Employee

_____

in the presence of (witness)

Name _____

Address _____

_____

Occupation_____

Signed for and on behalf of the Company

_____

Director

_____

Director/Secretary

Employee Disciplinary Report   Form E17

Employee _____

Department _____

☐ Written Warning   ☐ Final Warning

1.   Statement of the problem: _____

_____

_____

2.   Prior discussion or warnings on this subject, whether oral or written: _____

_____

_____

3.   Company policy on this subject: _____

_____

_____

4.   Summary of corrective action to be taken by the Company and/or Employee: _____

_____

_____

5.   Consequences of failure to improve performance or correct behaviour: _____

_____

_____

6.   Employee statement: _____

_____

_____

Employee Signature: _____   Date _____

Management Approval: _____   Date _____

Distribution: One copy to Employee, one copy to Supervisor and original to Personnel File.

Employee Dismissal for Lateness   Form E18

Date _____

To _____

_____

_____

Dear _____

Further to our meeting on _____ concerning your timekeeping, I am writing to inform you of my decision.

As discussed, despite receiving verbal and written warnings about your repeated lateness for work, on _____ you arrived late for work. You have been warned that any further lateness may result in the termination of your employment and as you were unable to provide any satisfactory explanation for your lateness, I regret that I have no other option than to give you _____ weeks' notice of the termination of your employment. Your last day of employment will therefore be _____.

If you wish to appeal against your dismissal, please notify me in writing within ___ working days.

Yours sincerely

_____

Before any decision to dismiss is made the statutory dismissal and disciplinary procedure and any contractual procedures may be followed to avoid legal repercussions.

Employee File   Form E19

Employee: _____

Address: _____

Phone: _____ National Insurance No.: _____

DOB: _____ Sex: ☐ M   ☐ F

Marital Status: ☐ Single ☐ Married ☐ Separated ☐ Widowed ☐ Divorced

Name of Spouse: _____No. Dependents _____

In Emergency Notify: _____

Address: _____

_____

_____

Education

Secondary School _____Years: _____

University/College _____Years: _____

Other _____Years: _____

Employment History

Date From /To	Position	Salary _____
_____	_____	£ _____
_____	_____	£ _____
_____	_____	£ _____
_____	_____	£ _____
_____	_____	£ _____
_____	_____	£ _____

Dismissal Information

Date dismissed: _____ Would we re-employ? ☐ Yes ☐ No

Reason for dismissal: _____

_____

_____

_____

_____

_____

Employee File

Employee Licence
(For a Furnished or Unfurnished House or Flat)

Form RT02

The PROPERTY _____

The LICENSOR _____

The LICENSEE _____

The PERIOD the period beginning on the date of this Agreement and ending on the date that the Licensee's employment with the Licensor ceases

(delete paragraph if not required) Subject to the right of the licensor at any time during the Period to end this Agreement earlier by giving to the licensee written notice of _____ week(s)/month(s)*

The LICENCE FEE £ _____ per week/month* payable in advance on the _____ of each week/month*

The Deposit £ _____

(delete if unfurnished) The Inventory means the list of the Licensor's possessions at the Property which has been signed by the Licensor and the Licensee

DATED _____

SIGNED _____   _____

_____   _____

(The Licensor)   (The Licensee)

THIS AGREEMENT comprises the particulars detailed above and the terms and conditions printed overleaf whereby the Property is hereby let by the Licensor and taken by the Licensee for the Period at the Licence Fee.

*delete as appropriate

Terms and Conditions on next page

Employee Licence Terms and Conditions (continued)   Form RT02

1. The Licensor requires the Licensee to reside at the Property in order to carry out his employment with the Licensor and on the termination of such employment this Agreement shall immediately terminate.

2. This Licence Agreement is personal to the Licensee

3. The Licensor may deduct the Licence Fee and any other payments due and outstanding from the Licensee under this Agreement from any wages or salary payable by the Licensor to the Licensee

4. The Licensee will pay:

    4.1 the Licence Fee at the times and in the manner set out in this Agreement

    4.2 pay all charges in respect of any electric, gas, water and telephonic or televisual services used at or supplied to the Property and Council Tax or any similar property tax that might be charged in addition to or replacement of it

    4.3 keep the interior of the Property in a good and clean state and condition and not damage or injure the Property or any part of it and if at the end of the Period any item on the Inventory requires repair, replacing, cleaning or laundering the Licensee will pay for the same (reasonable wear and tear and damage by an insured risk excepted)

    4.4 maintain at the Property and keep in a good and clean condition all of the items listed in the Inventory

    4.5 not make any alteration or addition to the Property nor without the Licensor's prior written consent (not to be unreasonably withheld) to do any redecoration or painting of the Property

    4.6 not do or omit to do anything on or at the Property which may be or become a nuisance or annoyance to any other occupiers of the Property or owners or occupiers of adjoining or nearby premises or which may in any way prejudice the insurance of the Property or cause an increase in the premium payable

    4.7 not without the Licensor's prior consent (not to be unreasonably withheld) allow or keep any pet or any kind of animal at the Property

    4.8 pay the Licensor's reasonable legal or other costs and expenses reasonably incurred as a result of any breaches by the Licensee of his obligations under this Agreement

    4.9 not use or occupy the Property in any way whatsoever other than as a private residence

    4.10 not part with or share possession of occupation of the Property or any part thereof provided however that members of the Licensee's immediate family may reside at the Property with the Licensee so long as no relationship of Licensor and Licensee is thereby created or allowed to arise between the Licensee and any family member

    4.11 allow the Licensor or anyone with the Licensor's written permission to enter the Property at reasonable times of the day to inspect its condition and state of repair, carry out any necessary repairs and gas inspections, or during the last month of the term, show the Property to prospective new licensee, provided the Licensor has given 48 hours written notice beforehand (except in emergency)

    4.12 provide the Licensor with a forwarding address when the Licence comes to an end and remove all rubbish and all personal items (including the Licensees own furniture and equipment) from the property before leaving

    4.13 pay interest at the rate of 4% above the Base Lending Rate for the time being of the Licensor's bankers upon any Licence Fee or other money due from the Licensee under this Agreement which is more than 14 days in arrears in respect of the period from when it became due to the date of payment

5. The Deposit

    5.1 will be held by the Licensor and will be refunded to the Licensee at the end of the Term (however it ends) but less any reasonable deductions properly made by the Licensor to cover any reasonable costs incurred by or losses caused to him by any breaches of the Licensee's obligations under this Agreement. No interest will be payable by the Licensor to the Licensee in respect of the Deposit money

    5.2 shall be repaid to the Licensee, at the forwarding address provided to the Licensor, as soon as reasonably practicable. However the Licensor shall not be bound to return the Deposit until he is satisfied that no money is repayable to the Local Authority if the Licensee has been in receipt of Housing Benefit and until after he has had a reasonable opportunity to assess the reasonable cost of any repairs required as a result of any breaches of his obligations by the Licensee or other sums properly due to the Licensor under clause 5.1 above, save that except in exceptional circumstances the Licensor shall not retain the Deposit for more than one month

    5.3 if at any time during the Term the Licensor needs to use any part of the Deposit to cover any reasonable costs incurred as a result of any breaches of his obligations by the Licensee or other sums properly due to the Licensor, the Licensee shall upon demand pay by way of additional rent to the Licensor any additional payments needed to restore the full amount of the Deposit

6. The Licensor will keep in repair

    6.1 the structure and exterior of the Property (including drains gutters and external pipes)

    6.2 the installations at the Property for the supply of water, gas and electricity and for sanitation (including basins, sinks, baths and sanitary conveniences), and

    6.3 the installations at the Property for space heating and heating water

    But the Licensor will not be required to:

    6.4 carry out works for which the licensee is responsible, eg by virtue of clauses 4.3 and 4.4 above

    6.5 reinstate the Property in the case of substantial damage or destruction.

7. In the event of substantial damage to or destruction the Licensee shall be relieved from payment of the Licence Fee to the extent that the Licensee's use and enjoyment of the Property is thereby prevented and from performance of its obligations as to the state and condition of the Property to the extent of and so long as there prevails such damage or destruction (except to the extent that the insurance is prejudiced by any act or default of the Licensee)

8. So long as the reference to a right of early termination in the definition of the 'PERIOD' overleaf (the 'early termination right') has not been deleted then Licensor may at any time during the Period terminate this Agreement by giving to the Licensee prior written notice to that effect, the length of such notice to be that stated in the early termination right, and upon the expiry of the notice period this Agreement shall end with no further liability of either party save for any existing breach, [provided that the Licensee will not be obliged to vacate the premises unless suitable alternative accommodation shall have been offered to him.]

9. Upon the termination of his employment the Licensee shall vacate the Property forthwith. Note that if possession of the Property has not been surrendered and anyone is living at the Property then the Licensor must obtain a court order for possession before reentering the Property. This clause does not affect the Tenant's rights under the Protection from Eviction Act 1977.

10. Where the context so admits:

    10.1 The 'Licensor' includes the persons for the time being entitled to the reversion expectant upon this Licence

    10.2 The 'Property' includes all of the Licensor's fixtures and fittings at or upon the Property

    10.3 The 'Period' shall mean the period stated in the particulars overleaf or any shorter or longer period in the event of an earlier termination or an extension or holding over respectively

11. All references to the singular shall include the plural and vice versa and any obligations or liabilities of more than one person shall be joint and several and an obligation on the part of a party shall include an obligation not to allow or permit the breach of that obligation

Employee Non-Competition and Confidentiality Agreement

Form E20

_____ ('the Employee'), of _____ (address) and employed or about to be employed by _____ ('the Company') hereby makes these convenants to the Company in consideration for the Company:

[hiring the Employee in the position of _____]*

[continuing to employ the Employee with the following change in the nature of the employment]*

*(delete as applicable)

Employee's Covenants:

BETWEEN:

(1) _____ (the 'Company'); and

(2) _____ (the 'Employee').

NOW IT IS HEREBY AGREED as follows:

In consideration of the employment or change in the nature of the employment of the Employee by the Company the Employee covenants as follows:

1. The Employee hereby agrees not directly or indirectly to compete with the business of the Company and its successors and assigns during the period of employment and for a period of _____ [months][years] following termination of employment and within a distance of _____ mile(s) of _____ notwithstanding the cause or reason for the termination or redundancy.

2. The phrase 'not compete with the business of' as used herein shall mean that the Employee shall not directly or indirectly own (whether as proprietor or as shareholder), manage, operate, act as consultant to or be employed in a business substantially similar to and in competition with any business of the Company of which the Employee had been engaged, save that this definition shall not extend to the ownership of shares in any public limited company.

3. The Employee further agrees, not for a period of _____ to solicit customers of the Company who have transacted business with the Company during the Employee's employment and that he will not for the like period solicit suppliers or employees of the Company with the intention of inducing them to cease to supply the Company or to leave the Company's employment.

4. The Employee acknowledges that the Company and its affiliates hold certain trade, business, and financial secrets in connection with the business. The Employee covenants not to divulge to any party at any time, directly or indirectly, during the term of employment or any time afterwards, unless directed by the Board of Directors, any confidential information acquired by the Employee about the Company or its affiliates, including, but not limited to, customer lists, trade secrets, documents, financial statements, correspondence, patents, processes, formulas, research, intellectual property, expenses, costs or other confidential information of any kind, or any other data that could be used by third parties to the disadvantage of the Company. This paragraph shall cease to apply to information that is in the public domain other than by way of unauthorised disclosure. This paragraph shall also not apply to disclosures that the Employee is entitled to make under the Public Interest Disclosure Act. The Employee further agrees that, throughout his employment and thereafter, he will not use such secrets, knowledge data or information for his purposes or for those of any third party.

Continued on next page

Employee Non-Competition and Confidentiality Agreement (continued)

5. If the Employee breaches this covenant, the Company shall have the right, in addition to all other rights available hereunder and by law, to prevent the Employee from continuing such breach. The Employee confirms the he/she has had the opportunity to discuss and negotiate this Covenant fully and confirm his/her understanding and acceptance of it. If any part of this Covenant is declared invalid, then the Employee agrees to be bound by a Covenant as near to the original as lawfully possible. This paragraph shall survive the term and termination of employment. The Employee shall further be liable for all costs of enforcement.

6. No waiver of a right by the Company constitutes a waiver of any other right of the Company, and a temporary waiver by the Company does not constitute a permanent waiver or any additional temporary waiver. These Covenants may be modified only in writing and signed by the Employee and the Company. If any portion of these Covenants is declared invalid, these Covenants shall continue in effect as if the invalid portion had never been part hereof.

7. This agreement shall be binding upon and inure to the benefit of the parties, their successors and assigns.

IN WITNESS OF WHICH the parties have signed this agreement the day and year first above written

_____   _____
Signed by the Employee   Signed for and on behalf of the Company

_____   _____
in the presence of (witness)   Director

Name _____

Address _____   _____

_____   Director/Secretary

Occupation _____

Health Warning: Restrictions on competition will not be enforceable unless they are necessary to protect the Employer's customer base and unless it is not practical to do so by a simple prohibition on soliciting or doing work for those customers. If you make the restriction too extensive, the court will not cut it back. Instead the restriction will fail altogether. As a guide, you should ask yourself what are the minimum restrictions which will stop your customers from following the Employee to his new job. Things to think about are: (1) how important is personal contact: for an accountant or a hairdresser; this will be more important than for a typist; (2) how frequently does a customer typically use your service: the more frequent the use, the quicker it is to get the customer to transfer his loyalty from your former employee to his replacement; (3) is your business in a town or in the country: an exclusion from working within a one mile radius may be reasonable in the country, but not in central London. If the restriction is important to you, consult a solicitor to make sure you get it right. Otherwise, think carefully before trying to impose an exclusion area of more than a half-mile radius or a time period of more than six months. Restrictions on disclosing confidential information, as opposed to restrictions on competition, however, need not be so limited.

It is important to ensure that this agreement is signed at the same time or before the time when the employment begins or changes. If you spring it on an Employee who is already working for you in the job which it is intended he should remain in, the court will be more likely to refuse to enforce it, both because there may be doubts as to whether the Employer is giving anything in exchange for the covenant (this is known as 'consideration') and because the Employer's actions may be regarded as oppressive. If the employment has already begun, take a solicitor's advice.

Employee Suspension Notice   Form E22

Date   _____

To   _____

_____

_____

Dear   _____

You have received informal notices that your conduct has been found to be unsatisfactory. On _____ a formal Warning Notice was placed on your permanent employment record. Your unacceptable conduct has continued; in particular you have:

_____

_____

_____

You are herewith suspended from work for a period of _____ commencing _____. Suspension shall be without pay; however, your health and pension benefits shall continue during the suspension providing you return to work immediately following the suspension period.

YOU MAY BE SUBJECT TO DISMISSAL IN THE FUTURE IF YOU CONTINUE TO VIOLATE COMPANY POLICY.

_____

Company Representative

ACKNOWLEDGED

Date   _____

_____

Employee

Note: An Employer is only entitled to suspend in this way if the contract allows it to do so, or if its disciplinary policy allows it to do so.

Employee Warning   Form E23

Date _____

To _____
_____
_____

Dear _____

Further to our meeting I write to confirm the outcome of our discussion. In this meeting we discussed your work performance and I informed you that your work performance is unsatisfactory for the following reasons: _____

_____
_____
_____
_____
_____
_____
_____

We discussed the reasons why your performance has fallen below the standard expected and we considered how an improvement might be achieved: _____

_____
_____.

We informed you that we expect immediate correction of the problem, and will monitor your performance for a period of _____ weeks/months to ensure an improvement is achieved.

If there is any question about this notice or if we can help you improve your performance or correct the difficulties, then please discuss this matter with your supervisor at the earliest possible opportunity.

_____
Company Representative

Employer's Request for Reference   Form E25

Date _____

Ref _____

To _____

_____

_____

Dear _____

Re _____

The above-named candidate has applied for a position within our company and has given your name as a previous employer reference. The information requested below will help us evaluate the candidate. We will consider your comments in strict confidence. Please fill in the details below and return this letter in the envelope provided. Thank you for your cooperation.

Yours sincerely

_____

Personnel Department

Please indicate:

    Position within your firm: _____

    Employed from _____to _____

    Salary £ _____

Please rate the applicant on the basis of his/her employment with you (good/ fair/ poor):

    Ability _____   Conduct _____   Attitude _____

    Efficiency _____   Attendance _____   Punctuality _____

    What was the reason for dismissal or redundancy? _____

    _____

    Would you re-employ him/her? _____. If not, please give reason: _____

    _____

_____

Signature and Title

Employment Confirmation Offer Letter — Form E26

Date _____

To _____

_____

_____

Dear _____

Following your interview at this office on_____

I am pleased to offer you the above position with _____ ('the Company') subject to satisfactory references[1] and a medical report.[2] It is the Company's final decision as to whether such references meet with its requirements. You are advised not to resign from your present position until I have confirmed to you that your references have been received and are satisfactory to us. We will endeavour to obtain your references as quickly as possible.

If you accept this offer of employment, your job will be based at _____.
Your employment will commence on _____ and the first four weeks will be treated as a probationary period during which time your employment may be terminated by yourself or by the Company on one week's notice.

Your duties and responsibilities will be as set out in the attached job description and you will be responsible to _____.

Your basic salary at the commencement of your employment will be _____ payable monthly in arrears by bank credit transfer on the last day of each month. Your normal weekly hours will be from _____.

You will be entitled to _____ holiday in every year, in addition to the normal statutory entitlement, of which no more than *two* weeks may be taken consecutively. The holiday year runs from _____.

The Company will be entitled to terminate your appointment by giving you written notice of _____.
You are required to give the Company *one week's* notice of your intention to terminate your employment with the Company.

Your other terms of employment will be provided on your first day of employment.[3]

Continued on next page

Employment Confirmation Offer Letter (continued)   Form E26

If you wish to accept this offer of employment, I would be grateful if you could confirm your acceptance by signing and returning one copy of this letter in the stamped addressed envelope enclosed.[4]

I do hope that you will accept this offer. In the meantime, if you wish to discuss any aspect of this offer, please do not hesitate to contact me.

Yours sincerely

_____

Personnel Manager

---

[1] References are usually taken up at this stage, the offer being made subject to satisfactory references. A candidate who receives a job offer subject to satisfactory references should not resign from his current employment until all the conditions have been satisfied. In the public sector, offers are usually made unconditional only after all the conditions are met.

[2] Medical examinations of prospective Employees are not a legal requirement, although Employers are recommended to carry them out now that health and safety in the workplace is so important. A prospective Employee is not obliged to agree to have a medical examination, although if he did refuse it would be reasonable for the prospective Employer not to make an offer.

[3] Alternatively, these may be set out in an enclosed statement of particulars of employment or incorporated into this letter.

[4] Once this offer has been accepted, the parties have entered into a contractual relationship and the Employer will need to issue either a full contract or a statement of particulars of employment.

Employment Contract   Form E27

THIS AGREEMENT IS MADE the _____.[1]

BETWEEN (1) _____ (the 'Employer') and (2)_____ (the 'Employee')

This document sets out the terms and conditions of employment which are required to be given to the Employee under section 1 of the Employment Rights Act 1996 and which apply at the date hereof.

1. Commencement and Job Title

The Employer agrees to employ the Employee from _____ in the capacity of _____. No employment with a previous employer will be counted as part of the Employee's period of continuous employment.[2] The Employee's duties which this job entails are set out in the job description attached to this statement. The job description may, from time to time, be reasonably modified as necessary to meet the needs of the Employer's business.

2. Salary

The Employer shall pay the Employee a salary of £_____ per year payable by credit transfer at monthly intervals on the last day of each month. The Company shall review the Employee's salary at such intervals as it shall, at its sole discretion, decide.

3. Hours of Employment

The Employee's normal hours of employment shall be _____ to _____ on _____ to _____ during which time the Employee may take up to one hour for lunch between the hours of _____ and _____, and the Employee may, from time to time, be required to work such additional hours as is reasonable to meet the requirements of the Employer's business at an overtime rate of £_____ per hour.

4. Holidays

The Employee shall be entitled to _____ days' holiday per calendar year at full pay in addition to the normal public holidays. Holidays must be taken at times convenient to the Employer and sufficient notice of the intention to take holiday must be given to the Employee's supervisor. No more than two weeks' holiday must be taken at any one time unless permission is given by the Employee's supervisor.

The Employee shall be entitled to payment in lieu of holiday accrued due but untaken at the date of termination of his employment. If, at the date of termination, the Employee has taken holiday in excess of his accrued entitlement, a corresponding deduction will be made from his final payment.

5. Sickness

5.1 If the Employee is absent from work on account of sickness or injury, he or someone on his behalf should inform the Employer of the reason for the absence as soon as possible but no later than *12.00pm* on the working day on which absence first occurs.

5.2 *The Company reserves the right to ask the Employee at any stage of absence to produce a medical certificate and/or to undergo a medical examination.*

5.3 The Employee shall be paid normal remuneration during sickness absence for a maximum of _____ in any period of _____ provided that the Employee provides the Employer with a medical certificate in the case of absence of more than _____. Such remuneration will be less the amount of any statutory sick pay or social security sickness benefits to which the Employee may be entitled. Entitlement to payment is subject to notification of absence and production of medical certificates as required above.[3]

Continued on next page

Employment Contract (continued)   Form E27

6. Collective Agreements

There are no collective agreements in force directly relating to the terms of your employment.[4]

7. Pension

The Employee shall be entitled to join the Employer's pension scheme, the details of which are set out in the Employer's booklet/leaflet which is entitled _____ and which is available on request. A contracting-out certificate under the Pension Schemes Act is in force in respect of this employment.[5]

8. Termination

The Employer may terminate this Agreement by giving written notice to the Employee as follows:

(a)   With not less than one week's notice during the first two years of continuous employment; then

(b)   With not less than a further one week's notice for each full year of continuous employment after the first two years until the 12th year of continuous employment; and

(c)   With not less than 12 weeks' notice after 12 years of continuous employment.[6] The Employer may terminate this Agreement without notice or payment in lieu of notice in the case of serious or persistent misconduct such as to cause a major breach of the Employer's disciplinary rules.

The Employee may terminate this Agreement by one week's written notice to the Employer.

After notice of termination has been given by either party, the Employer may in its absolute discretion give the Employee payments in lieu of all or any part of any notice; or, provided the Employee continues to be paid and to enjoy his full contractual benefits under the terms of this Agreement, the Employer may in its absolute discretion for all or part of the notice period exclude the Employee from the premises of the Employer and require that he carries out duties other than those specified in his job description or require that he carries out no duties at all until the termination of his employment.

The normal retirement age for the employment shall be 65.

9. Confidentiality

The Employee is aware that during his employment he may be party to confidential information concerning the Employer and the Employer's business. The Employee shall not, during the term of his employment, disclose or allow the disclosure of any confidential information (except in the proper course of his employment).

After the termination of this Agreement the Employee shall not disclose or use any of the Employer's trade secrets or any other information which is of a sufficiently high degree of confidentiality to amount to a trade secret. The Employer shall be entitled to apply for an injunction to prevent such disclosure or use and to seek any other remedy including without limitation the recovery of damages in the case of such disclosure or use.

The obligation of confidentiality both during and after the termination of this Agreement shall not apply to any information which the Employee is enabled to disclose under the Public Interest Disclosure Act 1998 provided the Employee has first fully complied with the Employer's procedures relating to such external disclosures.

10. Non-Competition

For a period of _____[7] after the termination of this Agreement the Employee shall not solicit or seek business from any customers or clients of the Employer who were customers or clients of the Employer at the time during the _____[8] immediately preceding the termination of this Agreement.

11. Dismissal, Discipline and Grievance

The Employer's Dismissal and Disciplinary Rules and Procedure and the Grievance and Appeal Procedure in connection with these rules are set out in the Employer's *Staff Handbook* which is attached hereto.

Continued on next page

Employment Contract (continued)   Form E27

12. Notices

All communications including notices required to be given under this Agreement shall be in writing and shall be sent either by personal service or by first class post to the parties' respective addresses.

13. Severability

If any provision of this Agreement should be held to be invalid it shall to that extent be severed and the remaining provisions shall continue to have full force and effect.

14. Staff Handbook

Further details of the arrangements affecting your employment are published in the *Staff Handbook* as issued and/or amended from time to time. These are largely of an administrative nature, but, so far as relevant, are to be treated as incorporated in this Agreement.

15. Prior Agreements

This Agreement cancels and is in substitution for all previous letters of engagement, agreements and arrangements (whether oral or in writing) relating to your employment,[9] all of which shall be deemed to have been terminated by mutual consent. This Agreement and the *Staff Handbook*[10] constitute the entire terms and conditions of your employment and any waiver or modification must be in writing and signed by the parties to this Agreement.

16. Governing Law

This Agreement shall be construed in accordance with the laws of England & Wales and shall be subject to the exclusive jurisdiction of the English courts.

Please acknowledge receipt of this statement and your agreement to the terms set out in it by signing the attached copy of this letter and returning it to _____.

IN WITNESS OF WHICH the parties hereto have signed this Agreement the day and year first above written.

SIGNED

_____   _____
Signed by or on behalf of   in the presence of (witness)

                                                          Name _____

                                                          Address _____

                                                          _____
Dated _____   Occupation _____

SIGNED

_____   _____
Signed by the employee   in the presence of (witness)

                                                          Name _____

                                                          Address _____

                                                          _____
Dated _____   Occupation _____

Continued on next page

Employment Contract (continued)   Form E27

[1] This must be no later than two months after the employment commences. Any changes must be notified to the Employee within one month of the change. No statement is required to be given to an Employee employed under a contract for less than one month.

[2] If employment with a previous Employer is to be counted as a period of continuous employment, this, and the date it began, must be stated.

[3] If the Employer does not wish to pay normal remuneration during sickness, it should state that the statutory sick pay rules apply.

[4] Where a collective agreement directly affects the terms and conditions of employment, the following should be inserted as clause 6: 'The terms of the collective agreement dated [_____] made between [_____] and [_____] shall be deemed to be included in this Agreement'.

[5] Where no pension scheme exists, this must be stated and where no contracting out certificate is in force, this must also be stated.

[6] These are the minimum periods required by law but they may be increased by agreement.

[7] The Employer may choose the number of months or years that are necessary to protect its business needs, but any more than two years is likely to render this clause unenforceable at law.

[8] This period should be between one and two years if it is to remain enforceable by the Employer.

[9] Where Opt-Out Agreement for Working Time Regulations purposes has already been signed, add the words 'other than an Opt-Out Agreement dated [_____]'.

[10] Where Opt-Out Agreement referred to in footnote 9 is signed, add the words 'and the Opt-Out Agreement dated [_____]'.

Enquiry on Overdue Account   Form CDC13

Date _____

To _____

_____

_____

Dear _____

We have not received payment on your overdue account, and would appreciate it if you could offer your explanation by completing this form. Please tick the applicable reason, fill in the details and return this form to us.

☐   We need copies of unpaid invoices: _____

☐   We have credits outstanding: _____

☐   Payment was sent on _____.

☐   Payment will be sent on _____.

☐   Other: _____

Thank you for your kind attention.

Yours sincerely

_____

Equal Opportunities Policy
Form E28

at _____ Limited

The Company's aim is to ensure that all of its employees and job applicants are treated equally irrespective of disability, race, colour, religion or religious belief, nationality, ethnic origin, age, sex, marital status or sexual orientation. This policy sets out instructions that all employees are required to follow in order to ensure that this is achieved.

Policy

1. There shall be no discrimination or harassment on account of disability, race, colour, religion or religious belief, nationality, ethnic origin, age, sex, marital status or sexual orientation.

2. The Company shall appoint, train, develop and promote on the basis of merit and ability.

3. Employees have personal responsibility for the practical application of the Company's Equal Opportunity Policy, which extends to the treatment of members of the public and employees.

4. Managers and supervisors who are involved in the recruitment, selection, promotion and training of employees have special responsibility for the practical application of the Company's Equal Opportunity Policy.

5. The Grievance Procedure is available to any employee who believes that he or she may have been unfairly discriminated against.

6. Disciplinary action under the Disciplinary Procedure shall be taken against any employee who is found to have committed an act of unlawful discrimination. Discriminatory conduct and harassment shall be regarded as gross misconduct.

7. If there is any doubt about appropriate treatment under the Company's Equal Opportunities Policy, employees should consult the Personnel Manager.

Exercise of Option   Form OLF14

Date   _____

To   _____

_____

_____

Dear   _____

You are hereby notified that I have elected to and hereby exercise and accept the option dated
_____, executed by you in my favour. I agree to all terms, conditions, and
provisions of the option.

Yours sincerely

_____

Signed

_____

Name

Address   _____

_____

_____

Expenses Record Form E29

EXPENSE CLAIM FORM MONTH CLAIMANT:

DATE	RECEIPT NUMBER	EXPENSE	TOTAL	VAT	FUEL/ MILEAGE	CAR EXPENSES	SUBSIST/ UK TRAVEL	OVERSEAS TRAVEL	ENTERTAINMENT CLIENT	ENTERTAINMENT STAFF	PHONE	OFFICE SUPPLIES	SUNDRIES
	1												
	2												
	3												
	4												
	5												
	6												
	7												
	8												
	9												
	10												
	11												
	12												
	13												
	14												
	15												
	16												
	17												
	18												
	19												
	20												
	21												
	22												
	23												
SUB TOTAL			£	£	£	£	£	£	£	£	£	£	£

TOTAL CLAIMED £

SIGNATURE: APPROVED:

Extension of Option to Purchase Property   Form OLF15

THIS DEED IS MADE the _____ day of _____ year _____

BETWEEN:

(1) _____(the 'Grantor'); and

(2) _____(the 'Holder').

WHEREAS:

(A)   The Grantor, as the owner of property located at _____

_____ (the 'Property') granted an option to buy the Property to

the Holder on _____ (the 'Original Option'), which expires on

_____. A copy of the said Original Option is attached to this agreement.

(B)   The Holder wishes to extend the term of the Option.

NOW IT IS HEREBY AGREED as follows:

1.   In consideration of the payment to the Grantor by the Holder of the sum of

_____Pounds (£_____),

the receipt of which is hereby acknowledged, the Grantor hereby grants to the Holder a further Option

in the same terms as those contained in the Original Option save that the Option herein granted will

expire at _____ on _____ and save as hereinafter appears.

2.   If the Holder exercises the Option before the expiry of the further term herein granted the payment for

the Option and the payment for extension of the expiration of the Option shall be applied towards the

purchase price of the Property and the Holder shall receive a credit on completion equal to the

amount(s) paid for the Option and any extension.

3.   If the Holder fails to exercise the Option before the expiry of the further term herein agreed the

Grantor shall be entitled to retain absolutely all payment made by the Holder to the Grantor for the

Option and the extension granted herein.

IN WITNESS OF WHICH the parties have signed this Deed the day and year first above written

_____   _____

Signed as a Deed by or on behalf of the Grantor   Signed as a Deed by or on behalf of the Holder

_____   _____

in the presence of (witness)   in the presence of (witness)

Name _____   Name _____

Address _____   Address _____

_____   _____

Occupation _____   Occupation _____

Family Tree

Name: _____

Father: _____   Mother: _____

Father's   **Mother's**

Father _____   Father _____

Mother _____   Mother _____

Father's Paternal   **Mother's Paternal**

Grandfather: _____   Grandfather _____

Grandmother: _____   Grandmother: _____

Father's Maternal   **Mother's Maternal**

Grandfather: _____   Grandfather _____

Grandmother: _____   Grandmother: _____

Your siblings _____

_____

Your half siblings _____

_____

Father's Siblings   Mother's Siblings _____

_____   _____

Children of each of Father's siblings   Children of each of Mother's siblings

_____   _____

Grandchildren of each of Father's siblings' children   Grandchildren of each of Mother's siblings' children

_____   _____

Father's half siblings   Mother's half siblings

_____   _____

Children of each of Father's half siblings   Children of each of Mother's half siblings

_____   _____

Paternal grandfather's siblings   Paternal grandmother's siblings

_____   _____

Maternal grandfather's siblings   Maternal Grandmother's siblings

_____   _____

_____   _____

Continued on next page

Family Tree (continued)   Form P113

Children of each of paternal grandfather's siblings

_____

_____

Children of each of paternal grandmother's siblings

_____

_____

Children of each of the children of
paternal grandfather

_____

_____

_____

Children of each of the children of
paternal grandmother

_____

_____

_____

Paternal grandfather's half siblings

_____

_____

Maternal grandfather's half siblings

_____

_____

Children of each of paternal grandfather's
half siblings

_____

_____

_____

Children of each of paternal grandmother's
half siblings

_____

_____

Children of each of maternal grandfather's siblings

_____

_____

Children of each of maternal grandmother's siblings

_____

_____

Children of each of the children of
maternal grandfather

_____

_____

_____

Children of each of the children of
maternal grandmother

_____

_____

_____

Paternal grandmother's half siblings

_____

_____

Maternal grandmother;s half siblings

_____

_____

Children of each of maternal grandfather's
half siblings

_____

_____

_____

Children of each of maternal grandmother's
half siblings

_____

_____

Final Notice Before Legal Proceedings   Form OLF16

Date _____

To _____

_____

_____

Dear _____

We have repeatedly requested payment of your long overdue account in the amount of
£ _____.

Unless we receive payment in full of this amount within seven days of the date of this letter we shall have no alternative but to refer your account to our solicitors for recovery.

[We also claim statutory interest from [_____] at the rate of [_____] per cent per annum and the amount of £_____ under the Late Payment of Commercial Debts (Interest) Act 1998.] / [We reserve our rights to statutory interest under the Late Payment of Commercial Debts (Interest) Act 1998].

Yours sincerely

_____

Note: Do not claim statutory interest under the Late Payment of Commercial Debts (Interest) Act 1998 unless the debt arises in connection with the supply of goods or services and unless (1) the debtor has entered into the contract in the course of a business and (2) the contract is not a regulated agreement under the Consumer Credit Act 1974.

Final Warning Before Dismissal   Form E30

Date _____

To _____

_____

_____

Dear _____

Further to our meeting, I write to confirm our discussion. You have already been warned about your conduct within this Company. Incidents that have since come to our notice are: _____

_____

_____

_____

_____

There has not been a satisfactory improvement in your conduct since your last warning. Accordingly, any continued violations of company policy or failure to conduct yourself according to the rules of the company shall result in immediate termination of your employment without further warning.

We remind you that you have the right of appeal against this warning according to the Terms and Conditions of Employment as supplied to you, and if you wish to exercise this right, please notify me in writing within _____ working days.

Please contact the undersigned or your supervisor if you have any questions.

Yours sincerely

_____

Final Warning for Lateness   Form E31

Date _____

To   _____

      _____

      _____

Dear _____

I refer to our meeting on _____. Despite our verbal and written warnings to you about your timekeeping, there has been no improvement and you have given no satisfactory explanation as to why you continue to be late for work.

Your behaviour is unacceptable. We therefore give you this final warning. If you are late again without offering a reasonable excuse, you will be dismissed.

We remind you that you have the right of appeal against this warning according to the Statement of Terms and Conditions of Employment as supplied to you, and if you wish to exercise this right please notify me in writing within ____ working days.

Please contact the undersigned or your superior if you have any questions.

Yours sincerely

_____

First Warning for Lateness Form E32

Date _____

To _____

_____

_____

Dear _____

I refer to our meeting on _____. You are aware that your hours of work are from _____ a.m. to _____ p.m. You have repeatedly arrived for work late.

You have been advised of your bad timekeeping and warned of the possible consequences. Despite those warnings you continue to be late for work and have offered no reasonable excuse.

Consider this a formal letter of warning. You must be at your place of work strictly in accordance with the terms of your employment and the hours set. If you are late again without reasonable excuse, disciplinary action will be taken.

This warning is being recorded on your personnel file. You have a right to appeal against this warning, and if you wish to exercise this right, please notify me in writing within ____ working days.

Yours sincerely

_____

Form of Letter from Testator to Executor Form PF07

Date _____

To _____
_____
_____

Dear _____

I am writing to confirm that I have named you as an executor of my Will dated
_____ .

- A copy of my Will is enclosed.*
- My signed original Will has been lodged with _____
- I have named _____as a co-executor.
- My solicitor is _____ at _____ .*

Please confirm to me in writing that you are willing to act as one of my executors.

Yours sincerely

_____

* delete as necessary

Form of Letter from Testator to Executor Form PF07

WARNING: DO NOT INCLUDE ANY OTHER INSTRUCTIONS TO YOUR EXECUTORS IN THIS LETTER.

Form of Resolution for Submission to Companies House   Form B08

_____ Limited

Company Number _____

The Companies Act 1985

Ordinary/Special/Extraordinary/Elective resolution of

_____ Limited/Public Limited Company

At an extraordinary general meeting of the above named company, duly convened and held at

_____ on the _____ day of _____ year _____ the following

[resolution][1] / [the resolution, a copy of which is attached hereto], was duly passed as an

ordinary/special/extraordinary/elective resolution[2]:

_____

_____

_____

_____

_____

_____

_____

_____

_____

Signature of Chairman

Note: A full list of the resolutions which need to be filed and of directions as to how to do this are available on the website of Companies House at www.companieshouse.gov.uk. From 1 October 2007 the need for annual general meetings will cease in the case of private companies and the types of resolutions which need to be filed will alter.

[1] If the resolution is oral, set out the text of it; if it is written, attach a copy.

[2] Section 380 of the Companies Act 1985 details resolutions that need to be filed at Companies House; special, extraordinary and elective resolutions must be filed but not all ordinary resolutions need to be filed. The resolution must be delivered to Companies House within 15 days of being passed, accompanied by the appropriate fee, if any.

Funeral Wishes   Form PF08

Funeral Wishes
of

_____ (Name)

Funeral (Burial/Cremation) _____

_____

_____

Undertaker _____

_____

_____

Place of Service _____

_____

_____

Type of service _____

_____

_____

Person Officiating _____

_____

_____

Music Selection _____

_____

_____

Reading Selection _____

_____

_____

Flowers _____

_____

_____

Special Instructions _____

_____

_____

Furnished House/Flat Rental Agreement

Form F301

The PROPERTY	_____
	_____
The LANDLORD	_____
	of _____
	_____
The TENANT	_____
	_____
The GUARANTOR	_____
	of _____
The TERM	_____ weeks/months* beginning on _____
The RENT	£ _____ per week/month* payable in advance on the _____ of each week/month*
The DEPOSIT	£_____ which will be registered with one of the Government authorised tenancy deposit schemes ("the Tenancy Deposit Scheme") in accordance with the Tenancy Deposit Scheme Rules.
The INVENTORY	means the list of the Landlord's possessions at the Property which has been signed by the Landlord and the Tenant
DATED	_____

Signed and executed as a Deed by the following parties

Landlord	**Tenant**	**Guarantor***
_____	_____	_____
Landlord(s)' name(s)	_____	_____
	Tenant(s)' name(s)	Guarantor's name
_____	_____	_____
Landlord(s)' signature(s)	_____	_____
	Tenant(s)' signature(s)	Guarantor's signature

In the presence of:

Witness signature _____	Witness signature _____	Witness signature _____
Full name _____	Full name _____	Full name _____
Address_____	Address_____	Address_____
_____	_____	_____

(*delete as appropriate)

Continued on next page

Furnished House/Flat Rental Agreement (continued) Form F301

THIS TENANCY AGREEMENT comprises the particulars detailed above and the terms and conditions printed overleaf whereby the Property is hereby let by the Landlord and taken by the Tenant for the Term at the Rent.

IMPORTANT NOTICE TO LANDLORDS:

1 The details of 'The LANDLORD' near the top of this Agreement must include an address for the Landlord in England or Wales as well as his/her name, or all names in the case of joint Landlords.

2 Always remember to give the written Notice Requiring Possession to the Tenant at least two clear months before the end of the Term.

3 Before granting the tenancy agreement, you should check whether your chosen deposit scheme provider requires you to insert any additional terms concerning the deposit into the tenancy agreement or to alter or delete any of the terms appearing in the form below. Details of the websites of the scheme providers are set out in Note 4 for tenants below. Currently only The Tenancy Deposit Scheme has any such requirements.

4. The information in 'Notice to Tenants' below is important to you as well, because it is relevant to whether or not you should use this form and whether you can get the Property back at the end of the term.

IMPORTANT NOTICE TO TENANTS:

1 In general, if you currently occupy Property under a protected or statutory tenancy and you give it up to take a new tenancy of the same or other accommodation owned by the same Landlord, that tenancy cannot be an Assured Shorthold Tenancy and this Agreement is not appropriate.

2 If you currently occupy Property under an Assured Tenancy which is not an Assured Shorthold Tenancy your Landlord is not permitted to grant you an Assured Shorthold Tenancy of that Property or of alternative property and this Agreement is not appropriate.

3 If the total amount of rent exceeds £25,000 per annum, an Assured Shorthold Tenancy cannot be created and this Agreement is not appropriate. Seek legal advice.

4 Further information about the Government-authorised Tenancy Deposit Schemes can be obtained from their websites: The Deposit Protection Service at www.depositprotection.com, Tenancy Deposit Solutions Ltd at www.mydeposits.co.uk and The Tenancy Deposit Scheme at www.tds.gb.com.

Terms and Conditions on next page

Furnished House/Flat Rental Agreement
Terms and Conditions

Form F301

1. This Agreement is intended to create an Assured Shorthold Tenancy as defined in the Housing Act 1988, as amended by the Housing Act 1996, and the provisions for the recovery of possession by the Landlord in that Act apply accordingly. The Tenant understands that the Landlord will be entitled to recover possession of the Property at the end of the Term.

2. The Tenant's obligations:

2.1 To pay the Rent at the times and in the manner set out above.

2.2 To pay all charges in respect of any electric, gas, water, sewage and telephonic or televisual services used at or supplied to the Property and Council Tax or any property tax that might be charged in addition to or replacement of it during the Term.

2.3 To keep the items on the Inventory and the interior of the Property in a good and clean state and condition and not damage or injure the Property or the items on the Inventory (fair wear and tear excepted).

2.4 To yield up the Property and the items on the Inventory at the end of the Term in the same clean state and condition it/they was/were in at the beginning of the Term (but the Tenant will not be responsible for fair wear and tear caused during normal use of the Property and the items on the Inventory.

2.5 Not to make any alteration or addition to the Property and not without the prior written consent of the Landlord (consent not to be withheld unreasonably) do any redecoration or painting of the Property.

2.6 Not do anything on or at the Property which:

(a) may be or become a nuisance or annoyance to any other occupiers of the Property or owners or occupiers of adjoining or nearby premises

(b) is illegal or immoral

(c) may in any way affect the validity of the insurance of the Property and the items listed on the Inventory or cause an increase in the premium payable by the Landlord

(d) will cause any blockages in the drainage system and in the case of breach of this clause the Tenant to be responsible for the reasonable cost of such repair or other works which will be reasonably required.

2.7 Not without the Landlord's prior consent (consent not to be withheld unreasonably) allow or keep any pet or any kind of animal at the Property.

2.8 Not use or occupy the Property in any way whatsoever other than as a private residence.

2.9 Not assign, sublet, charge or part with or share possession or occupation of the Property (but see clause 5.1 below).

2.10 To allow the Landlord or anyone with the Landlord's written permission to enter the Property at reasonable times of the day to inspect its condition and state of repair, carry out any necessary repairs and gas inspections, and during the last month of the Term, show the Property to prospective new tenants, provided the Landlord has given at least 24 hours' prior written notice (except in emergency).

2.11 To pay the Landlord's reasonable costs reasonably incurred as a result of any breaches by the Tenant of his obligations under this Agreement, and further to pay the Landlord's reasonable costs of responding to any request for a consent which the Tenant may make of the Landlord under this Agreement.

2.12 To pay interest at the rate of 4% above the Bank of England base rate from time to time prevailing on any rent or other money lawfully due from the Tenant under this Agreement which remains unpaid for more than 14 days, interest to be paid from the date the payment fell due until payment.

2.13 To provide the Landlord with a forwarding address when the tenancy comes to an end and to remove all rubbish and all personal items (including the Tenant's own furniture and equipment) from the Property before leaving.

3. The Landlord's obligations:

3.1 The Landlord agrees that the Tenant may live in the Property without unreasonable interruption from the Landlord or any person rightfully claiming under or in trust for the Landlord.

3.2 To insure the Property and the items listed on the Inventory and use all reasonable efforts to arrange for any damage caused by an insured risk to be remedied as soon as possible and to provide a copy of the insurance policy to the Tenant if requested.

3.3 To keep in repair (where provided by the Landlord)

3.3.1 the structure and exterior of the Property (including drains gutters and external pipes)

3.3.2 the installations at the Property for the supply of water, sewage, gas and electricity and for sanitation (including basins, sinks, baths and sanitary conveniences)

3.3.3 the installations at the Property for space heating and heating water

3.4 But the Landlord will not be required to

3.4.1 carry out works for which the Tenant is responsible by virtue of his duty to use the Property in a tenant-like manner

3.4.2 reinstate the Property in the case of damage or destruction if the insurers refuse to pay out the insurance money due to anything the Tenant has done or failed to do

3.4.3 rebuild or reinstate the Property in the case of destruction or damage of the Property by a risk not covered by the policy of insurance effected by the Landlord.

3.5 If the property is a flat or maisonette within a larger building then the Landlord will be under similar obligations for the rest of the building but only in so far as any disrepair will affect the Tenant's enjoyment of the Property and in so far as the Landlord is legally entitled to enter the relevant part of the larger building and carry out the required works or repairs.

3.6 To arrange for the Tenant's Deposit to be protected by an authorised Tenancy Deposit Scheme and provide the Tenant with the required information in accordance with the provisions of the Housing Act 2004 within 14 days of receipt, and to comply with the rules of the Tenancy Deposit Scheme at all times.

4. Guarantor

If there is a Guarantor, he guarantees that the Tenant will keep to his obligations in this agreement. The Guarantor agrees to pay on demand to the Landlord any money lawfully due to the Landlord by the Tenant.

5. Ending this Agreement

5.1 The Tenant cannot normally end this Agreement before the end of the Term. However after the first three months of the Term, if the Tenant can find a suitable alternative tenant, and provided this alternative tenant is acceptable to the Landlord (the Landlord's approval not to be unreasonably withheld) the Tenant may give notice to end the tenancy on a date at least one month from the date that such approval is given by the Landlord. On the expiry of such notice, and upon (i) payment by the Tenant to the Landlord of the reasonable expenses reasonably incurred by the Landlord in granting the necessary approval and in

Continued on next page

Furnished House/Flat Rental Agreement
Terms and Conditions (continued)

granting any new tenancy to the alternative tenant, and (ii) the execution by the alternative tenant of a new tenancy agreement in the form of this Agreement for a period of 6 months or for a period not less than the unexpired portion of the term of this Agreement (if that be greater than 6 months), or for such other period as the Landlord shall approve, this tenancy shall end.

5.2 If the Tenant stays on after the end of the fixed term, a new tenancy will arise that will run from month to month or week to week ('a periodic tenancy'). This periodic tenancy can be ended by the Tenant giving at least one month's written notice to the Landlord, the notice to expire at the end of the rental period.

5.3 If at any time
5.3.1 any part of the Rent is outstanding for 21 days after becoming due (whether formally demanded or not) and/or
5.3.2 there is any breach, non-observance or non-performance by the Tenant of any covenant and/or other term of this Agreement which has been notified in writing to the Tenant and the Tenant has failed within a reasonable period of time to remedy the breach and/or pay reasonable compensation to the Landlord for the breach and/or
5.3.3 any of the grounds set out as Grounds 2, 8 or Grounds 10-15 (inclusive) (which relate to breach of any obligation by a Tenant) contained in the Housing Act 1988 Schedule 2 apply

the Landlord may recover possession of the Property and this Agreement shall come to an end. The Landlord retains all his other rights in respect of the Tenant's obligations under this Agreement. Note that if possession of the Property has not been surrendered and anyone is living at the Property or if the tenancy is an Assured or Assured Shorthold Tenancy then the landlord must obtain a court order for possession before re-entering the Property. This clause does not affect the Tenant's rights under the Protection from Eviction Act 1977.

6. The Deposit
6.1 The Deposit will be held in accordance with the Tenancy Deposit Scheme Rules as issued by the relevant Tenancy Deposit Scheme.
6.2. No interest will be payable to the Tenant by the Landlord in respect of the Deposit save as provided by the Rules of the relevant Tenancy Deposit Scheme.
6.3. Subject to any relevant provisions of the rules of the relevant Tenancy Deposit Scheme, the Landlord shall be entitled to claim from the Deposit the reasonable cost of any repairs or damage to the Property or its contents caused by the Tenant (including any damage caused by the Tenant's family and visitors) and for any rent in arrears and for any other financial losses suffered or expenditure incurred by the Landlord as a result of the Tenant's breach of these terms and conditions, provided the sum claimed by the Landlord is reasonably incurred and is reasonable in amount. The Landlord is not entitled to claim in respect of any damage to the Property or its contents which is due to 'fair wear and tear' i.e. which is as a result of the Tenant and his family (if any) living in the property and using it in a reasonable and lawful manner.

7. Other provisions
7.1 The Landlord hereby notifies the Tenant under Section 48 of the Landlord & Tenant Act 1987 that any notices (including notices in proceedings) should be served upon the Landlord at the address stated with the name of the Landlord overleaf.
7.2 The Landlord shall be entitled to have and retain keys for all the doors to the Property but shall not be entitled to use these to enter the Property without the consent of the Tenant (save in an emergency) or as otherwise provided in this Agreement.
7.3 Any notices or other documents (including any court claim forms in legal proceedings) shall be deemed served on the Tenant during the tenancy by either being left at the Property or by being sent to the Tenant at the Property by first-class post. Notices shall be deemed served the day after being left at the property or the day after posting.
7.4 Any person other than the Tenant who pays the rent due hereunder or any part thereof to the Landlord shall be deemed to have made such payment as agent for and on behalf of the Tenant which the Landlord shall be entitled to assume without enquiry.
7.5 Any personal items left behind at the end of the tenancy after the Tenant has vacated (which the Tenant has not removed in accordance with clause 2.13 above) shall be considered abandoned if they have not been removed within 14 days of written notice to the Tenant from the Landlord, or if the Landlord has been unable to trace the Tenant by taking reasonable steps to do so. After this period the Landlord may remove or dispose of the items as he thinks fit. The Tenant shall be liable for the reasonable disposal costs which may be deducted from the proceeds of sale (if any), and the Tenant shall remain liable for any balance. Any net proceeds of the sale to be returned to the Tenant at the forwarding address provided to the Landlord.
7.6 In the event of destruction to the Property or of damage to it which shall make the same or a substantial portion of the same uninhabitable, the Tenant shall be relieved from paying the rent by an amount proportional to the extent to which the Tenant's ability to live in the Property is thereby prevented, save where the destruction or damage has been caused by any act or default by the Tenant or where the Landlord's insurance cover has been adversely affected by any act or omission on the part of the Tenant.
7.7 Where the context so admits:
7.7.1 The 'Landlord' includes the persons from time to time entitled to receive the Rent.
7.7.2 The 'Tenant' includes any persons deriving title under the Tenant.
7.7.3 The 'Property' includes any part or parts of the Property and all of the Landlord's fixtures and fittings at or upon the Property.
7.7.4 All references to the singular shall include the plural and vice versa and any obligations or liabilities of more than one person shall be joint and several (this means that they will each be liable for all sums due under this Agreement, not just liable for a proportionate part) and an obligation on the part of a party shall include an obligation not to allow or permit the breach of that obligation.
7.7.5 All references to 'he', 'him' and 'his' shall be taken to include 'she', 'her' and 'hers'.

Garage Service Bill Complaint   Form GS08

Date   _____

To   _____

_____

_____

Dear   _____

On _____ I brought in my _____ registration number_____ for repairs which your reception mechanic estimated would cost £_____. However, when I came to pick the car up on _____ I was dismayed at being presented with a bill for £_____. I had to pay the bill in order to drive the car away, but did so expressly under protest, saying I would take the matter up in writing.

[Your reception mechanic never indicated to me that the figure which he quoted was provisional or that I might have to pay a greater sum. I am therefore entitled, as a matter of contract, to hold you to the figure quoted. I am therefore entitled to the sum of £_____ representing the difference between the figure quoted and the figure charged.]

[Even if you were to be correct in saying that no set price had been agreed for the work]/[Although we had not agreed a set price for the work] I am by law only obliged to pay a reasonable price for your services. Judging by your initial estimate and also by the enclosed copies of estimates I have since obtained from [other garages]/[the RAC]/[the AA] of £_____ and £_____ for the same work, I am exercising my rights under law by rejecting your bill as unreasonably high.

I estimate that the work done on my car was worth £_____, taking into consideration your original estimate and the others I have obtained, but no more. Please therefore send me a cheque for £_____, representing the amount you overcharged me within 10 days.

I look forward to hearing from you.

Yours sincerely

_____

Name

_____

Address

_____

Tel

Garage Service Claim   Form GS09

Date _____

To _____
_____
_____

Dear _____

Re Model _____ Reg. No._____

On _____ I brought in the above vehicle for [a full service] / [repairs to _____].
I was subsequently informed that the following needed attention _____
and agreed to have the necessary work carried out. On picking up the car on _____ I paid the
bill for £_____ in full and received a schedule of the parts tested and work carried out.

However, on _____, just _____ days after it was returned to me, the vehicle developed the
following problems _____ which should not have arisen
after [a full service] / [the above repairs]. I had to have the defect remedied at a cost of £_____, as
evidenced by the enclosed receipt.

Under the Supply of Goods and Services Act of 1982, you are responsible for supplying quality goods and
satisfactory service. Your failure to return my car in satisfactory condition constitutes your breach of contract
and you are liable for the expenses I incurred in having the car repaired.

Please send me a cheque for this sum within 10 days. Otherwise, I shall have no alternative but to issue you
a county court claim for recovery of the amount owed to me without further notice.

Yours sincerely

_____
Name

_____
Address

_____
Tel.

General Assignment   Form TA08

THIS AGREEMENT IS MADE the _____ day of _____ year _____

BETWEEN

(1) _____(the 'Assignor');and

(2) _____(the 'Assignee').

NOW IT IS HEREBY AGREED as follows:

1.   In consideration for the payment of £_____, receipt of which the Assignor hereby
      acknowledges, the Assignor hereby unconditionally and irrevocably assigns and transfers to the
      Assignee all right, title and interest in the following: _____

      _____

      _____

      _____

2.   The Assignor fully warrants that it has full rights and authority to enter into this assignment and that
      the rights and benefits assigned hereunder are free and clear of any lien, encumbrance, adverse claim
      or interest by any third party.

3.   The Assignor will, at the behest of the Assignee, forthwith give such notice of this Assignment, as the
      Assignee may require, to any person who is under any obligation which is assigned to the Assignee
      under this Agreement.

4.   This assignment shall be binding upon and inure to the benefit of the parties, and their successors and
      assigns.

IN WITNESS OF WHICH the parties have signed this agreement as a Deed the day and year first above
written

_____   _____

Signed by or on behalf of the Assignee   Signed by or on behalf of the Assignor

_____   _____

in the presence of (witness)   in the presence of (witness)

Name _____   Name _____

Address _____   Address _____

_____   _____

Occupation _____   Occupation _____

Health Warning: It is essential for the Assignee's protection that the person affected by the assignment (e.g. the debtor under an
assigned debt) should be given notice of the assignment.

Note: This form is not to be used for assignments by way of security (i.e. where the Assignee is making a loan to the Assignor and
where it is intended that the assignor should get back the thing which is assigned once he has paid the debt).

If the assignment is by way of gift (i.e. if no consideration is to be payable in exchange for the assignment) the assignment must be
by Deed.

General Power of Attorney

Form PF09

(Pursuant to the Powers of Attorney Act 1971, Section 10)

THIS GENERAL POWER OF ATTORNEY is made

this_____ day of _____ year _____

BY   _____

       OF _____

            _____

I APPOINT   _____

             _____

             _____

[jointly]/[jointly and severally] to be my attorney(s) in accordance with section 10 of the Powers of Attorney Act 1971.

IN WITNESS whereof I have hereunto set my hand the day and year first above written.

SIGNED as a Deed and Delivered by the said

_____   _____

in the presence of:

Witness's Signature   _____

Full name   _____

Address   _____

                       _____

Occupation   _____

Note:

1. If you are giving this power to more than one person, specify 'jointly' which means that they must all act together and cannot act separately; or 'jointly and severally' which means that they can act together, but also separately if they want to.

2. This form may not be valid if you are a trustee and if you wish to use it to delegate your powers as a trustee. If this applies to you, you should take legal advice.

General Proxy   Form B09

_____ LIMITED

I/We _____ of _____, a member/members of the above

company, hereby appoint _____ of _____

_____, as a proxy to vote in my/our name(s) and on my/our behalf at the

annual/extraordinary general meeting of the company to be held at   _____

on _____ year____ and at any adjournment thereof.

_____

Shareholder

_____

Shareholder

_____

Date

Note:

1. This form complies with the requirements of Article 6 of Table A, the provision most commonly applicable to companies. However, you should check the Articles of your company to make sure that this form is compatible with the procedure set out in them.

2. The Companies Act 1985 requires that the notice of the appointment be lodged with the company (or at such address in the UK as may be specified by the notice of the meeting for which the proxy is to be appointed) 48 hours before the meeting is due to begin. When the Companies Act 2006 section 327 comes into force on 1 October 2007, then any day which is not a working day will no longer count towards the 48 hours. Therefore, if a meeting is due to start at 3pm on the Tuesday following a bank holiday Monday, the deadline for giving notice will be 3pm the previous Thursday.

General Release   Form OLF17

THIS DEED IS MADE the _____ day of _____ year _____

BETWEEN

(1) _____ (the 'First Party');and

(2) _____ (the 'Second Party').

NOW IT IS HEREBY AGREED as follows:

1.   The First Party forever releases, discharges, acquits and forgives the Second Party from any and all claims, actions, suits, demands, agreements, liabilities, judgment, and proceedings no matter when the same may have arisen and as more particularly related to or arising from:

_____

_____

_____

_____

2.   This release shall be binding upon and inure to the benefit of the parties, their successors and assigns.

IN WITNESS OF WHICH the parties have executed this deed the date and year first above written

(Individual)   (Company)

                                                Signed for and on behalf of
_____
Signed by the First Party   _____Ltd

_____   _____
in the presence of (witness)   Director

Name _____

Address _____   _____

_____   Director/Secretary

Occupation _____

                                                Signed for and on behalf of
_____
Signed by the Second Party   _____Ltd

_____   _____
in the presence of (witness)   Director

Name _____

Address _____   _____

_____   Director/Secretary

Occupation _____

General Subordination Agreement Between Creditors   Form OLF18

THIS DEED IS MADE the _____ day of _____ year _____

BETWEEN

(1) _____ (the 'First Creditor');and

(2) _____ (the 'Second Creditor').

WHEREAS:

(A)   The First Creditor has a claim against _____ (the 'Debtor') for monies owed to the First Creditor by the Debtor.

(B)   The Second Creditor also has a claim against the Debtor for monies owed to the Second Creditor by the Debtor.

(C)   The Parties agree that the Second Creditor's debt be subordinated to that of the First Creditor.

NOW THIS DEED WITNESSES as follows:

1.   The Second Creditor hereby agrees to subordinate its claims for debts now or hereinafter due to the undersigned from the Debtor to any and all debts that may now for a period of _____ years[1] from the making of this Agreement become or hereinafter be due to the First Creditor from the Debtor.

2.   This subordination shall be unlimited as to amount or duration and shall include the subordination of any secured or unsecured obligation.

3.   At any time when the Debtor may be indebted to the First Creditor, the Second Creditor may not receive payment of any debt owed to the Second Creditor, whether such payment be made by the Debtor or by any guarantor of the Debtor's indebtedness, except as follows: _____.

4.   If the Second Creditor shall receive any payment which it is not entitled under this Agreement to receive, or if any indebtedness which the Second Creditor may have to the Debtor should become the subject of any set-off of any indebtedness which the Debtor may have to the Second Creditor, the Second Creditor shall pay to the First Creditor a sum equal to the amount of such payment or set-off, and in the case of any such sums paid to the Second Creditor, the Second Creditor shall hold the same upon trust for the First Creditor.

5.   This subordination agreement shall be binding upon and inure to the benefit of the parties, their successors and assigns.

Continued on next page

General Subordination Agreement
Between Creditors (continued)

IN WITNESS OF WHICH the parties have executed this Deed the day and year first above written

(Individual)

_____

Signed by the First Creditor

_____

in the presence of (witness)

Name _____

Address _____

_____

Occupation _____

_____

Signed by the Second Creditor

_____

in the presence of (witness)

Name _____

Address _____

_____

Occupation _____

(Company)

Signed for and on behalf of

_____Ltd

_____

Director

_____

Director/Secretary

Signed for and on behalf of

_____Ltd

_____

Director

_____

Director/Secretary

General Subordination Agreement

¹ The period should not exceed 80 years.

Grievance Procedure   Form E33

GRIEVANCE PROCEDURE
at _____ Limited

1. The following procedure shall be applied to settle all disputes or grievances concerning an employee or employees of the Company (but excluding those relating to redundancy selection).

2. Principles:

    (i)   It is the intention of both parties that employees should be encouraged to have direct contact with management to resolve their problems.

    (ii)   The procedure for resolution of grievances and avoidance of disputes is available if the parties are unable to agree a solution to a problem.

    (iii) Should a matter be referred to this procedure for resolution, both parties should accept that it should be progressed as speedily as possible, with a joint commitment that every effort will be made to ensure that such a reference takes no longer than seven working days to complete.

    (iv)   Pending resolution of the grievance, the same conditions prior to its notification shall continue to apply, except in those circumstances where such a continuation would have damaging effects upon the Company's business.

    (v)   It is agreed between the parties that where the grievance is of a collective nature, i.e. affecting more than one employee, it shall be referred initially to (ii) of the procedure.

    (vi)   If the employee's immediate supervisor/manager is the subject of the grievance and for this reason the employee does not wish the grievance to be heard by him or her, it shall be referred initially to (ii) of the procedure.

3. The Procedure:

    (i)   Where an employee has a grievance, he shall raise the matter with his or her immediate supervisor/manager. If the grievance concerns the performance of a duty by the Company in relation to an employee, the employee shall have the right to be accompanied by a fellow worker or trade union official if he makes a request to be so accompanied.

    (ii)   If the matter has not been resolved at (i), it shall be referred to a more senior manager or director and the shop steward, full-time trade union officer, or fellow employee, if requested shall be present. A statement summarising the main details of the grievance and the reasons for the failure to agree must be prepared and signed by both parties.

    (iii) In the event of a failure to agree, the parties will consider whether conciliation or arbitration is appropriate. The Company may refer the dispute to the Advisory Conciliation and Arbitration Service, whose findings may, by mutual prior agreement, be binding on both parties.

Guarantee Form LB03

THIS AGREEMENT IS MADE the _____ day of _____ year _____

BETWEEN

(1) _____ (the 'Guarantor');and

(2) _____ (the 'Creditor').

NOW IT IS HEREBY AGREED as follows:

1. As an inducement for the Creditor, from time to time to extend credit to _____
    _____(the 'Customer'),
    it is hereby agreed that the Guarantor does hereby guarantee to the Creditor the prompt, punctual
    and full payment of all monies now or hereinafter due to the Creditor from the Customer.

2. Until termination, this Guarantee is unlimited as to amount or duration and shall remain in full force
    and effect notwithstanding any extension, compromise, adjustment, forbearance, waiver, release or
    discharge of any party or guarantor, or release in whole or in part of any security granted for the said
    indebtedness or compromise or adjustment thereto, and the Guarantor waives all notices thereto.

3. The obligations of the Guarantor shall be primary and not secondary and the Creditor shall not be
    required to exhaust its remedies as against the Customer prior to enforcing its rights under this
    Guarantee against the Guarantor.

4. The Guarantee hereunder shall be unconditional and absolute and the Guarantor waives all rights of
    subrogation and set-off until all sums due under this guarantee are fully paid.

5   In the event payments due under this Guarantee are not paid punctually upon demand, then the
    Guarantor shall pay all reasonable costs and solicitors fees necessary for the collection and
    enforcement of this Guarantee.

6. This guarantee may be terminated by the Guarantor upon fourteen (14) days written notice of
    termination being delivered to the Creditor. Such termination shall extend only to credit extended by
    the Creditor after the expiry of the said fourteen (14) day period and not to prior extended credit, or
    goods in transit received by the Customer after the expiry of the fourteen day period.

7. The Guarantor warrants and represents it has full authority to enter into this Guarantee.

8. This Guarantee shall be binding upon and inure to the benefit of the parties, their successors and
    assigns.

Continued on next page

Guarantee (continued)   Form LB03

9.   This Guarantee is subject to English law and the parties agree to submit to the exclusive jurisdiction of the English courts in connection with any dispute hereunder.

IN WITNESS OF WHICH the parties have signed this agreement the day and year first above written

_____

Signed by or on behalf of the Guarantor

_____

in the presence of (witness)

Name _____

Address _____

_____

Occupation _____

_____

Signed by or on behalf of the Creditor

_____

in the presence of (witness)

Name _____

Address _____

_____

Occupation _____

Health | warning: This form should not be used if the original agreement is one which is regulated under the Consumer Credit Act 1974. Broadly speaking the Act, at the time of writing, applies to any loan, hire or hire purchase agreement for £25,000 or less. There are some exceptions. The most important are that (1) an agreement is not regulated if the borrower or hirer is a limited company or (2) the agreement is 'non-commercial', meaning that it is not made in the course of a business or is a mere one-off. There are other exceptions as well, but you should take a solicitor's advice before deciding that any of these apply to you. If the Act does regulate the original agreement, it will also regulate any variation to the agreement (such as this one). In those circumstances, this form will not comply with the requirements of the Act and the agreement may therefore be unenforceable. Note also that by the time you use this form, the law may have changed so as to apply to loans of more than £25,000.

Holiday Letting Agreement
(for a Holiday Let of Furnished Property)

Form RT03

The PROPERTY _____

_____

The LANDLORD _____

_____

_____

The TENANT _____

_____

_____

_____

_____

The TERM _____day(s)/week(s)/month(s)* beginning at 12 noon on _____

and expiring at 10 am on _____

The RENT £ _____ per week/month* payable in advance on the _____of each week/month*

or

£_____ payable in advance on the date of this Agreement

The DEPOSIT £ _____

The INVENTORY means the list of the Landlord's possessions at the Property which has been _____

signed by the Landlord and the Tenant

DATED _____

SIGNED _____   _____

_____   _____

(The Landlord)   _____

(The Tenant)

THIS RENTAL AGREEMENT comprises the particulars detailed above and the terms and conditions printed overleaf whereby the Property is hereby let by the Landlord and taken by the Tenant for the Term at the Rent.

(*delete as appropriate)

IMPORTANT NOTICE TO LANDLORDS:

This Form is intended for use only for a Holiday Let. If the circumstances make it clear that the letting is NOT for the purposes of the Tenant's holiday, for example because the Term is so long, the Courts may hold that it is an Assured Shorthold Tenancy (and you will not be able to obtain an order for possession of the Property for at least six months from the beginning of the tenancy).

Terms and Conditions on next page

Holiday Letting Agreement Terms and Conditions   Form RT03

1. The Tenant shall be entitled to occupy the Property for holiday purposes only and this Agreement shall not confer on the Tenant any security of tenure within the terms of the Housing Act 1988 pursuant to which the occupation shall be deemed to be by way of an excluded tenancy

2. The Tenant will:

   2.1 pay the Rent at the times and in the manner aforesaid

   2.2 keep the interior of the Property in a good, clean and tenantable state and condition and not damage or injure the Property or any part of it

   2.3 yield up the Property at the end of the Term in the same clean state and condition it was in at the beginning of the Term reasonable wear and tear and damage by insured risks excepted

   2.4 maintain at the Property and keep in a good and clean condition all of the contents of the Property as listed on the Inventory, if any, and to replace, repair or cleanse any item(s) which become broken or damaged during the Term

   2.5 not make any alteration or addition to the Property nor to do any redecoration or painting of the Property

   2.6 not do or omit to do anything on or at the Property which may be or become a nuisance or annoyance to any other occupiers of the Property or owners or occupiers of adjoining or nearby premises or which may in any way prejudice the insurance of the Property or cause an increase in the premium payable therefor

   2.7 not without the Landlord's prior written consent (consent not to be withheld unreasonably) allow or keep any pet or any kind or animal at the Property. If any pets are permitted they must be kept under strict control at all times and must not be left unattended in the Property. The Tenant will be responsible for all damage and any extra cleaning caused by the pet(s)

   2.8 not use or occupy the Property in any way whatsoever other than as a private holiday residence for a maximum of _____ persons

   2.9 not assign, sublet, charge or part with or share possession of occupation of the Property or any part thereof

   2.10 allow the Landlord or anyone with the Landlord's written permission to enter the Property at reasonable times of the day to inspect its condition and state of repair, and carry out any necessary repairs and gas inspections, provided the Landlord has given reasonable prior notice (except in emergency)

   2.11 pay interest at the rate of 4% above the Base Lending Rate for the time being of the Landlord's bankers upon any Rent or other money due from the Tenant under this Agreement which is more than 3 days in arrears in respect of the period from when it became due to the date of payment

   2.12 provide the Landlord with a forwarding address when the tenancy comes to an end and remove all rubbish and all personal items (including the Tenant's own furniture and equipment) from the Property before leaving

3. Subject to the Tenant paying the rent and performing his/her obligations under this Agreement the Tenant may peaceably hold and enjoy the Property during the term without interruption from the Landlord or any person rightfully claiming under or in trust for the Landlord

4. In the event of the Rent being unpaid for more than 10 days after it is due (whether demanded or not) or there being a breach of any other of the Tenant's obligations under this Agreement then the Landlord may recover possession of the Property and this Rental Agreement shall thereupon end but without prejudice to any of the Landlord's other rights and remedies in respect of any outstanding obligations on the part of the Tenant. This clause does not affect the Tenant's statutory rights and the Landlord will need to obtain a court order while anyone is living at the Property

5. The Deposit

   5.1 The Deposit will be held by the Landlord and will be refunded to the Tenant at the end of the Term (however it ends) at the forwarding address provided to the Landlord but less any reasonable deductions properly made by the Landlord to cover any reasonable costs incurred or losses caused to him by any breaches of the obligations in his Agreement by the Tenant. No interest will be payable to the Tenant in respect of the Deposit money

   5.2 The Deposit shall be payable to the Tenant as soon as reasonably practicable, however the Landlord shall not be bound to return the Deposit until after he has had a reasonable opportunity to assess the reasonable cost of any repairs required as a result of any breaches of his obligations by the Tenant or other sums properly due to the Landlord under clause 6.1 However, the Landlord shall not, save in exceptional circumstances, retain the Deposit for more than one month after the end of the tenancy

   5.3 If at any time during the Term the Landlord is obliged to deduct from the Deposit to satisfy the reasonable costs occasioned by any breaches of the obligations of the Tenant the Tenant shall make such additional payments as are necessary to restore the full amount of the Deposit

6. The Landlord hereby notifies the Tenant under Section 48 of the Landlord & Tenant Act 1987 that any notices (including notices in proceedings) should be served upon the Landlord at the address stated with the name of the Landlord overleaf

7. In the event of damage to or destruction of the Property by any of the risks insured against by the Landlord the Tenant shall be relieved from payment of the Rent to the extent that the Tenant's use and enjoyment of the Property is thereby prevented and from performance of its obligations as to the state and condition of the Property to the extent of and so long as there prevails such damage or destruction (except to the extent that any policy of insurance that the Landlord may have taken out is prejudiced by any act or default of the Tenant)

8. Where the context so admits:

   8.1 The 'Landlord' includes the persons for the time being entitled to the reversion expectant upon this Tenancy

   8.2 The 'Tenant' includes any persons deriving title under the Tenant

   8.3 The 'Property' includes all of the Landlord's fixtures and fittings at or upon the Property

   8.4 The 'Term' shall mean the period stated in the particulars overleaf or any shorter or longer period in the event of an earlier termination or an extension respectively

9. All references to the singular shall include the plural and vice versa and any obligations or liabilities of more than one person shall be joint and several and an obligation on the part of a party shall include an obligation not to allow or permit the breach of that obligation

House Rules   Form RT04

1.   The price for the use of the room (with bed and breakfast and evening meal*) is £ _____ per week

     payable in advance on _____

     of each week.

2.   The room will be cleaned and sheets changed on _____ of each week.

3.   Guests are requested to keep the room tidy and not to bring any food into it.

4.   No overnight visitors are permitted. Any visitors must leave the premises at 10 p.m. when the doors

     will be locked.

5.   The volume control on any television, radio, audio system or musical instrument must be turned low so

     that they are not audible from outside the room. The owner reserves the right to require these to be

     turned off if they cause annoyance to them or other occupiers.

6.   Communal bathroom and kitchen facilities (if any) must be left clean and tidy by guests after use.

7.   Guests may use the sitting room.

8.   Guests have use of the bedroom assigned to them but they do not have exclusive possession of it. The

     owner reserves the right to require the guest to move to another room at short notice.

9.   Guests must not move furniture, pictures or wall hangings without the consent of the owner, nor

     should they install their own furniture, pictures or wall hanging without such consent.

10. Guests returning to the house after 10 p.m. without prior arrangement with the owner are liable to be

     locked out.

* Delete as appropriate

Note: Guests should be asked to sign a copy of these rules.

House/Flat Share Agreement (Non-Resident Owner)   Form F304

The PROPERTY _____

_____

The DESIGNATED ROOM _____

The SHARED PARTS _____

The LANDLORD _____

of _____

_____

The TENANT _____

The GUARANTOR* _____

of _____

The TERM _____ weeks/months* beginning on _____

The RENT £ _____ per week/month* payable in advance on the _____ of each

week/month*

The DEPOSIT £ _____ which will be registered with one of the Government

authorised tenancy deposit schemes ('the Tenancy Deposit Scheme') in

accordance with the Tenancy Deposit Scheme Rules

The INVENTORY means the list of the Landlord's possessions at the Property which has been

signed by the Landlord and the Tenant

DATED _____

Signed and executed as a Deed by the following parties

Landlord	Tenant	Guarantor*
_____	_____	_____
_____	_____	_____
Landlord(s)' name(s)	_____	_____
	Tenant(s)' name(s)	Guarantor's name
_____	_____	_____
Landlord(s)' signature(s)	_____	_____
	Tenant(s)' signature(s)	Guarantor's signature

In the presence of:

Witness signature _____   Witness signature _____   Witness signature _____

Full name _____   Full name _____   Full name _____

Address_____   Address_____   Address_____

_____   _____   _____

(*delete as appropriate)

Continued on next page

House/Flat Share Agreement (Non-Resident Owner) (cont)   Form F304

THIS TENANCY AGREEMENT comprises the particulars detailed above and the terms and conditions printed overleaf whereby the Designated Room, with the right to share the use of the Shared Parts with such other persons as the Landlord grants or has granted the right to use those Shared Parts, is hereby let by the Landlord and taken by the Tenant for the Term at the Rent.

IMPORTANT NOTICE TO LANDLORDS:

1 The details of 'The LANDLORD' near the top of this Agreement must include an address for the Landlord in England or Wales as well as his/her name, or all names in the case of joint Landlords.

2 Always remember to give the appropriate written Notice to Terminate to the Tenant two clear months before the end of the Term.

3 Before granting the tenancy agreement, you should check whether your chosen deposit scheme provider requires you to insert any additional terms concerning the deposit into the tenancy agreement or to alter or delete any of the terms appearing in the form below. Details of the websites of the scheme providers are set out in Note 4 for tenants below. Currently only The Tenancy Deposit Scheme has any such requirements.

4. The information in 'Notice to Tenants' below is important to you as well, because it is relevant to whether or not you should use this form and whether you can get the Property back at the end of the term.

IMPORTANT NOTICE TO TENANTS:

1 In general, if you currently occupy this Property under a protected or statutory tenancy and you give it up to take a new tenancy of the same or other accommodation owned by the same Landlord, that tenancy cannot be an Assured Shorthold Tenancy and this Agreement is not appropriate.

2 If you currently occupy this Property under an Assured Tenancy which is not an Assured Shorthold Tenancy your Landlord is not permitted to grant you an Assured Shorthold Tenancy of this Property or of alternative property and this Agreement is not appropriate.

3 If the total amount of rent exceeds £25,000 per annum, an Assured Shorthold Tenancy cannot be created and this Agreement is not appropriate. Seek legal advice.

4 Further information about the Government authorised Tenancy Deposit Schemes can be obtained from their websites: The Deposit Protection Service at www.depositprotection.com, Tenancy Deposit Solutions Ltd at www.mydeposits.co.uk and The Tenancy Deposit Scheme at www.tds.gb.com.

Terms and Conditions on next page

House/Flat Share Agreement (Non-Resident Owner)
Terms and Conditions

Form F304

1. This Agreement is intended to create an assured shorthold tenancy as defined in the Housing Act 1988, as amended by the Housing Act 1996, and the provisions for the recovery of possession by the Landlord in that Act apply accordingly. The Tenant understands that the Landlord will be entitled to recover possession of the Property at the end of the Term. Under this Agreement, the Tenant will have exclusive occupation of the Designated Room and will share with other occupiers of the Property the use and facilities of the Shared Parts of the Property.

2. The Tenant's obligations:

   2.1 To pay the Rent at the times and in the manner set out above.

   2.2 To make a proportionate contribution to the costs of all charges in respect of any electric, gas, water and telephone or televisual services used at or supplied to the Property and Council Tax or any similar property tax that might be charged in addition to or replacement of it during the Term.

   2.3 To keep the items on the Inventory and the interior of the Designated Room and Shared Parts of the Property in a good and clean state and condition and not damage or injure the Designated Room and Shared Parts of the Property or the items on the Inventory (fair wear and tear excepted).

   2.4 To yield up the Designated Room and Shared Parts of the Property and the items on the Inventory at the end of the Term in the same clean state and condition it/they was/were in at the beginning of the Term (but the Tenant will not be responsible for fair wear and tear caused during normal use of the Property and the items on the Inventory or for any damage to the Shared Parts of the Property and its contents caused by other tenants and/or their visitors).

   2.5 Not make any alteration or addition to the Property and not without the prior written consent of the Landlord (consent not to be withheld unreasonably) do any redecoration or painting of the Property.

   2.6 Not do anything on or at the Property which:

      (a) may be or become a nuisance or annoyance to any other occupiers of the Property or owners or occupiers of adjoining or nearby premises;

      (b) is illegal or immoral;

      (c) may in any way affect the validity of the insurance of the Property and the items listed on the Inventory or cause an increase in the premium payable by the Landlord.

      (d) will cause any blockages in the drainage system and in the case of breach of this clause the Tenant to be responsible for the reasonable cost of such repair or other works which will be reasonably required.

   2.7 Not without the Landlord's prior consent allow or keep any pet or any kind of animal at the Property.

   2.8 Not use or occupy the Property in any way whatsoever other than as a private residence.

   2.9 Not assign, sublet, charge or part with or share possession or occupation of the Property (but see clause 5.1 below).

   2.10 To allow the Landlord or anyone with the Landlord's written permission to enter the Property at reasonable times of the day to inspect its condition and state of repair, carry out any necessary repairs and gas inspections, and during the last month of the Term, show the Property to prospective new tenants, provided the Landlord has given 24 hours' prior written notice (except in emergency).

   2.11 To pay the Landlord's reasonable costs reasonably incurred as a result of any breaches by the Tenant of his obligations under this Agreement, and further to pay the Landlord's reasonable costs of responding to any request for a consent which the Tenant may make of the Landlord under this Agreement.

   2.12 To pay interest at the rate of 4% above the Bank of England base rate from time to time prevailing on any rent or other money lawfully due from the Tenant under this Agreement which remains unpaid for more than 14 days, interest to be paid from the date the payment fell due until payment.

   2.13 To provide the Landlord with a forwarding address when the tenancy comes to an end and to remove all rubbish and all personal items (including the Tenant's own furniture and equipment) from the Designated Room and Shared Parts of the Property before leaving.

3. The Landlord's obligations:

   3.1 The Landlord agrees that the Tenant may live in Designated Room and Shared Parts of the Property without unreasonable interruption from the Landlord or any person rightfully claiming under or in trust for the Landlord.

   3.2 To insure the Property and the items listed on the Inventory and use all reasonable efforts to arrange for any damage caused by an insured risk to be remedied as soon as possible and to provide a copy of the insurance policy to the Tenant if requested.

   3.3 To keep in repair (where provided by the Landlord)

      3.3.1 the structure and exterior of the Property (including drains gutters and external pipes)

      3.3.2 the installations at the Property for the supply of water, sewage, gas and electricity and for sanitation (including basins, sinks, baths and sanitary conveniences)

      3.3.3 the installations at the Property for space heating and heating water

   3.4 But the Landlord will not be required to

      3.4.1 carry out works for which the Tenant is responsible by virtue of his duty to use the Property in a tenant-like manner

      3.4.2 reinstate the Property in the case of damage or destruction if the insurers refuse to pay out the insurance money due to anything the Tenant has done or failed to do

      3.4.3 rebuild or reinstate the Property in the case of destruction or damage of the Property by a risk not covered by the policy of insurance effected by the Landlord.

   3.5 If the property is a flat or maisonette within a larger building then the Landlord will be under similar obligations for the rest of the building but only in so far as any disrepair will affect the Tenant's enjoyment of the Property and in so far as the Landlord is legally entitled to enter the relevant part of the larger building and carry out the required works or repairs.

   3.6 To arrange for the Tenant's Deposit to be protected by an authorised Tenancy Deposit Scheme in accordance with the provisions of the Housing Act 2004 within 14 days of receipt, and to comply with the rules of the Tenancy Deposit Scheme at all times.

4. Guarantor

   If there is a Guarantor, he guarantees that the Tenant will keep to his obligations in this agreement. The Guarantor agrees to pay on demand to the Landlord any money lawfully due to the Landlord by the Tenant.

5. Ending this Agreement

   5.1 The Tenant cannot normally end this Agreement before the end of the Term. However after the first three months of the Term, if the Tenant can find a suitable alternative tenant, and provided this alternative tenant

Continued on next page

House/Flat Share Agreement (Non-Resident Owner)   Form F304
Terms and Conditions (continued)

is acceptable to the Landlord (the Landlord's approval not to be unreasonably withheld) the Tenant may give notice to end the tenancy on a date at least one month from the date that such approval is given by the Landlord. On the expiry of such notice and upon (i) payment by the Tenant to the Landlord of the reasonable expenses reasonably incurred by the Landlord in granting the necessary approval and in granting any new tenancy to the alternative tenant, and (ii) the execution by the alternative tenant of a new tenancy agreement in the form of this Agreement for a period of 6 months or for a period not less than the unexpired portion of the term of this Agreement (if that be greater than 6 months), or for such other period as the Landlord shall approve this tenancy shall end.

5.2   If the Tenant stays on after the end of the fixed term, a new tenancy will arise that will run from month to month or week to week (a 'periodic tenancy'). This periodic tenancy can be ended by the Tenant giving at least one month's written notice to the Landlord, the notice to expire at the end of the rental period.

5.3   If at any time

5.3.1   any part of the Rent is outstanding for 21 days after becoming due (whether formally demanded or not) and/or

5.3.2   there is any breach, non-observance or non-performance by the Tenant of any covenant and/or other term of this Agreement which has been notified in writing to the Tenant and the Tenant has failed within a reasonable period of time to remedy the breach and/or pay reasonable compensation to the Landlord for the breach and/or

5.3.3   any of the grounds set out as Grounds 2, 8 or Grounds 10-15 (inclusive) (which relate to breach of any obligation by a Tenant) contained in the Housing Act 1988 Schedule 2 apply

the Landlord may recover possession of the Property and this Agreement shall come to an end. The Landlord retains all his other rights in respect of the Tenant's obligations under this Agreement. Note that if possession of the Property has not been surrendered and anyone is living at the Property or if the tenancy is an Assured or Assured Shorthold Tenancy then the landlord must obtain a court order for possession before re-entering the Property. This clause does not affect the Tenant's rights under the Protection from Eviction Act 1977.

6.   The Deposit

6.1   The Deposit will be held in accordance with the Tenancy Deposit Scheme Rules as issued by the relevant Tenancy Deposit Scheme.

6.2.   No interest will be payable to the Tenant by the Landlord in respect of the Deposit save as provided by the Rules of the relevant Tenancy Deposit Scheme.

6.3.   Subject to any relevant provisions of the rules of the relevant Tenancy Deposit Scheme, the Landlord shall be entitled to claim from the Deposit the reasonable cost of any repairs or damage to the Property or its contents caused by the Tenant (including any damage caused by the Tenant's family and visitors) any rent in arrears and for any other financial losses suffered or expenditure incurred by the Landlord as a result of the Tenant's breach of these terms and conditions, provided the sum claimed by the Landlord is reasonably incurred and is reasonable in amount. The Landlord is not entitled to claim in respect of any damage to the Property or its contents which is due to 'fair wear and tear' i.e. which is as a result of the Tenant and his family (if any) living in the property and using it in a reasonable and lawful manner.

7.   Other provisions

7.1   The Landlord hereby notifies the Tenant under Section 48 of the Landlord & Tenant Act 1987 that any notices (including notices in proceedings) should be served upon the Landlord at the address stated with the name of the Landlord overleaf.

7.2   The Landlord shall be entitled to have and retain keys for all the doors to the Property but shall not be entitled to use these to enter the Designated Room without the consent of the Tenant (save in an emergency) or as otherwise provided in this Agreement.

7.3   Any notices or other documents shall be deemed served on the Tenant during the tenancy by either being left at the Property or by being sent to the Tenant at the Property by first-class post. If notices or other documents are served on the Tenant by post they shall be deemed served on the day after posting.

7.4   Any person other than the Tenant who pays the rent due hereunder or any part thereof to the Landlord shall be deemed to have made such payment as agent for and on behalf of the Tenant which the Landlord shall be entitled to assume without enquiry.

7.5   Any personal items left behind at the end of the tenancy after the Tenant has vacated (which the Tenant has not removed in accordance with clause 2.13 above) shall be considered abandoned if they have not been removed within 14 days of written notice to the Tenant from the Landlord, or if the Landlord has been unable to trace the Tenant by taking reasonable steps to do so. After this period the Landlord may remove or dispose of the items as he thinks fit. The Tenant shall be liable for the reasonable disposal costs which may be deducted from the proceeds of sale (if any), and the Tenant shall remain liable for any balance. Any net proceeds of the sale to be returned to the Tenant at the forwarding address provided to the Landlord.

7.6   In the event of destruction to the Property or of damage to it which shall make the same or a substantial portion of the same uninhabitable, the Tenant shall be relieved from paying the rent by an amount proportional to the extent to which the Tenant's ability to live in the Property is thereby prevented , save where the destruction or damage has been caused by any act or default by the Tenant or where the Landlord's insurance cover has been adversely affected by any act or omission on the part of the Tenant.

7.7   Where the context so admits:

7.7.1   The 'Landlord' includes the persons from time to time entitled to receive the Rent.

7.7.2   The 'Tenant' includes any persons deriving title under the Tenant.

7.7.3   The 'Designated Room' and 'Shared Parts' includes any part or parts of the Designated Room and Shared Parts and all of the Landlord's fixtures and fittings in the Designated Room and Shared Parts.

7.7.4   All references to the singular shall include the plural and vice versa and any obligations or liabilities of more than one person shall be joint and several (this means that they will each be liable for all sums due under this Agreement, not just liable for a proportionate part) and an obligation on the part of a party shall include an obligation not to allow or permit the breach of that obligation. Note that joint and several liability will only apply to two or more Tenants signing this Agreement together. Tenants will not have joint and several liability with other tenants in the Property who have signed separate agreements with the Landlord.

7.7.5   All references to 'he', 'him' and 'his' shall be taken to include 'she', 'her' and 'hers'.

Household Inventory

Form RT07

Re _____(the Property)

No.	Living Room
____	
____	Armchair
____	Ashtray
____	Chairs
____	Coffee table
____	Curtains
____	Cushions
____	Framed picture
____	Stereo system
____	Mirror
____	Net curtains
____	Plant
____	Rug
____	Sofa
____	Table
____	Table lamp
____	Telephone
____	Television
____	Vase
____	Video
____	Wall clock
____	
____	

No.	Kitchen/Dining Room
____	
____	Apron
____	Baking tray
____	Bottle opener
____	Bread bin
____	Carving knives
____	Casserole dish
____	Cheese grater
____	Chopping board
____	Coffee pot

____ Corkscrew
____ Cups
____ Dessert spoons
____ Dinner plates
____ Dishwasher
____ Draining board
____ Egg cups
____ Forks
____ Fridge/Freezer
____ Fruit bowl
____ Frying pans
____ Garlic crusher
____ Glasses
____ Kettle
____ Knives
____ Liquidiser
____ Measuring jug
____ Microwave
____ Milk jug
____ Mugs
____ Mug tree
____ Oven & Hob
____ Pie dishes
____ Potato peeler
____ Pudding/Soup dishes
____ Pyrex dish
____ Roasting dish
____ Rolling pin
____ Salt & pepper pots
____ Sauce pans
____ Scales
____ Serving dishes
____ Side plates
____ Sieve
____ Soup spoons
____ Spatula

____ Storage jars
____ Sugar jug
____ Swing bin
____ Table
____ Tablecloth
____ Table mats
____ Teapot
____ Tea spoons
____ Tea towels
____ Tin opener
____ Toaster
____ Tray
____ Washing machine
____ Washing up bowl
____ Wok
____ Wooden spoons
____
____

No.	Bedroom One
____	
____	Blankets
____	Bed sheets
____	Chair
____	Chest of drawers
____	Curtains
____	Double bed
____	Dressing table
____	Duvet
____	Duvet cover
____	Framed picture
____	Lamp
____	Mattress cover
____	Net curtains
____	Pillows
____	Pillow cases

Continued on next page

Household Inventory (continued)   Form RT07

_____ Side table
_____ Single bed
_____ Table mirror
_____ Wall mirror
_____ Wardrobe
_____
_____

No.	Bedroom Two

_____
_____ Blankets
_____ Bed sheets
_____ Chair
_____ Chest of drawers
_____ Curtains
_____ Double bed
_____ Dressing table
_____ Duvet
_____ Duvet cover
_____ Framed picture
_____ Lamp
_____ Mattress cover
_____ Net curtains

_____ Pillows
_____ Pillow cases
_____ Side table
_____ Single bed
_____ Table mirror
_____ Wall mirror
_____ Wardrobe
_____
_____

No.	Bathroom

_____
_____ Basket
_____ Floor mat
_____ Lavatory brush
_____ Shower curtain
_____ Soap dish
_____ Towels
_____ Wall mirror
_____ Wooden chair
_____
_____

No.	Storage cupboard

_____
_____ Broom
_____ Bucket
_____ Clothes horse
_____ Dustpan & brush
_____ Iron
_____ Ironing board
_____ Mop
Vacuum cleaner
_____
_____

No.	Hall

_____
_____ Coat stand
_____ Framed picture
_____
_____

Signed _____   _____
(Landlord/Owner)   (Tenant/Sharer)

Indemnity Agreement   Form OLF19

THIS AGREEMENT[1] IS MADE the _____ day of _____ year _____

BETWEEN

(1) _____(the 'First Party');and

(2) _____ (the 'Second Party').

[NOW THIS DEED WITNESSES as follows:]

1. [In consideration of the Second Party [engaging the First Party as a subcontractor to carry out certain of the works which the First Party has undertaken to complete for _____ under a contract dated _____('the Main Contract').The First Party agrees to indemnify and save harmless the Second Party and its successors and assigns, from any claim, action, liability, loss, damage or suit, arising from the following:

   [any breach, non -performance, act or omission by the First Party its employees or agents by reason of which the Second Party is rendered liable for breach of the Main Contract or in negligence or for breach of any statutory duty to _____ or to any other person or persons, provided that nothing in this Agreement shall make the First Party liable for any negligence or breach of duty on the part of the Second Party its employees or agent.]

2. In the event of any asserted claim as aforesaid, the Second Party shall provide the First Party immediate written notice of the same, and thereafter the First Party shall pay forthwith upon demand by the Second Party, such costs of defending against the Claim as the Second Party may incur and shall at its own expense give all reasonable assistance to the defence against such claim and shall, protect and save harmless the Second Party from the same and from any loss or liability thereunder.

3. The Second Party shall have the right at its sole discretion to defend, pay or settle the claim on its own behalf without notice to the First Party and with full rights of recourse against the the First Party for all fees, costs, expenses and payments made or agreed to be paid to discharge the claim.

4. Upon default, the First Party further agrees to pay all reasonable solicitor's fees incurred in enforcing this Agreement against the First Party.

5. This Agreement shall be unlimited as to amount or (save as aforesaid) duration.

6. This Agreement shall be binding upon and inure to the benefit of the parties, their successors and assigns.

[7. Nothing in this Agreement is intended to confer any benefit on a third party whether under the Contracts (Rights of Third Parties) Act or otherwise].

Continued on next page

Indemnity Agreement (continued)   Form OLF19

IN WITNESS OF WHICH the parties have executed this Deed the day and year first above written

(Individual)   (Company)

                                                 Signed for and on behalf of

_____   _____Ltd

Signed by the First Party

                                                 _____

_____   Director

in the presence of (witness)

Name _____   _____

Address _____   Director/Secretary

_____

Occupation _____

_____   Signed for and on behalf of:

Signed by the Second Party   _____Ltd

_____   _____

in the presence of (witness)   Director

Name _____

Address _____   _____

_____   Director/Secretary

Occupation _____

Note: This is merely an example of the sort of transaction which could make an indemnity agreement desirable and which could furnish consideration for it.

¹ If there is no consideration for the indemnity, this document should be stated to be a Deed and executed as such.

Independent Contractor Agreement   Form E34

THIS AGREEMENT IS MADE the _____ day of _____ year _____

BETWEEN:

(1 _____ (the 'Owner');and

(2 _____ (the 'Contractor').

WHEREAS:

(A)   The owner resides or operates a business at _____ (the 'Site') and

wishes to have certain services performed at the Site.

(B)   The Contractor agrees to perform such services under the terms and conditions set forth in this

agreement.

NOW IT IS HEREBY AGREED as follows:

1.   Description of Work: In return for the payment agreed hereunder the Contractor will perform services

of the following description at the Site: _____

_____

_____

_____

_____

_____

_____

_____

_____

_____

_____

2.   Payment: The Owner will pay the Contractor the sum of _____Pounds (£_____)

for the work performed under this agreement, in accordance with the following schedule: _____

_____

_____

_____

_____

_____

3.   Relationship of the Parties: This agreement creates an independent contractor-owner relationship. The

Owner is interested only in the results to be achieved. [The Contractor is free to decide how those

results will be achieved, and who is to be engaged by him to achieve those results without reference

to the Contractor, save that _____]¹

[The Contractor is entitled to carry out the work himself or to engage other persons to carry out in his

stead as he may in his discretion decide]. The Contractor is solely responsible for the conduct and

control of the work. The Contractor is not an agent or employee of the Owner for any purpose.

Employees of the Contractor are not in any contractual relationship with the Owner and are not

entitled to any benefits that the Owner provides to the Owner's employees. This is not an exclusive

Continued on next page

Independent Contractor Agreement (continued) Form E34

agreement. Both parties are free to contract with other parties for similar services. [Save for the particular assignments mentioned in the above schedule, the Owner shall not be obliged to provide work for the Contractor, and the Contractor shall not be obliged to do any work or supply any services].

4. Liability: The Contractor assumes all risk connected with work to be performed, whether in respect of the premises (or access thereto) on which the work is to be carried out or for providing a safe system of work to those engaged in that work. [The Contractor also accepts all responsibility for the provision of tools and equipment used in the performance of this agreement. To the extent that the Owner's tools and equipment are used, the Contractor shall be responsible for ensuring that they are safe to use and appropriate for the work to be done. If the Contractor shall decide that any tools or equipment are unsafe to use or inappropriate for the work, the Contractor shall provide such tools and equipment which in the Contractor's opinion are necessary. Tools and equipment so provided shall belong to and be at the risk of the Contractor. The Contractor will carry for the duration of this agreement public liability insurance [employers' liability insurance] [and] [contract works insurance] in an amount and on terms acceptable to the Owner. The Contractor agrees to indemnify the Owner for any and all liability or loss arising from the performance of this agreement.

5. Duration: Either party may cancel this agreement with _____ days' written notice to the other party; otherwise, the contract shall remain in force for a term of _____ _____ from the date hereof, [but this term shall not be construed so as to require the Contractor to perform any work or the Owner to provide any work, save as specifically provided for in this Agreement].

IN WITNESS OF WHICH the parties have signed this agreement the day and year first above written

_____   _____

Signed by or on behalf of the Owner   Signed by or on behalf of the Contractor

_____   _____

in the presence of (witness)   in the presence of (witness)

Name _____   Name _____

Address _____   Address _____

_____   _____

Occupation _____   Occupation _____

Note: If you wish to avoid an employer/employee relationship you cannot achieve this by simply calling yourselves independent contractors. A court would look at the reality of the relationship and make an evaluation in all the circumstances. Important factors would be the degree of control which one party has over the way in which the other works, whether the work is to be done by an individual personally, or whether he is free to delegate performance; whether one party is bound to offer, and the other to do, the work and above all the extent to which the contractor is part of the organisation for which he is working (e.g. whether he is brought in to achieve one project or whether he carries out work of a type which always requires someone to be on hand to do it). In this form there are many parts in square brackets. Include all of those which suit your arrangement, as the more you include, the more likely it will be that you will avoid the relationship of employer/employee. Note that it is generally easier to avoid this relationship if you take on temporary staff through an employment agency. You should consult a solicitor if any doubt arises.

[1] Here insert any restrictions as to times of work, qualifications of workers or such other restrictions on the Contractor's freedom to carry out the work in the manner he chooses as may be necessary.

Insurance Claim Notice   Form PF10

Date _____

To _____

_____

_____

Dear _____

You are hereby notified that I have incurred a loss which I believe is covered by my insurance policy number _____ . Details of the loss are as follows:

1.   Type of loss or claim: _____

2.   Date and time incurred: _____

3.   Location: _____

4.   Estimated loss: _____

Please forward a claim form to me as soon a possible.

Yours sincerely

Name _____

Address _____

_____

Telephone No. (Work) _____

Telephone No. (Home) _____

Policy Number _____

Note: that you will have to follow this up with a claim on the insurance company's form and that you must submit it within the time limits set out in your policy.

Internal Customer Complaint Memorandum　　Form BS19

Please complete and return this memorandum to Customer Services

Date:	Ref:	Complaint taken by:
Customer:		Telephone/Letter/Fax
		Contact:
		Tel:
		Fax:
Nature of complaint:		Product code:
		Supplier:
		Qty:
Action required: By whom: Date:		
Action completed:		Signed off:
		Date:

Joint Venture Agreement (Non-Partnership) Form B10

THIS JOINT VENTURE AGREEMENT IS MADE the ____ day of _____ year ____

BETWEEN:

(1) _____ of _____(the 'First Party")

the proprietor of a business known as _____; and

(2) _____ of _____ (the 'Second Party') the proprietor of a

business known as _____

In consideration of the terms, conditions and covenants hereinafter set forth, the parties agree as follows:

1. The Parties hereby agree to co operate for the purposes of enabling their separate businesses to co-operate with one another in the following respects: _____

_____

2. The term of the this Agreement shall be _____

3. The Parties shall from time to time contribute equally to meeting the expenses arising under this Agreement without reference to the receipts or profitability of either business. For the avoidance of doubt, nothing in this agreement shall confer upon any Party a right to share in the profits of any other Party or Parties.

4. The relationship between the Parties shall be limited to the performance of the terms and conditions of this agreement. Nothing herein shall be construed to create a partnership between the Parties or to authorise any Party to act as a general agent for another, or to permit any Party to bind the other or others except as set forth in this agreement, or to borrow money on behalf of another Party or Parties, or to use the credit of any Party or Parties for any purpose.

5. This agreement may not be assigned without the prior written consent of all of the other Parties hereto.

6. This agreement shall be governed by and interpreted under the law of England and Wales. Any claim arising out of or relating to this agreement, or the breach thereof, shall be settled by arbitration in accordance with the Rules of the Chartered Institute of Arbitrators and judgment upon the award rendered by the arbitrator(s) may be entered in any court having jurisdiction thereof.

7. Any and all notices to be given pursuant to or under this agreement shall be sent to the party to whom the notice is addressed at the address of the Party stated above and to all the other parties thereto.

8. This agreement constitutes the entire agreement between the Joint Venturers pertaining to the subject matter contained in it, and supersedes all prior and contemporaneous agreements, representations, warranties and understandings of the parties. No supplement, variation or amendment of this agreement shall be binding unless executed in writing by all the parties hereto. No waiver of any of the provisions of this agreement shall be deemed, or shall constitute, a waiver of any other provision, whether similar or not similar, nor shall any waiver constitute a continuing waiver. No waiver shall be binding unless in writing signed by the party making the waiver.

Continued on next page

Joint Venture Agreement (Non-partnership) (continued)   Form B10

IN WITNESS OF WHICH the parties have signed this agreement the day and year first above written

_____   _____
Signed by or on behalf of the First Joint Venturer   Signed by or on behalf of the Second Joint Venturer

_____   _____
in the presence of (witness)   in the presence of (witness)

Name _____   Name _____

Address _____   Address _____

_____   _____

Occupation _____   Occupation _____

Health Warning: Business people occasionally attempt to dress up their arrangements as non-partnership agreements when they are in fact partners. They do this because they know that one partner has the ability to undertake obligations on behalf of all of the other partners and because each individual partner is liable for all of the debts of the firm, even if they were run up without his knowledge or consent and even if he was defrauded.

If things go wrong, and if a court has to decide whether you were in a partnership or not, it will not do you any good merely to point to a form which says that you were not partners. Partnership is defined by the Partnership Act 1890 as 'the relation which subsists between persons carrying on a business in common with a view of profit.' If that is what you are doing, then you are partners, with all that that entails. There is no single test for whether you are in fact partners or not. However, if you share only gross receipts, rather than profits, and if you each run your separate businesses without interference of the other, and if you merely co operate with each other in various limited ways, then you are unlikely to be regarded as partners. An example would be if you share shop premises and take turns looking after each others merchandise and serving each others customers. Another example would be if one of you owns land, and you let the other farm it in exchange for your having a share of what he sells the produce for (as opposed to a share of what he earns after deducting his expenses).

Note also that even if you are not partners in fact, you will be treated as if you were partners if you give outsiders the impression that that is what you are. Avoid using stationery which has both your names on it and make it obvious to everyone that you are running separate businesses.

The form above should help you to frame a co operation agreement where you are not partners. Because of the importance of whether you are partners or not, we strongly recommend that you run your draft agreement past your solicitor.

Note that if a partnership is what you want, and if you also to avoid unlimited liability, the law now permits you to have a Limited Liability Partnership. Ask your solicitor about how you can form one.

Landlord's Reference Requirements   Form RT08

EMPLOYMENT			
Work reference – stating	(a) Job Title	☐ Yes	☐ No
	(b) Length of Employment	☐ Yes	☐ No
	(c) Salary	☐ Yes	☐ No
Last three payslips		☐ Yes	☐ No
If self-employed	(a) Copy of last set of accounts	☐ Yes	☐ No
	(b) accountant's letter – stating		
	(i) length of time known to accountant	☐ Yes	☐ No
	(ii) indication of yearly income	☐ Yes	☐ No

BANK/BUILDING SOCIETY		
Last three bank statements	☐ Yes	☐ No
Building society book	☐ Yes	☐ No

OTHER		
Student identification (e.g. student card or letter of acceptance)	☐ Yes	☐ No
Personal reference (e.g. professional friend)	☐ Yes	☐ No
Reference from current landlord stating:		
(a) how long residing at current address;	☐ Yes	☐ No
(b) whether payment of rent and observance of covenants of your letting agreement has been satisfactory. If you have been residing at your current address for less than 6 months, you must also provide a similar reference from your previous landlord.	☐ Yes	☐ No

Letter Accepting Liability   Form BS20

Date _____

To _____

_____

_____

Dear _____

We have now had an opportunity to investigate your complaint fully.

Whilst we do impose the most rigorous quality control on all our products, unfortunately, on rare occasions, human error allows a product to be despatched that does not reach the standards that we have set ourselves. We accept that this is one of those rare occasions.

We are prepared, at your choice, either to replace the product free of charge to you or to refund your purchase money in full. In either case, we would ask you please to return to us the item in question. We will, of course, reimburse you the cost of postage.

Please accept our apologies for the trouble caused you.

Yours sincerely

_____

Note: By sending this letter you are making a statement which is admissible in evidence in a claim brought by the buyer for 'consequential loss' that is, loss which goes beyond the mere loss of the purchase price. This could be, for example, losses of profits which would have been earned from a machine if it had not been faulty, or disappointment caused by a bad holiday experience.

If you think that there is some doubt about your liability, or if you are worried about a claim for consequential loss, you should put the words 'without prejudice' at the top of the letter, and add before the last paragraph the words 'this offer is conditional upon your accepting it in full satisfaction of any claims you may have arising out of the sale of the above mentioned products'.

Letter Accepting Return of Goods

Form BS21

Date _____

To _____

_____

_____

Re: Your order No. _____

Dear _____

We understand that you are rejecting the goods sent to you under the above order because

_____

_____

_____

_____

Whilst we do not accept your claim, we do not wish any customer to be dissatisfied and for that reason we will accept return of the goods.

Yours sincerely

_____

Letter Accompanying Unsolicited Goods   Form BS22

Date _____

To _____

_____

_____

Dear _____

In order to introduce you to our range of products, we enclose a sample together with a leaflet specifying the prices and normal business terms which we offer.

I will telephone you within the next few days, after you have had an opportunity to inspect the samples, to discuss with you any questions you may have. You are, of course, under no obligation to purchase any of the samples. [If you decide not to purchase we will arrange for their return at our expense, and in the meantime they will be at our risk.][1]/[Whatever decision you may make about future purchases, you are welcome to keep these samples with our compliments.][2]

I look forward to speaking to you, and the pleasure of doing business with you.

Yours sincerely

_____

Health Warning: If you send unsolicited goods with a view to their being acquired by the recipient, then if they are to be acquired for the recipient otherwise than for his business, he is entitled to keep them as if you had made a gift.

If you send unsolicited goods with a view to their being acquired by the recipient for the purposes of his business, you are entitled to ask for them back, but the recipient is under no duty to look after the goods before you arrange for their collection.

Whether or not the goods are sent for the purposes of the recipient's business it is usually a criminal offence to demand payment for them. Do not do this under any circumstances without consulting a solicitor first.

[1] Include this if the goods are intended for use in the recipient's business.

[2] Include this if the goods are not intended for use in the recipient's business.

Letter Acknowledging Complaint   Form BS23

Date   _____

To   _____

    _____

    _____

Dear   _____

I was sorry to hear of your complaint that   _____

_____

I am investigating the matter fully and will contact you again as soon as possible.

Please be assured that we will do our very best to rectify any problem we discover, and if the fault is due to any error or omission on our part, we will discuss appropriate compensation with you.

Yours sincerely

_____

Letter Acknowledging Request for Trade Credit — Form CDC14

Date _____

To _____

_____

_____

Dear _____

To enable us to accommodate your request for trade credit, please let us have the name, address and sort code of your bank to whom we may apply for a reference together with your account number. Please also provide two trade references of companies with whom you have done business over the past three years.

Your bank and trade referees will require your permission to communicate with us about you. Please therefore write to them immediately saying that you wish them to provide us with a reference for you and that they have your authority to discuss your credit worthiness with us. It will be helpful if you provide us with a copy.

We should be grateful if you would let us know the extent of the orders that you anticipate placing with us. Our normal payment terms require full payment within _____ days of invoice.

Yours sincerely

_____

Letter Agreeing Appointment of an Estate Agent Form BS24

Date _____

To _____

_____

_____

Dear _____

Re _____

We hereby instruct you [as sole agents]* to sell the above mentioned property at a price not less than £ _____ and agree to pay your fees and charges as set out in your letter of _____ subject to the terms in this letter. However, we give you no authority to accept any offer (whether or not 'subject to contract') without our prior written consent.

We reserve the right to withdraw these instructions at any time [and without notice]/[on _____ days' notice], and thereafter to appoint another agent [or to move to a non-exclusive basis with you]*. In such circumstances we shall be under no liability to you unless we proceed to an exchange of contracts with a prospective purchaser whom you have introduced to us [or to whom we have been otherwise introduced during the period of your sole agency].*

Yours sincerely

_____

Delete if the agency is not to be an exclusive agency

Letter Agreeing to Trade Terms   Form CDC15

Date _____

To _____

_____

_____

Dear _____

We confirm that we are pleased to extend to you our normal trade terms. We enclose our terms and conditions of trade and draw your attention in particular to the requirement that accounts are due and payable _____ days from the date of invoice. Interest at the rate of _____% per month is payable on overdue accounts.

The maximum credit allowed will be £ _____. These trade terms may be altered or withdrawn by us at our discretion at any time.

Please sign and return one copy of this letter to confirm these terms. Until the signed copy is received, orders will be accepted on a cash on delivery basis.

Yours sincerely

_____

Letter Alleging Passing Off   Form CDC16

Date _____

To _____

_____

_____

Dear _____

We notice that you are advertising or promoting goods/services under the following [name and/or description]. This will or may mislead prospective purchasers that your goods/services are ours.

We have long marketed goods/services under the name and description '_____

_____.' Your use of the name '_____

_____' is misleading and likely to cause confusion with our product.

We demand that you cease further use of this name and make clear to those with whom you have previously dealt that you are not connected with our business and that the product that you offer has no connection with ours.

Unless you confirm this to us within the next ten days, we shall have no option but to instruct our solicitors to commence proceedings against you for an injunction and damages.

Yours sincerely

_____

Health Warning: If you have a registered trade mark, do not mention it in this letter without first taking legal advice, as a groundless complaint of trade mark infringement can lead to your being sued under the Trade Marks Act 1994 Section 21.

Letter Confirming Appointment of Independent Consultant

Form E35

Date   _____

To   _____

_____

_____

Re   _____

Dear   _____

We are writing to confirm your engagement as a consultant for_____ (the 'Company')

commencing on   _____.

The terms of your engagement will be:

1. Your engagement shall continue (subject to Paragraph 7) [for a period of _____months from today]/[for the duration of a project consisting of _____]/[until determined by either of us giving to the other not less than _____ months' written notice].[1]

2. [Your work will include the following:[2]

   _____

   _____]

   [Your work will include such work of the following

   description_____ as we may from time to time offer

   you and as you may undertake to carry out]. [For the avoidance of doubt, we are not under any

   obligation to offer you work, and you are not under an obligation to accept any work we may offer.]

3. [You will devote up to _____ hours per week to the performance of your duties].[3]
   [You shall be free to carry out your work during any hours which are consistent with the proper completion of your work].

4. Your place of work shall be _____ [You will, however, be free to work elsewhere at your discretion to the extent that this is consistent with the proper completion of your work].

5. We shall require regular progress reports on projects in which you are involved.

Continued on next page

Letter Confirming Appointment of Independent Consultant (continued)

Form E35

6. The manner in which work is carried out will be entirely for you to decide but you must comply with all reasonable requests from the board of the company. You must ensure that your work is carried out in such manner whereby the company is in no way prejudiced.

7. [In consideration of you carrying out your work we will pay to you a fee of £ _____ per _____ in arrears].[4] [In consideration of your carrying out your work, we will pay to you a fee of £___ per _____]/[such fee as may be agreed in respect of the same]. You will render us _____ invoices in respect of these fees. If you are registered for VAT, you must show VAT separately on the invoices. Our accountants shall have full access to all records supporting these invoices so as to enable them to audit the invoices rendered. [Payment will be made within 30 days of the rendering of your invoice unless within that time we question it].

8. You will be responsible for all out-of-pocket expenses incurred by you in the performance of your duties.

9. You will be responsible for all income tax liabilities and National Insurance or similar contributions in respect of your fees and will indemnify us against all claims that may be made against us in respect of income tax or similar contributions relating to your services.

10. [In addition to the right of determination declared in Paragraph 1], we shall be entitled to terminate your engagement forthwith, without any payment, compensation or damages, if you are guilty of any serious misconduct or material or persistent breach of any of the terms and conditions of your engagement, or you wilfully neglect or refuse to carry out your work or to comply with any instructions reasonably given to you by the board, if you are unable to carry out your work properly, if you bring the name of the company into disrepute, if you have a bankruptcy order made against you or compound with or enter into any voluntary arrangement with your creditors, or if you are convicted of any criminal offence. This will not prejudice any other rights or remedies which we may have against you.[5]

11. One matter upon which we are most insistent concerns confidentiality. You will, in providing your services, gain knowledge of our business, our business contacts, our employees and many of our business secrets. It is fundamental that you will not disclose to anyone or use for your own or another's benefit any confidential information that you acquire. This is both during and after your engagement. In particular, you must not solicit, for the benefit of yourself or any other person, business from any customer or employee of the company for a period of two years after you have last done work for the company. Any and all records or papers of any description which are provided to you by the company or which you may bring into being in the course of carrying out your work for the company are the property of the company and must be immediately delivered to the company on the termination of your engagement.

Continued on next page

Letter Confirming Appointment of Independent Consultant (continued)   Form E35

12.   This agreement shall be governed by the laws of England and Wales to the non-exclusive jurisdiction of whose courts both we and you hereby submit.[6]

If you agree to these terms please sign and return one copy of this letter.

We look forward to working with you.

Yours faithfully

_____

Agreed and accepted

_____

Consultant

Note: If you wish to avoid an employer/employee relationship you will not achieve this simply by calling the worker a 'consultant'. A court would look at the reality of the relationship and make an evaluation in all the circumstances. Important factors would be the degree of control which you have over the way in which the other works, whether the work is to be done by an individual personally, or whether he is free to delegate performance; whether you are bound to offer, and the other to do, the work and above all the extent to which the consultant is part of your organisation (e.g. whether he is brought in to achieve one project or whether he carries out work of a type which always requires someone to be on hand to do it). In the form below there are many parts in square brackets. Include all of those which suit your arrangement, as the more you include, the more likely it will be that you will have avoided the relationship of employer/employee. Note that it is generally easier to avoid this relationship if you take on temporary staff through an employment agency. Because of the importance of the distinction between the relationship of employee and that of independent contractor, you would be wise to consult a solicitor if any doubt arises.

[1] You should delete this clause if you can arrange matters so that you are not obliged to offer any work and if the consultant is not obliged to accept it. If you cannot do that, then you might prefer to provide for a fixed period of the engagement or for the engagement to be for the duration of a particular project. One of the matters which a court would look at in deciding whether a relationship of employer/employee exists is whether there is a duty on one party to provide work for the other, and a duty on the other party to do the work. As always, of course, what you write must reflect the reality of your arrangement with the other party, as the courts are very quick to spot a sham.

[2] If possible, provide only for the consultant to do such work as from time to time may be offered and as they may choose to accept.

[3] This clause should be deleted if possible.

[4] If possible, delete this sentence because payment for a period of time can be an indication of employment.

[5] If you have provided that the engagement is for a fixed period, delete the words 'in addition to the right of determination declared in paragraph 1'. If you have provided that there is no obligation on you to provide work or on the consultant to accept it, then delete this paragraph altogether.

[6] Delete the prefix 'non' if you wish to avoid the possibility of litigation in a foreign court.

Letter Confirming Reason for Instant Dismissal   Form E36

Date _____

To _____

_____

_____

Dear _____

Further to the disciplinary hearing held on _____ ,

I write to confirm, formally, your instant dismissal for gross misconduct effective from today for the following reason(s):

_____

_____

_____

_____

_____

_____

_____

You are aware of the code of discipline (a copy of which is enclosed) which makes it quite clear that this type of behaviour will result in immediate dismissal. You have a right to appeal against this decision, and if you wish to exercise this right, please notify me in writing within _____ working days.

Yours sincerely

_____

Letter Denying Liability on Complaint   Form BS25

Date   _____

To   _____

_____

_____

Dear   _____

We have investigated the complaint contained in your letter of dated_____.
I am satisfied that we are not at fault for the following reasons:

_____

_____

_____

_____

[However, if you remain of the opinion that we were at fault, then I am willing to consider the possibility that the matter be referred to mediation in order to reach a compromise in this dispute. If you agree, we can discuss the appointment of an mediator.]

Yours sincerely

_____

Letter Expelling Partner from Continuing Partnership   Form B11

Date _____

Ref _____

To _____

_____

_____

Dear _____

In accordance with clause _____ of our partnership agreement dated _____,

I/we wish to inform you that you are expelled from the partnership. Your rights to any share in the

partnership profits and assets will be dealt with in accordance with the terms of the partnership agreement.

Yours sincerely

_____

Partner's signature

_____

Partner's signature

Health Warning: If the partnership agreement states that a partner can only be expelled for a reason, you must be satisfied that one of the reasons, set out in the agreement as justifying expulsion, actually exists and that you have acted fairly to the expelled partner in coming to your decision. You should specify the reason in this letter. Before any decision to expel is made, the partner who is to be expelled should be informed of the reason why his expulsion is under consideration, and he should be given an opportunity to answer the allegations which are made against him and to say why he should be allowed to continue as a partner.

Where there is no provision in the agreement requiring that a partner be expelled only for cause, it would still be wise not to do it unless there is a reasonable cause, and to specify that cause in the letter of expulsion. This is because partners are obliged to act with good faith towards one another and because it is possible (although controversial) that a good reason for expulsion may have to be given even where the agreement does not expressly call for this.

If the partnership agreement gives a right to expel for reasons having nothing to do with conduct, for example upon the reaching of a particular age, it is usually best to rely upon this right rather than to raise matters of conduct. However, you should only rely upon such a provision it is in practice is applied to everyone.

Above all, remember that expulsions from partnerships often give rise to bitter and expensive disputes. It is usually a good idea to consult a solicitor before you take any action.

Letter from Employee Intending to Resume Work Before End of Ordinary Maternity Leave

Form E37

Date   _____

To   _____

_____

_____

Dear   _____

This is to inform you that I intend to return to work before the end of my maternity leave period and I am giving you at least eight weeks' notice as required by law.

I intend to return to work on _____.

Your sincerely

_____

Letter Inviting Candidate to Attend Interview   Form E68

Date   _____

To   _____

        _____

        _____

Dear Miss Porter

Thank you for sending me your application for the post of _____.

I would very much like to discuss this matter further with you and have arranged an interview at
_____ at these offices. I
should be grateful if you would confirm your attendance.

I look forward to meeting you.

Yours sincerely

_____
Personnel Manager

Letter of Claim Addressed to a Carrier   Form BS26

Date   _____

To   _____

_____

_____

Dear Sirs

Re: _____

We refer to consignment note no._____ concerning _____ collected by you from

_____ for delivery to   _____ .

We have been notified by the recipient that goods to the value of £ _____ were received which were damaged or missing from the consignment.

We wish formally to notify you of this circumstance under the terms of clause _____of our contract dated _____ .

We have inspected the goods and estimate the replacement cost to be £ _____ and should be grateful if you would arrange for that sum to be forwarded to us within _____ days of the date hereof, failing which we shall be compelled to refer this matter to our solicitors.

Yours faithfully

_____

Letter of Redundancy   Form E38

Date   _____

To   _____

_____

_____

Dear   _____

Further to our meeting on   _____,
it is with deep regret that I must advise you that your employment with us will end on   _____
_____, by reason of redundancy. As you are aware, the company has
experienced a serious decline in business.

Our selection criteria has been as follows_____. Wherever
possible, we have offered employees other employment, but unfortunately we have been unable to find a
suitable alternative position for you. You are entitled to receive a payment based upon the scale laid down
by law and a tax-free cheque for the amount due is enclosed together with a statement reflecting how this
has been calculated. You are also entitled to _____ [weeks']/[months'] notice [which you will be required to
work]/[which you will not be required to work and subsequently we enclose a cheque in lieu of your notice
period].

We hope that you soon find other suitable employment. If you need a reference from us, please submit our
name with the confidence that our reference will be a good one. You have a right to appeal against this
decision and if you wish to exercise this right, please notify me in writing within [_____] days.

Yours sincerely

_____

Letter Offering to Purchase Leasehold Property Form OLF20

Date _____

To _____

_____

_____

Dear _____

Re _____

Following my inspection of the above-named property, I am prepared to offer the sum of

£ _____ for your existing lease, on the following terms but subject to contract:

1. Receipt of a satisfactory survey from my surveyors.
2. Receipt of my solicitor's advice on the terms of the lease, confirming that it contains no provisions adverse to my interests and that it is a lease for _____ years from_____ at a ground rent of £ _____ per annum payable quarterly in advance (reviewable every three years, the next review being in _____).
3. Your giving us vacant possession by _____.

My company's solicitors are Messrs. _____ , to whom I have copied this letter. Please instruct your solicitors to send a draft contract and copy of the lease to my solicitors. I hope we are able to proceed to a swift exchange of contracts.

Yours sincerely

_____

[For and on behalf of _____Limited]

Letter re. Landlord's Agent's Authority   Form RT09

Date _____

Ref _____

To _____ (name of Tenant(s))

_____

_____

Dear Tenant(s)

Re. _____(the Property)

Please note that _____

_____

_____(name and address of agent(s))

is/are now authorised to deal with the above property on my/our behalf so that you should until further

notice pay the rent and any other payments due under the tenancy to him/her and deal with him/her/them

in respect of any other matters relating to the property.

Notices, including notices in proceedings, can be received [by me at _____] or [on my

behalf by _____ at _____] in respect of your tenancy.[1] This notice is give pursuant to

Section 48 of The Landlord and Tenant Act 1987.

Yours faithfully

_____

(Landlord's signature and printed name and address)

Letter re. Landlord's Agent's Authority   Form RT09

[1] The address for receiving notices must be in England or Wales.

Letter re. Bills   Form RT10

Date _____

Ref _____

To _____   (name and address of Authority)

_____

_____

Dear Sir(s)

Re. _____(the Property)

I am/we are the landlord(s) of the above property and write to advise you that with effect from

_____(date of start of tenancy)

the property has been let to _____

_____

_____(name(s) of Tenant(s))

who will therefore be responsible with effect from that date for the [council tax] [electricity charges] [gas charges] [telephone charges] [water rates] in respect of the property.

Yours faithfully

_____

(Landlord's signature and printed name and address)

Letter Refusing Return of Goods   Form BS27

Date   _____

To   _____

_____

_____

Dear   _____

Re: Your Order No. _____

Today your carrier attempted to return the goods identified in the above order.

We refuse to accept the return of the goods because we have given no permission to you either expressly or implicitly to return the goods without good reason. We therefore ask you to remove them immediately as we can accept no liability for them or for any damage that they may suffer whilst left on our premises.

Yours sincerely

_____

Note: Before using this form and acting upon it, make certain that your customer did not have the right in law to return the goods. In particular note that the customer has the right to return the goods if they are not as described, if they are not fit for the stated purpose for which they were bought, if they do not conform to sample, if they are not of satisfactory quality, or if the correct quantity has not been delivered. The rules as to quantity and satisfactory quality are slightly relaxed in the case of commercial (as opposed to consumer) sales, but again you must proceed with caution. Note also that while the law does not impose a particularly high duty of care on you to look after the goods (assuming them to have been wrongly rejected by the customer) you must not be reckless with them either. Do not leave them out in the rain or in a place where they can be easily stolen.

Letter Refusing Trade or Financial References   Form CDC17

Date _____

To _____

_____

_____

Dear _____

Re _____

We regret that we are unable to comply with your request for a reference in respect of the above named company as it is a policy in this company not to give such references.

Please do not take this letter as any indication whatsoever of the commercial or financial standing of the company. We suggest that you ask them for an alternative referee.

Yours sincerely

_____

Letter Refusing Trade Terms   Form CDC18

Date   _____

To   _____
       _____
       _____

Dear   _____

We have carefully considered your request for trade terms. Unfortunately, we regret that we are not prepared to extend trade terms to you until you first establish a satisfactory pattern of trade with us. We hope you understand our position on the matter.

Yours sincerely

_____

Letter Refusing Trade Terms   Form CDC18

Letter Rejecting Conditions of Order and   Form BS28
Reimposing Conditions of Sale

Date   _____

To   _____

     _____

     _____

Dear   _____

Re: Your Order No. _____

We refer to your order number _____ which is expressed to be on your standard terms and conditions.

Unfortunately, your standard terms and conditions are unacceptable. We can only supply goods on our standard terms and conditions of sale, a copy of which is enclosed.

[We are despatching your ordered goods on our standard terms and conditions in 48 hours. Acceptance of delivery by you will constitute acceptance of our terms. If you are not prepared to accept our terms you must return the goods immediately, although you may do so at our expense] or [If you would care to confirm your acceptance of our terms by return, we will be delighted to fulfill your order by _____. If, however, you feel you are unable to accept our terms, then regretfully we will have to decline your offer].

Yours sincerely

_____

Letter Rejecting Incorrect Goods   Form BS29

Date _____

To _____

_____

_____

Dear _____

Re: Our Order No _____

Today your carrier attempted to deliver goods identified on the numbered order above.

On examination, the goods delivered were found not to correspond with the [sample] or [description] we had received and we therefore refused to accept delivery of the goods. The carrier was instructed to return them to you.

Yours sincerely

_____

Letter Requesting Trade Terms of Payment — Form CDC19

Date   _____

To   _____

_____

_____

Dear Sirs

We wish to place orders with you for the following:

_____

_____

_____

Please advise us of your normal trade terms of payment.

If you wish to have references we suggest that you refer to our bankers who are:

_____

_____.

You may also like to refer to   _____, with whom we have had business relations.

[We have already given our authority to the above to discuss our credit worthiness with you].

Yours faithfully

_____

Letter Sending a Copy of an Agreement Regulated Under the Consumer Credit Act 1974

Form CDC20

Date _____

To _____

_____

_____

Dear _____

Re: Hire Purchase Agreement No. _____

I refer to the above Hire Purchase Agreement which you signed on _____.

As explained to you when you signed the above agreement, you have time to reconsider your decision. If you wish to do so you may still cancel the agreement by posting to us a written notice of cancellation as indicated in the document(s) which accompany this letter.

Yours sincerely

_____

Note: To be sent within seven days of signature of the agreement. The Consumer Credit Act has provisions governing the questions of when copies of an agreement and notices of cancellation rights have to be provided to the customer. The agreements themselves and notices of rights to cancel have to follow a formula set out in the Consumer Credit Act 1974 and in regulations made under that Act. **It is essential that you take legal advice** as to what you must provide to your client, and when you must do it. Failure to observe these requirements may result in your not being able to enforce your agreement.

Letter Taking Up Bank Reference   Form CDC21

Date _____

To: The Manager _____

_____

_____ Bank plc

Dear Sir

Re _____ Limited

The above-named company, whose address is _____

_____,

has applied to us for trade credit. They tell us that you are their bankers and that their account number is

_____.

The amount involved will be in the order of £ _____ per month. We should be grateful if you would supply us with a statement as to their creditworthiness and let us know whether they can be considered good for the amount involved.

Yours faithfully

_____

Letter Taking Up Trade Reference — Form CDC22

Date _____

To _____

_____

_____

Dear _____

Re _____Limited

The above-named company has applied to us for trade credit. They tell us that they have a credit account with you and have given us your name as a reference. They have suggested that the amount of their trade with us would be in the order of £ _____ per month.

Would you please let us know, in confidence, whether their account with you has been maintained satisfactorily and whether all invoices have been paid on the date they are due.

A stamped and addressed envelope is enclosed for your reply.

Yours sincerely

_____

Letter Terminating Contract and Invoking Retention of Title Clause

Form OLF21

Date _____

To _____
_____
_____

Dear _____

We have received notification that you have been [put into receivership] / [made subject to a winding up order].

Accordingly, pursuant to our Terms and Conditions, we notify you that we consider our contract with you terminated, and that the full price of the goods delivered to you is immediately due and payable.

It is also the case that under our Terms and Conditions, title in the goods, until they have been paid for in full, remains vested in us [and that you hold on trust for us the proceeds of sale of any goods which you have sold without paying for the same].

We therefore require that you forthwith make payment to us in full, and that you undertake that unless and until payment in full is made, you will not dispose of any of our goods without our express permission.

Yours sincerely

_____

Letter to a Solicitor to Collect a Debt   Form CDC23

Date   _____

To   _____

_____

_____

Dear   _____

Re   _____

Debt £_____

Please issue proceedings to recover £ _____ from the above named company.

We enclose a copy of our invoice together with our complete file relating to this debt. Please let us know if you require any further information.

No complaint has been received in respect of this debt and all our applications for payment have been ignored. We draw your attention to our last letter in which we gave warning that unless payment was received, proceedings would be commenced without further notice.

We will let you know immediately if any payment is received by us.

Yours sincerely

_____

Letter to Credit Reference Agency for Report   Form CDC24

Date   _____

To   _____

         _____

         _____

Dear   _____

Re   _____

We request a detailed credit report on the above. They have requested credit terms representing a monthly risk to us of approximately £ _____. We enclose our cheque for £ _____ and would ask you to fax or post your report to us as soon as possible.

[We enclose a copy letter from the above which authorises credit reference agencies to disclose to us information as to their credit-worthiness].

Yours sincerely

_____

Letter to Credit Reference Agency Requesting Personal Data

Form CDC25

Date _____

To _____

_____

_____

Dear _____

Re: Data Protection Act 1998 (the 'Act')

Please let me know if you hold any personal data concerning me on your records. If you do, I should be grateful for a copy of any such data according to my entitlement under the Act. Accordingly, please indicate to me the evidence of my identity which you require in order that you may honour this request. If it is your practice to deal with these requests via a standard form, please furnish me with a copy. If you wish to make a charge for the supply of this information, please let me know the amount of the charge and the statutory provision under which you are entitled to levy the same.

My details and address are as follows _____.

Yours sincerely

_____

Letter to Customer who has Exceeded Credit Limit   Form CDC26

Date _____

To _____

_____

_____

Dear _____

As you know, your credit limit with us is £ _____. Your account today stands in the sum of £ _____, which is in excess of the credit allowed. Until this amount has been paid we regret that we are not prepared to accept any further orders from you on trade terms.

[Interest at the rate of _____ per cent per month is payable on outstanding accounts [under the terms of our conditions of trading] / [under the Late Payment of Commercial Debts (Interest) Act 1998][1] and this interest will be added to your statement.]

Yours sincerely

_____

---

[1] Do not use the wording which refers to the Late Payment of Commercial Debts (Interest) Act 1998 if the sale was to a person purchasing as a consumer.

Letter to Employee Concerning Salary Rise   Form E39

Date _____

To _____

_____

_____

Dear _____

It is with pleasure that I write to let you know of our decision to increase your salary. The increase is

£ _____ per _____ .

This increase is only partly in recognition of the increase in the cost of living since your last rise. It is also made to reward your loyal and conscientious work, and to let you know that your efforts have been recognised. The increase will take effect from the beginning of this month.

Yours sincerely

_____

Letter to Employee, Absent Believed Sick   Form E41

Date   _____

To   _____

_____

_____

Dear   _____

You have not been to work since _____ , and have failed to contact me to let me know why.

Please let me know at once the reason for your absence from work and, if you are unwell, provide me with a certificate from your doctor. Without this certificate, you are not entitled to any sick pay.

In case you do not know about the sickness regulations, employees are only entitled to statutory sick pay when they are absent from work for four or more consecutive days, up to a limit of 28 weeks in a three-year period. After that you must claim state benefit.

Yours sincerely

_____

Letter to Former Employee Who is Using Confidential Information

Form E43

Date _____

To _____

_____

_____

Dear _____

It has come to our attention that you are informing our customers that you can supply them at prices below our current price list. You are clearly using the information about our customers and prices that you gained whilst working for us, which is in breach of your duty of confidentiality.

Unless you return to us within seven days all customer and price lists relating to our business that you have in your possession and give us your written promise not to make use of your knowledge of our customers and business, our solicitors will be instructed to make an immediate application to the courts for an injunction to prevent you approaching our customers, and they will be instructed also to bring proceedings to claim damages from you.

Yours sincerely

_____

Letter to Receiver or Liquidator Reclaiming Goods Form BS30

Date _____

To _____

_____

_____

Dear _____

Re: Our Invoice No. _____

The goods referred to in the above invoice were delivered to _____

_____ which is now in [receivership] or [liquidation]. The goods were sold

on the condition that legal title remains with us until such time as they are paid for in full and that if they

are not paid for in full within _____ days, under such conditions we reserved the right to enter premises

to recover our goods. A copy of the invoice and of our standard conditions is enclosed.

We have not received payment for the goods within the specified period, and therefore we intend to enter

upon their premises on _____ to reclaim our goods. Please may we have your

undertaking by return not to sell, deal with or otherwise dispose of the goods until such time as they have

been paid for in full or collected by us?

Yours sincerely

_____

| **Letter to Shareholders and Auditors with Resolution to be Passed** | Form B13 |

Date _____

To _____

_____

_____

Dear _____

The company directors propose:

_____

_____

_____

To give effect to this proposal it is necessary for the shareholders to pass a formal resolution to be recorded in the company's minute book. As I understand that all shareholders have been approached and agree to the proposal, I enclose a formal written resolution.

If you confirm that you are in agreement, please sign the form where indicated and return it to me.

An identical form of resolution has been sent to all other shareholders and to the auditors.

[Under the Companies Act 2006 unanimous consent is no longer required to a written resolution. However, it will require a vote of the holders of a [simple majority][1] [75 per cent majority][2] of the voting shares. If consent is not given by the necessary majority before _____ the resolution will be defeated.

In order to indicate your consent to the resolution, you will need to send a signed and witnessed statement to the registered office on or before _____ identifying the resolution in question and stating that you agree to it].

Yours sincerely

_____

Director/Company Secretary

Note: At present the rule is that unanimous consent is needed to approve a resolution that is not passed at a general meeting. However, when Chapter Two Part 13 of the Companies Act 2006 comes into force on 1 October 2007, it will be possible to pass a resolution with the same sorts of majorities which are needed for resolutions that are passed in general meetings. The catch is that new procedures will have to be followed. Therefore copies of the resolutions must be circulated to all members at the same time and the resolution will have to be accompanied by a notice stating that there is a deadline for passing the motion, and that it will be treated as having been defeated if it is not passed by that date. Unless the articles say otherwise, the period will be 28 days from the circulation of the resolution. Another requirement is that the notice should also state what needs to be done by the member to approve the resolution.

Once the new provisions are in force, you will not require unanimous consent for a written resolution, but the letter will need to include the text which appears in square brackets.

Note, this procedure cannot be used to remove an auditor or director before the end of his or her term and is available only to private companies, not to public ones.

[1] For ordinary resolutions.

[2] For special resolutions.

Written Resolution   Form B13

_____LIMITED

COMPANY NUMBER:_____

The following ordinary/extraordinary/special/elective resolution is signed as a written resolution pursuant to [Section 381A of the Companies Act 1985] or [Section Part 13 Chapter Two of the Companies Act 2006][1] [by the holders of all issued shares] or [by the holders of a majority of _____per cent] in the capital of the company conferring a right to vote thereon as if the resolution had been proposed at a general meeting of the company at the date hereof:

_____

_____

_____

_____

_____

_____

_____

Dated this _____ day of _____ year ____

_____

Shareholder's signature

[1] Delete reference to the 1985 Act from 1 October 2007.

Refer to footnote in the letter to shareholders and auditors on the preceding page.

Note that it is a legal requirement to retain copies of all resolutions for 10 years.

Letter to Auditor   Form B13

Date   _____

Ref   _____

To Messrs.   _____   Chartered Accountants

_____

_____

_____

Dear   _____

I enclose a copy of a letter sent to all the shareholders and also a copy of the resolution that we wish to pass. As you can see, we are hoping to pass the motion by written resolution rather than by voting at a general meeting.

A copy of the proposed resolution is being sent to you in accordance with the provisions of section 381(B)(i) of the Companies Act 1985.

Yours sincerely

_____

Company Secretary

Note: Until 1 October 2007, failure to send a letter in this form will be a criminal offence. After that date the requirement is abolished for private companies.

Letter to Unsuccessful Candidate   Form E44

Date   _____

To   _____

        _____

        _____

Dear   _____

I regret to inform you that, after considering your application and meeting to interview you, I am unable to offer you the position you have applied for. Whilst you were adequately qualified for the position, another applicant was more suited to the position.

I am grateful to you for giving your time and wish you every success in the future.

Yours sincerely

_____

Letter Treating Breach of Contract as Repudiation and Claiming Damages

Form BS31

Date _____

To _____

_____

_____

Dear _____

We refer to the contract between us, under which you agreed to perform the following:

_____

_____

_____

You to have failed to perform your obligation under the contract in the following respects:

_____

_____

_____

Despite our previous protests you have not made good your failure.

We have considered the matter fully and conclude that your failure is a repudiation by you of your obligations under the contract. We consider the contract terminated because of your conduct. We are taking advice from our solicitors as to the remedies available to us and you will hear from them shortly.

[As a result of your breaches we have suffered the following losses and been put to the following expense:_____].[1]

[We require you to repay the sum of £_____ which we have paid to you under the contract, the benefit of which he have lost as a result of your breach].[2]

Yours sincerely

_____

Health warning: Unless the contract says specifically that the particular breach you are complaining of entitles you to treat the contract as at an end, it can be very risky to send this letter. Only the most serious breaches of contract will entitle you to do this. If you send this letter when you are not entitled to do so, you could be said to have repudiated the contract and the other side would be able to sue you. That is why we have included the words 'We have referred this matter to our solicitors.' This is something which you should do in all but the clearest cases.

[1] Add this if you are not referring the matter to your solicitor and if it is applicable.

[2] Add this if you are not referring the matter to your solicitor and if it is applicable.

Licence for use of a Car Parking Space   Form OLF22

Date   _____

To   _____

        _____

        _____

Dear   _____

Premises _____

This is to confirm that we are giving you a licence to park _____ motor car(s) in the car parking area adjacent to the above premises (the 'Licence') subject to the following conditions:

(a)   Only _____ motor car(s) may be parked under the Licence and those motor car(s) shall only be parked in the spaces that we indicate. No special place is reserved for you and we can at any time change the area in which you may park. We accept no liability for any loss or damage to the car(s) or their contents.

(b)   You will provide us with the registration number of the car(s) that will be using this permission. [No vehicle may be parked by virtue of this licence, unless notice of that number has been so provided to us.]

(c)   No vehicle may obstruct the access to the parking area and our vehicle that is parked so as to obstruct the parking or movement of any vehicle belonging to us or any other person will be removed immediately. It is a fundamental condition of this Licence that you agree that we may at any time move any car that we consider is in breach of this term and that, unless it is caused negligently, we shall not be liable for any damage caused by our taking this action.

(d)   You will pay us £_____ per _____ for this Licence, the payment to be made in advance. The first payment shall be made today and subsequent payments shall be made on the _____ day of each _____.

(e)   This licence is personal to you.

(f)   This licence is personal to you and may not be assigned.

[(g)   The parking area is kept locked [daily] from _____ to _____during which time you will not have access to it] or [You will be furnished with a key to the parking area. You are not to duplicate this key without our written permission] / [Your access to the parking area shall be [daily] from _____ to _____].

(h)   You will take care not to cause damage to the parking area or to any property thereon. You will not there engage in unlawful activity nor any activity whereby any policy of insurance may be avoided, you will not allow oil to leak from your vehicle(s) and you will not create any untidiness.

Continued on next page

Licence for use of a Car Parking Space (continued)   Form OLF22

(i)   In the event of any breach of this licence, we shall be entitled to terminate it forthwith, and you shall be liable to indemnify us for such breach and any loss or damage thereby caused.

(i)   This Licence may be terminated by either of us giving to the other seven clear days' notice. [Upon termination of this Licence you shall immediately return to us your key and any copy which you may have received or had made].

Yours sincerely

_____

Health Warning: If the arrangement is for the giving of exclusive use of any garage or parking space, as opposed to shared use, then you should consult a solicitor, as otherwise you might create a tenancy with statutory protection under the Landlord and Tenant Act 1954.

Licence to use Copyright Material   Form OLF23

THIS LICENCE IS MADE the _____ day of _____ year _____

BETWEEN:

(1) _____ of _____(the 'Licensor'); and

(2) _____ of _____(the 'Licensee').

NOW IT IS HEREBY AGREED as follows:

1. In consideration of the sum of £ _____, receipt of which the Licensor hereby acknowledges, the Licensor grants to the Licensee a licence to use, reprint and publish the following material (the 'Copyright Material'):

    _____

    _____

2. The Copyright Material shall be used by the Licensee only in the following manner or publication and for the following period:

    _____

    _____

3. The Copyright Material shall be used by the Licensee only in the following territory of the world:

    _____

    _____

4. The Licence confers [exclusive] / [non-exclusive] rights to the Copyright Material in the aforementioned territory during the aforementioned time.

5. The Licensee agrees that the Licensor shall retain the worldwide copyright in the Copyright Material, and the moral rights of the author of the Copyright Material are hereby asserted.

6. [This Licence shall be binding upon and inure to the benefit of the parties, their successors and assigns] / [This Licence is personal to the Licensee and may not be assigned without the express consent of the Licensor].

7. Nothing in this Agreement is intended to confer any benefit on a third party whether under the Contracts (Rights of Third Parties) Act or otherwise.

IN WITNESS OF WHICH the parties have agreed this licence the day and year first above written

_____   _____

Signed by or on behalf of the Licensor   Signed by or on behalf of the Licensee

_____   _____

in the presence of (witness)   in the presence of (witness)

Name _____   Name _____

Address _____   Address _____

Occupation _____   Occupation _____

Note: If payment is to be other than a single lump sum, there should be a clause which says that if payment of any instalment is delayed by more than a period of _____, the Licensor will be at liberty to terminate the Licence by notice. There should also be a clause in those circumstances which provides that interest at the rate of ___ per cent a year will be payable on any licence fees unpaid at the date when they fall due.

Limited Guarantee

Form LB04

THIS DEED IS MADE the _____ day of _____ year _____

BETWEEN:

(1) _____(the 'Guarantor'); and

(2) _____ (the 'Creditor').

NOW IT IS HEREBY AGREED as follows:

1. As an inducement to the Creditor to extend credit from time to time to _____
    (the 'Customer') the Guarantor unconditionally guarantees to the Creditor the prompt and punctual
    payment of all sums and the discharge of all obligations due to the Creditor from the Customer,
    whether such indebtedness or obligations shall exist at the date of this agreement or arise hereafter,
    and whether such indebtedness or obligation be actual or contingent, or whether it be by way of
    primary liability or under a guarantee and whether the Customer be solely liable or liable jointly or
    jointly and severally with any other person or persons, provided that the liability of the Guarantor
    hereunder shall be limited to the amount of £ _____ as a maximum liability and that the
    Guarantor shall not be liable under this Guarantee for any greater or further amount.

2. The Guarantor agrees to remain fully bound under this Guarantee, notwithstanding any extension,
    giving of time, forbearance, indulgence or waiver, or release or discharge to the Customer or the
    substitution or the release or substitution of any surety or collateral or security for the debt. In the
    event of default, the Creditor may seek payment directly from the Guarantor without need to proceed
    first against the Customer.

3. The obligations of the Guarantor shall be as a principal debtor and will arise whether or not the
    Customer is in default of any obligation.

4. The Guarantor shall pay all costs incurred by the Creditor in enforcing the performance of the
    obligations of the Customer to discharge its indebtedness and other obligations to the Creditor
    provided that the total of such costs and any indebtedness of the debtor which the Guarantor may
    pay shall not exceed the aforementioned sum of £_____ . The Guarantor shall further pay all
    costs incurred by the Creditor in enforcing this Guarantee. For the avoidance of doubt, these costs will
    be payable, notwithstanding that the total of such costs and other sums due hereunder may exceed
    the aforementioned limit.

5   This guarantee may be terminated by the Guarantor upon fourteen (14) days written notice of
    termination being delivered to the Creditor. Such termination shall apply only to credit extended by
    the Creditor after the expiry of the said fourteen (14) day period and not to prior extended credit, or
    goods in transit received by the Customer after the expiry of the fourteen day period.

Continued on next page

Limited Guarantee (continued)   Form LB04

[6.   The person signing on behalf of the Guarantor warrants and represents he has full authority to bind the Guarantor to this guarantee.]

7.   Until all debts of the Customer are fully paid, the Guarantor shall not exercise any rights of subrogation or set-off in competition with the Creditor.

8.   This guarantee shall be binding upon and inure to the benefit of the parties, their successors and assigns.

9.   This guarantee is subject to English law and the parties agree to submit to the exclusive jurisdiction of the English courts in connection with any dispute hereunder.

IN WITNESS OF WHICH the parties have signed this deed the day and year first above written.

(Individual)   (Company)

                                                          Signed for and on behalf of

_____   _____Ltd

Signed by the Guarantor

_____   _____

in the presence of (witness)   Director

Name _____

Address _____   _____

_____   Director/Secretary

Occupation Solicitor _____

 I hereby certify that I have explained this Guarantee to the Guarantor and that he/she is entering into it of his/her own free will

                                                          Signed for and on behalf of:

_____   _____Ltd

Signed by the Creditor

_____   _____

in the presence of (witness)   Director

Name _____

Address _____

_____   _____

Occupation _____   Director/Secretary

Health warning: This guarantee should not be used in the case of any indebtedness governed by the Consumer Credit Act 1974. Note also that if there is any personal or family relationship between the parties (even if they are also business partners), you should not accept this guarantee unless the guarantor has seen a solicitor, who has then certified to you that he has advised the guarantor about the guarantee and that the guarantor is willing to enter into it. The name of the solicitor must be given to you by the guarantor, not by the customer.

Limited Proxy   Form B14

_____ LIMITED

FORM OF PROXY FOR USE BY ORDINARY SHAREHOLDERS
FOR THE ANNUAL GENERAL MEETING TO BE HELD ON

_____

I _____ of _____ being a member

of the above-named company, hereby appoint _____

of _____ or, failing him/her, _____

of _____ or failing him/her the duly appointed chairman of

the meeting as my proxy at the annual general meeting of the company to be held on

_____and at any adjournment thereof and to vote on my behalf as

directed below.

RESOLUTIONS

Please indicate how you wish your proxy to vote by placing an 'X' in the appropriate box. Unless otherwise

indicate the proxy will exercise his discretion as to how he votes and whether he abstains from voting. __

		For	Against
1.	[Insert text of resolution]	☐	☐
2.	[Insert text of resolution]	☐	☐

_____

Dated

_____

Signature

Notes:

(a) This form of proxy, together with the power of attorney or other authority (if any) under which it was signed, or an office or notarially certified copy thereof, must be lodged [at the company's registered office] not later than 48 hours before the meeting.[1]

(b) A proxy need not be a member of the company.

(c) In the case of joint holders the signature of the first-named will be accepted to the exclusion of all others.

(d) In the case of a corporation this form of proxy should be under its common seal or under the hand of an officer or attorney duly authorised.

(e) Any alterations to this form of proxy should be initialled.

(f) The completion of this form of proxy will not preclude the member from attending and voting in person if he/she so wishes.

[(g) Unless the articles provide otherwise, proxies may only vote on a poll] or [members have the right to appoint more than one proxy provided that such proxy is appointed in respect of the rights of different shares or blocks of shares. All proxies have the right to attend, speak or vote at the meeting.][2]

The notes above should be included in the form as sent out to the members.

[1] The Articles of the Company should be checked on this point as some permit proxies to be lodged up until the commencement of the meeting.

[2] After the Companies Act 2006 section 284 comes into effect on 1 October 2007, you must delete in note G above the first passage in square brackets from the form and you must include the second passage in square brackets.

Living Will   Form PF11

PERSONAL DETAILS

Name   _____

Address   _____

Date of birth   _____

Doctor's details   _____

National Health Number   _____

I, _____, am of sound mind and make this Advance Directive now on my future medical care to my family, my doctors, other medical personnel and anyone else to whom it is relevant, for a time when, for reasons of physical or mental incapacity, I am unable to make my views known.

INSTRUCTIONS

MEDICAL TREATMENT I **DO NOT** WANT:

I REFUSE medical procedures to prolong my life or keep me alive by artificial means if (including but not limited to the intravenous administration of food or fluids where this is not necessary to ensure my comfort) if:

TICK <u>ONE</u> OF THE BOXES ONLY

(1)   I suffer from a severe physical illness or from severe consequences of a physical injury from which in the opinion of _____ independent medical practitioners it is unlikely that I will ever recover or experience any significant improvement where that illness, or the consequences of that injury (a) cause(s) severe and frequent pain or loss of the use of all of my limbs or (b) is terminal;

or

(2)   I have a severe mental incapacity which, in the opinion of _____ independent medical practitioners, has no likelihood of improvement and in addition I have a severe physical illness or suffer from severe consequences of a physical injury from which in the opinion of _____ medical practitioners it is unlikely that I will ever recover or experience any significant improvement where that illness or the consequences of that injury (a) cause(s) severe and frequent pain or loss of the use of all my limbs or (b) is terminal;

or

(3)   I am permanently unconscious and have been so for a period of at least ___ months and in the opinion of ___ independent medical practitioners there is no likelihood that I will ever recover.

or

(4)   I have a severe mental incapacity which, in the opinion of _____ independent medical practitioners, has no likelihood of improvement and which causes me severe emotional distress.

Continued on next page

Living Will (continued)   Form PF11

MEDICAL TREATMENT I **DO** WANT:

I DO wish to receive any medical treatment which will alleviate pain or distressing symptoms or will make me more comfortable. I accept that this may have the effect of shortening my life.

☐

If I am suffering from any of the conditions above and I am pregnant, I wish to RECEIVE medical procedures which will prolong my life or keep me alive by artificial means only until such time as my child has been safely delivered.

☐

HEALTH CARE PROXY

I wish to appoint _____ of _____

as my Health Care Proxy. S/he should be involved in any decisions about my health care options if I am physically or mentally unable to make my views known. I wish to make it clear that s/he is fully aware of my wishes and I request that his/her decisions be respected.

ADDITIONAL DIRECTIONS ON FUTURE HEALTH CARE

_____

_____

_____

_____

_____

_____

The above directions are to apply even if my life is at risk.

SIGNATURES

Signature _____ Date _____

Witness's signature _____ Date_____

I confirm that my views are still as stated above.

	Date	Signature	Witness' signature
1)	_____	_____	_____
2)	_____	_____	_____
3)	_____	_____	_____
4)	_____	_____	_____

Note: This form operates as a refusal of medical treatment which in some circumstances may be legally binding on your doctors. The effect of signing this form could therefore be to shorten your life in circumstances where your doctors could prolong it. Although you can revoke this Living Will at any time, and although you can permit medical treatment at any time even if you have not revoked it, remember that of course you can only do either of these things if you are conscious and able to express yourself at the time.

For the form to be validly executed: (1) you must sign the form or it must be signed by someone by your direction in your presence; and (2) the signature must be made or acknowledged by you in the presence of a witness; and (3) the witness must sign it or acknowledge his signature in your presence.

Loan Agreement

Form LB05

THIS AGREEMENT IS MADE the _____ day of _____ year _____

BETWEEN:

(1) _____ (the 'Borrower'); and

(2) _____ (the 'Lender').

NOW IT IS HEREBY AGREED as follows:

1. Loan: Subject to and in accordance with this agreement, its terms, conditions and covenants the Lender agrees to lend to the Borrower on _____ (the 'Loan Date') the principal sum of _____ Pounds (£_____) (the 'Loan').

2. Note: The terms of the Loan shall be evidenced by and further particularised in a Note in the form attached hereto and marked 'A' (the 'Note') executed by the Borrower and delivered to the Lender on the Loan Date.

3. Interest: The Loan shall bear interest on the unpaid principal at an annual rate of_____ percent (_____%). In the event of the default in payment interest at the aforesaid interest rate shall additionally accrue on any overdue payment until the same is discharged.

4. Payment: Payment shall be in accordance with the terms contained in the Note. The Note may, at any time and from time to time, be paid or prepaid in whole or in part without premium or penalty, except that any partial prepayment shall be (a) in multiples of £_____, and (b) of a minimum of £_____. All payments shall be applied firstly to the discharge of any interest which may be due by virtue of a default on the part of the Borrower, and secondly to the instalments (if any) due under the Note in the inverse order of their maturity. [Upon the payment of the outstanding principal in full or all of the instalments, if any, the interest on the Loan shall be computed and shall be paid within five (5) days of the receipt of notice from the Lender, in default of which any such unpaid interest will in turn bear interest at the aforementioned rate.][1]

5. Security: The Borrower agrees to secure the repayment of the Loan by executing those security documents attached hereto as Exhibit B (the 'Security Documents') and shall deliver the Security Documents on the Loan Date. From time to time the Lender may demand, and the Borrower shall execute, additional loan documents which in the Lender's view are reasonably necessary to perfect the Lender's security interests.

6. Representations and Warranties: The undersigned signatory on behalf of the Borrower represents and warrants: (i) that the execution, delivery and performance of this agreement, and the Note and Security Documents have been duly authorised by the Borrower; (ii) that the financial statement submitted to the Lender truly and fairly presents the financial condition of the Borrower as of the date of this agreement knowing that the Lender has relied thereon in granting the Loan; (iii) that the Borrower has no contingent obligations not disclosed or reserved against in said financial statement, and at the present time there are no material, unrealised or anticipated losses from any present commitment of the Borrower; (iv) that there will be no material adverse changes in the financial condition of the Borrower at the time of the Loan Date; (v) that the Borrower will advise the Lender of material adverse changes which occur at any time prior to the Loan Date and thereafter to the date of final payment;

Continued on next page

Loan Agreement (continued)   Form LB05

and (vi) that the Borrower has good and valid title to all of the property given as security hereunder. The said Undersigned represents and warrants that such representations and warranties shall be deemed to be continuing representations and warranties during the entire life of this agreement.

7.   Default: In addition to the grounds set out in the Loan Note, the Borrower shall be in default: (i) if any payment due hereunder is not made within (___) days of the date due; (ii) in the event of assignment by the Borrower for the benefit of creditors, or the entry of the Borrower into any voluntary arrangement or the passing of a resolution for the winding up of the Borrower otherwise than for the purpose of amalgamation or reconstruction; (iii) upon the filing of any voluntary or involuntary petition for the bankruptcy or liquidation of the Borrower or the appointment of a receiver or administrator of the Borrower; or (iv) if the Borrower has breached any representation or warranty specified in this agreement. In the event of any such default the entire capital sum and interest due hereunder shall on demand fall due forthwith.

8.   If the Borrower shall comprise more than one person, the Borrower's obligations herein shall be joint and several.

9.   Governing Law: This agreement, the Note(s) and the Security Documents shall be governed by, construed and enforced in accordance with the law of England and Wales to the jurisdiction of which the parties hereto submit.

IN WITNESS OF WHICH the parties have signed this agreement the day and year first above written

(Borrower)   (Lender)

_____   _____

Signed by the Borrower   Signed by the Lender

_____   _____

in the presence of (witness)   in the presence of (witness)

Name _____   Name _____

Address _____   Address _____

_____   _____

Signed for and on behalf of   Signed for and on behalf of:

_____Ltd   _____Ltd

_____   _____

Director   Director

_____   _____

Director/Secretary   Director/Secretary

Note: This form is to be used in conjunction with the Loan Note (Short Form). This form must only be used in connection with agreements which are not regulated under the Consumer Credit Act 1974. Broadly speaking the Act, at the time of writing, applies to any loan, hire or hire purchase agreement for £25,000 or less. There are some exceptions. The most important are that an agreement is not regulated if the borrower or hirer is a limited company. By the time you use this form, however, the law may have changed so as to regulate agreements for more than £25,000. Therefore, you must check the current position.

¹ Include this passage **only** if you are using the Loan Note and it does not provide for instalments to include interest as well as principal.

Loan Note (Long Form)   Form LB06

THIS DEED IS MADE the _____ day of _____ year _____

BETWEEN:

(1) _____ of _____ (the 'Borrower'); and

(2) _____ of _____ (the 'Lender').

NOW THIS DEED WITNESSES as follows:

1. The Borrower hereby promises to pay to the order of the Lender the sum of _____ _____ Pounds (£_____), which the Lender has lent to the Borrower (receipt of which the Borrower hereby acknowledges) together with interest thereon at the rate of _____% per annum on the unpaid balance. The said amount shall be paid in the following manner:

    _____

    _____

    _____

2. The terms of this Loan shall be governed by the Loan Agreement of the same date made between the Lender and the Borrower and attached hereto.

3. This note shall at the option of any holder thereof be immediately due and payable upon the occurrence of any of the following:

    (a) Failure of the Borrower to make any payment due hereunder within _____ days of its due date.

    (b) Breach of any condition of any mortgage, loan agreement, or guarantee granted as collateral security for this note.

    (c) Breach of any condition of any loan agreement or mortgage, if any, having a priority over any loan agreement or mortgage on security granted, in whole or in part, as collateral security for this note.

    (d) Upon the death, incapacity, dissolution, receivership, insolvency or liquidation of either of the parties hereto, or any endorser or guarantor of this note.

4. In the event that the Borrower shall be in default of any obligation under the Loan Agreement or this note then the Borrower will pay all reasonable solicitors fees and costs. All payments hereunder shall be made to such address as may from time to time be designated to the Borrower by the Lender.

5. If the Borrower shall comprise more than one person, the liability of each such person in respect of the obligations herein shall be joint and several.

Continued on next page

Loan Note (Long Form) (continued)   Form LB06

IN WITNESS OF WHICH the parties have signed this deed the day and year first above written

(Borrower)   (Lender)

_____   _____

Signed by the Borrower   Signed by the Lender

_____   _____

in the presence of (witness)   in the presence of (witness)

Name _____   Name _____

Address _____   Address _____

_____   _____

Signed for and on behalf of   Signed for and on behalf of:

_____Ltd   _____Ltd

_____   _____

Director   Director

_____   _____

Director/Secretary   Director/Secretary

Note: This form must only be used in connection with agreements which are not regulated under the Consumer Credit Act 1974. Broadly speaking the Act, at the time of writing, applies to any loan, hire or hire purchase agreement for £25,000 or less. There are some exceptions. The most important are that an agreement is not regulated if the borrower or hirer is a limited company. By the time you use this form, however, the law may have changed so as to regulate agreements for more than £25,000. Therefore, you must check the current position.

Loan Note (Short Form)

Form LB07

THIS DEED is made the _____ day of _____ year_____

BY:

_____ of _____ (the 'Borrower').

WHEREAS:

The Borrower is indebted to _____(the 'Lender') in the sum of £ _____

NOW THIS DEED WITNESSES as follows:

[This Loan Note is subject to the terms of the Loan Agreement dated _____ which is attached hereto. The two terms of the Loan Agreement dated _____ which is attached hereto. The two documents are to be read as one document, but if there is any conflict between them, the terms of this Loan Note shall prevail.]

1. The Borrower promises to pay to the order of the Lender the sum of _____ _____ Pounds (£ _____), with annual interest of _____ % on any unpaid balance.

2. This note shall be paid in _____ consecutive and equal instalments of £ _____ each with the first payment being made from the date hereof, and the same amount on the same day of each _____ thereafter. The instalments shall be in discharge of [both principal and interest due hereunder] / [principal only, the interest being payable in accordance with the Loan Agreement after the repayment of the principal].

3. This note may be prepaid without penalty.

4. If any instalment shall be unpaid more than _____ days after the same shall fall due, the same shall bear interest at the aforementioned rate until paid. All payments shall be first applied to such default interest and the balance to instalments in the order in which the same fell due.

5. This note shall be due and payable upon demand by any holder hereof should the Borrower default in any payment beyond _____ days of its due date.

Continued on next page

Loan Note (Short Form) (continued)   Form LB07

IN WITNESS OF WHICH the Borrower has executed this deed the day and year first above written

(Borrower)   (Lender)

_____   _____
Signed by the Borrower   Signed by the Lender

_____   _____
in the presence of (witness)   in the presence of (witness)

Name _____   Name _____

Address _____   Address _____

_____   _____

Signed for and on behalf of   Signed for and on behalf of:

_____Ltd   _____Ltd

_____   _____
Director   Director

_____   _____
Director/Secretary   Director/Secretary

Note: This form may be used in conjunction with the Loan Agreement form LB05. This form must only be used in connection with agreements which are not regulated under the Consumer Credit Act 1974. Broadly speaking the Act, at the time of writing, applies to any loan, hire or hire purchase agreement for £25,000 or less. There are some exceptions. The most important are that an agreement is not regulated if the borrower or hirer is a limited company. By the time you use this form, however, the law may have changed so as to regulate agreements for more than £25,000. Therefore, you must check the current position.

If it is intended for the loan to be governed by the Loan Agreement in this book as well as the Loan Note on this page, appropriate deletions will have to be made in order to avoid contradiction. That is because one of the options in the Loan Note permits instalments to pay off both interest and principal, whereas the Loan Agreement calls for the instalments to be of capital only, with the interest to be paid off at the end.

Loan Payment Record

Form LB08

Borrower: _____ Creditor: _____

Terms: _____

Date Due	Date Paid	Amount	Balance	Arrears	Interest Accruing on Arrears	Payments of Interest Accruing on Arrears
_____	_____	£ _____	£ _____	£ _____	£ _____	£ _____
_____	_____	£ _____	£ _____	£ _____	£ _____	£ _____
_____	_____	£ _____	£ _____	£ _____	£ _____	£ _____
_____	_____	£ _____	£ _____	£ _____	£ _____	£ _____
_____	_____	£ _____	£ _____	£ _____	£ _____	£ _____
_____	_____	£ _____	£ _____	£ _____	£ _____	£ _____
_____	_____	£ _____	£ _____	£ _____	£ _____	£ _____
_____	_____	£ _____	£ _____	£ _____	£ _____	£ _____
_____	_____	£ _____	£ _____	£ _____	£ _____	£ _____
_____	_____	£ _____	£ _____	£ _____	£ _____	£ _____
_____	_____	£ _____	£ _____	£ _____	£ _____	£ _____
_____	_____	£ _____	£ _____	£ _____	£ _____	£ _____
_____	_____	£ _____	£ _____	£ _____	£ _____	£ _____
_____	_____	£ _____	£ _____	£ _____	£ _____	£ _____
_____	_____	£ _____	£ _____	£ _____	£ _____	£ _____
_____	_____	£ _____	£ _____	£ _____	£ _____	£ _____
_____	_____	£ _____	£ _____	£ _____	£ _____	£ _____
_____	_____	£ _____	£ _____	£ _____	£ _____	£ _____
_____	_____	£ _____	£ _____	£ _____	£ _____	£ _____
_____	_____	£ _____	£ _____	£ _____	£ _____	£ _____
_____	_____	£ _____	£ _____	£ _____	£ _____	£ _____
_____	_____	£ _____	£ _____	£ _____	£ _____	£ _____
_____	_____	£ _____	£ _____	£ _____	£ _____	£ _____
_____	_____	£ _____	£ _____	£ _____	£ _____	£ _____
_____	_____	£ _____	£ _____	£ _____	£ _____	£ _____
_____	_____	£ _____	£ _____	£ _____	£ _____	£ _____
_____	_____	£ _____	£ _____	£ _____	£ _____	£ _____
_____	_____	£ _____	£ _____	£ _____	£ _____	£ _____
_____	_____	£ _____	£ _____	£ _____	£ _____	£ _____
_____	_____	£ _____	£ _____	£ _____	£ _____	£ _____
_____		£ _____	£ _____	£ _____	£ _____	£ _____

Location of Important Documents and Summary of Personal Information   Form PF12

Location of Important Documents and
Summary of Personal Information

OF

Name _____

Will   _____
              _____

Birth Certificate   _____
                    _____

Marriage Certificate   _____
                       _____

Divorce Decree   _____
                 _____

Title Deeds   _____
              _____

Mortgage Documents   _____
                     _____

Life Insurance Policies   _____
                          _____

Pension Details   _____
                  _____

Share Certificates   _____
                     _____

Other Investment Certificates   _____
                                _____

Loan and H.P. Agreements   _____
                           _____

Continued on next page

Location of Important Documents and Summary of Personal Information (continued)

Form PF12

Bank Account Details
_____
_____

Building Society Passbooks
_____
_____

Donor Cards
_____
_____

Passport
_____
_____

Household Insurance
_____
_____

Driver's Licence
_____
_____

Tenancy Agreement
_____
_____

Car Insurance
_____
_____

Lodger Agreement   Form F303

The PROPORTY   _____

_____

The ROOM   means the room at the Property which has been nominated by the Owner and agreed

to by the Lodger

The OWNER   _____

_____whose address is the Property above

The LODGER   _____

_____

The TERM   _____ weeks/months* beginning on _____

EARLY   Either party may at any time end this Agreement earlier than the end of the Term   (*delete as
TERMINATION   by giving to the other written notice of _____ week(s)/month(s)*   appropriate)

The PAYMENT   £ _____ per week/month* payable in advance on the _____ of each week/month*

The DEPOSIT   £ _____

The INVENTORY   means the list of the Owner's possessions at the Property/Room* which has been

signed by the Owner and the Lodger

DATED   _____

SIGNED   _____   _____

_____   _____

(The Owner)   (The Lodger)

THIS HOUSE/FLAT SHARE AGREEMENT comprises the particulars detailed above and the terms and conditions printed overleaf whereby the Room is licensed by the Owner and taken by the Lodger for occupation during the Term upon making the Payment.

IMPORTANT NOTICE:

1   This form of Agreement is for use in those cases where the Room is part of a house or flat which the Owner occupies as his/her only or principal home, so that an Assured Shorthold Tenancy is not created.

2   This form of Agreement does not require either party to give any form of notice to the other at the end of the fixed Term, but if either party wishes to end this Agreement early, as referred to in the definition of the TERM near the middle of this Agreement, then a Notice to Terminate may be used.

Terms and Conditions on next page

Lodger Agreement (Terms and Conditions)   Form F303

1. This Agreement is personal to the Lodger, is not assignable, and will terminate automatically without any notice if the Lodger ceases to reside at the Property or at any time more than two of the payments are due and unpaid.

2. The Lodger will:

    2.1 only in conjunction with the occupation of the Room be allowed to share with the other occupiers of the Property the use and facilities of the common parts of the Property (including such bathroom, toilet, kitchen and sitting room facilities as may be at the Property);

    2.2 pay the Payment at the times and in the manner aforesaid;

    2.3 keep the interior of the Room in a good and clean state and condition and not damage or injure the Property or any part of it;

    2.4 yield up the Room at the end of the Term in the same clean state and condition it was in at the beginning of the Term;

    2.5 maintain in the Room and keep in a good and clean condition all of the items listed in the Inventory;

    2.6 not make any alteration or addition to the Room nor without the Owner's prior written consent do any redecoration or painting of the Room;

    2.7 not do or omit to do anything on or at the Property which may be or become a nuisance or annoyance to the Owner or any other occupiers of the Property or Sharers or occupiers of adjoining or nearby premises or which may in any way prejudice the insurance of the Property or cause an increase in the premium payable therefor;

    2.8 not without the Owner's prior consent allow or keep any pet or any kind of animal at the Property;

    2.9 not use or occupy the Room in any way whatsoever other than as a private residence;

    2.10 not to let or purport to let or share any rooms at the property or take in any lodger or paying guest or, without the consent of the Owner to permit any person to sleep, or stay at the property;

    2.11 provide the Owner with a forwarding address when the Agreement comes to an end and remove all rubbish and all personal items (including the Lodger's own furniture and equipment) from the Property before leaving;

    2.12 pay interest at the rate of 4% above the Base Lending Rate for the time being of the Owner's bankers upon any payment or other money lawfully due from the Lodger under this Agreement which is more than 14 days in arrears in respect of the period from when it become due down to the date of payment;

    2.13 make a reasonable and proportionate contribution to the cost according to use of all charges in respect of any electric, gas, water and telephonic or televisual services used at or supplied to the Property and Council Tax or any similar tax that might be charged in addition to or replacement of it during the Term.

3. The Deposit

    3.1 The Deposit will be held by the Owner and will be refunded to the Lodger at the end of the Term (however it ends) but less any reasonable deductions properly made by the Owner to cover any reasonable costs incurred by or losses caused to him by any breaches of the Lodger's obligations under this Agreement. No interest will be payable by the Owner to the Lodger in respect of the deposit money.

    3.2 The Deposit shall be repaid to the Lodger, at the forwarding address provided to the Owner, as soon as reasonably practicable. However the Owner shall not be bound to return the Deposit until he is satisfied that no money is repayable to the Local Authority if the Lodger has been in receipt of Housing Benefit and until after he has had a reasonable opportunity to assess the reasonable cost of any repairs required as a result of any breaches of his obligations by the Lodger or other sums properly due to the Owner under clause 3.1 above, save that except in exceptional circumstances the Owner shall not retain the Deposit for more than one month.

    3.3 At any time during the Term the Owner may apply any part of the Deposit to cover any reasonable costs incurred as a result of any breaches of his obligations by the Lodger or other sums properly due to the Owner, in which case the Lodger shall upon demand pay by way of additional Payment to the Owner any additional payments needed to restore the full amount of the Deposit.

4. In the event of destruction to the Property or of damage to it which shall make the same or a substantial portion of the same uninhabitable, the Lodger shall be relieved from making the payment by an amount proportionate to the extent to which the Lodger's ability to live in the Property is thereby prevented, save where the destruction or damage has been caused by any act or default by the Lodger or where the Owner's insurance cover has been adversely affected by any act or omission on the part of the Lodger.

5. To enable the Lodger to comply with clause 4 above, the Owner will upon request provide to the Lodger a copy of his insurance policy (if any) or an extract of the relevant terms.

6. The Lodger shall not have exclusive possession of the Room and the identity of any other occupiers of the Property shall be in the absolute discretion of the Owner.

7. It is hereby agreed that if the parties agree to the Lodger continuing in occupation of the Room after the end of the Term, his occupation shall still be subject to the Terms and Conditions set out in this Agreement, save that it shall be terminable by either party on [one month's] notice. Such notice may expire at any time, whether or not on a date specified for payment on or at the end of a period of this Agreement or otherwise. If such notice expires on a date other than a date specified for payment, the Lodger shall be entitled to a refund of such part of the final payment as is proportionate to the number of days which follows the expiry of the notice or the end of his occupancy, whichever shall be the later, and this will continue unless and until a new agreement is signed or the Lodger vacates the Property.

8. Where the context so admits:

    8.1 the 'Owner' includes the successors in title to the Owner's interest in the Property;

    8.2 the 'Property' includes all of the Owner's fixtures and fittings at or upon the Property and all of the items listed in the Inventory and (for the avoidance of doubt) the Room;

    8.3 the 'Term' shall mean the period stated in the particulars overleaf or any shorter or longer period in the event of an earlier termination or an extension or holding over respectively.

    8.4 All references to the singular shall include the plural and vice versa and any obligations or liabilities of more than one person shall be joint and several and an obligation on the part of a party shall include an obligation not to allow or permit the breach of that obligation.

    8.5 All references to 'he', 'him' and 'his' shall be taken to include 'she', 'her' and 'hers'.

Lodger/Bed and Breakfast Licence (For a Room in a Furnished House)

Form RT22

The PROPERTY _____

_____

The ROOM means the room at the Property which has been agreed between the Licensor and Licensee to be taken by the Licensee

The LICENSOR _____

_____whose address is the Property above

The LICENSEE _____

of _____

The PERIOD

(delete paragraph if not required)

_____weeks/months* beginning on _____

Subject to the right for either party at any time during the Period to end this Agreement earlier by giving to the other written notice of _____ week(s)/month(s)*

The SERVICES means the services that the Licensor hereby agrees to provide to the Licensee being to [clean the Room and Property] [provide clean sheets] [provide breakfast] [provide dinner]*

The PAYMENT £ _____ per week/month* payable in advance on the _____ of each week/month*

being payment for the Room and Services

The DEPOSIT £_____

The INVENTORY means the list of the Licensor's possessions at the Property which has been signed by the Licensor and the Licensee

DATED _____

SIGNED _____   _____

_____   _____

(The Licensor)   (The Licensee)

THIS AGREEMENT comprises the particulars detailed above and the terms and conditions printed overleaf whereby the Room is licensed by the Licensor and taken by the Licensee for occupation during the Period upon making the Payment.

(* delete as appropriate)

Terms and Conditions on next page

Lodger/Bed and Breakfast Licence Terms and Conditions   Form RT22

1. This Licence is personal to the Licensee, is not assignable, and will terminate automatically without any notice if the Licensee ceases to reside at the Property or if at any time more than two of the payments are due and unpaid

2. The Licensee will:

   2.1 only in conjunction with the occupation of the Room be allowed to share with the other occupiers of the Property the use and facilities of the common parts of the Property (including such bathroom, toilet, kitchen and sitting room facilities as may be at the Property)

   2.2 pay the Payment at the times and in the manner aforesaid

   2.3 [keep the interior of the Room in a good and clean state and condition and]* not damage or injure the Property or any part of it

   2.4 yield up the Room at the end of the Period in the same clean state and condition it was in at the beginning of the Period

   2.5 maintain in the Room and keep in a good [and clean]* condition all of the items listed in the Inventory

   2.6 not make any alteration or addition to the Room nor without the Licensor's prior written consent to do any redecoration or painting of the Room

   2.7 not do or omit to do anything on or at the Property which may be or become a nuisance or annoyance to the Licensor or any other occupiers of the Property or owners or occupiers of adjoining or nearby premises or which may in any way prejudice the insurance of the Property or cause an increase in the premium payable therefor

   2.8 not without the Licensor's prior consent allow or keep any pet or any kind of animal at the Property

   2.9 not use or occupy the Room in any way whatsoever other than as a private residence

   2.10 not to let or purport to let or share any rooms at the property or take in any lodger or paying guest or, without the consent of the Licensor (not to be unreasonably withheld) to permit any person to sleep, or stay at the property

   2.11 provide the Licensor with a forwarding address when the licence agreement comes to an end and remove all rubbish and all personal items (including the Licensee's own furniture and equipment) from the property before leaving

   2.12 pay interest at the rate of 4% above the Base Lending Rate for the time being of the Licensor's bankers upon any payment or other money due from the Licensee under this Agreement which is more than 14 days in arrears in respect of the period from when it become due down to the date of payment

   2.13 make a reasonable and proportionate contribution to the cost according to use of all charges in respect of any electric, gas, water and telephonic or televisual services used at or supplied to the Property and Council Tax or any similar tax that might be charged in addition to or replacement of it during the Period

   2.14 to register with the Local Authority as a Council Tax payer in respect of the room or of the house as the Local Authority may decide and to pay such Council Tax as may be assessed. If the Licensee shall pay less than ___ per cent of the Council Tax which is payable in respect of the [room]/[Property] the Licensee will reimburse the Licensor or any occupant who may be obliged to make up the shortfall. If the Licensee is obliged to pay more than the aforementioned portion of the Council Tax, the Licensor shall reimburse him for the excess The term 'Council Tax' shall include any similar tax that might be charged in addition to or replacement of it during the Period

3. The Deposit

   3.1 The Deposit will be held by the Licensor and will be refunded to the Licensee at the end of the Period (however it ends) but less any reasonable deductions properly made by the Licensor to cover any reasonable costs incurred by or losses caused to him by any breaches of the Licensee's obligations under this Licence. No interest will be payable by the Licensor to the Licensee in respect of the deposit money

   3.2 The Deposit shall be repaid to the Licensee, at the forwarding address provided to the Licensor, as soon as reasonably practicable. However the Licensor shall not be bound to return the Deposit until he is satisfied that no money is repayable to the Local Authority if the Licensee has been in receipt of Housing Benefit and until after he has had a reasonable opportunity to assess the

Continued on next page

Lodger/Bed and Breakfast Licence
Terms and Conditions (cont)

Form RT22

reasonable cost of any repairs required as a result of any breaches of his obligations by the Licensee or other sums properly due to the Licensor under clause 3.1 above, save that except in exceptional circumstances the Licensor shall not retain the Deposit for more than one month

3.3 If at any time during the Period the Licensor needs to use any part of the Deposit to cover any reasonable costs incurred as a result of any breaches of his obligations by the Licensee or other sums properly due to the Licensor, the Licensee shall upon demand pay by way of additional Payment to the Licensor any additional payments needed to restore the full amount of the Deposit

4. In the event of damage to or destruction of the Property by fire or other catastrophe not caused by the Licensee shall be relieved from making the Payment to the extent that the Licensee's use and enjoyment of the Property is thereby prevented and from performance of its obligations as to the state and condition of the Property to the extent of and whilst there prevails any such damage or destruction (except to the extent that the insurance is prejudiced by any act or default of the Licensee)

5. So long as the reference to a right of early termination in the definition of 'the PERIOD' overleaf (the 'early termination right) has not been deleted then either party may at an time during the period terminate this Agreement by giving to the other prior written notice to that effect, the length of such notice to be that stated in the early termination right, and upon the

expiry of said notice this Agreement shall end with no further liability for either party save for any existing breach

6. The Licensee shall not have exclusive possession of the Room and the identity of any other occupiers of the Property shall be in the absolute discretion of the Licensor

7. Where the context so admits:
   7.1 the 'Licensor' includes the successors in title to the Licensor's interest in the Property
   7.2 the 'Property' includes all of the Licensor's fixtures and fittings at or upon the Property and all of the items listed in the Inventory and (for the avoidance of doubt) the Room
   7.3 the 'Period' shall mean the period stated in the particulars overleaf or any shorter or longer period in the event of an earlier termination or an extension or holding over respectively

8. All references to the singular shall include the plural and vice versa and any obligations or liabilities of more than one person shall be joint and several and an obligation on the part of a party shall include an obligation not to allow or permit the breach of that obligation

*Delete as appropriate

Note: If you are providing meals (not just a packet of cereal in the morning, for example) or other substantial services such as cleaning and laundry, or if the occupant is sharing the room with someone else and you genuinely have the right to decide who the sharer is, then the arrangement is a licence and can be brought to an end, simply by your serving a written notice giving the minimum term of notice which the licence prescribes. After expiry of the notice, you can bring proceedings for possession. Note that there are only limited cases that you can expel a lodger without bringing court proceedings, and that you must be sure that your case is one of them before you do so. It can be a criminal offence if you get it wrong.

Remember also that the courts are keen to detect sham arrangements and that therefore the provision of meals or the right to determine sharers must reflect reality. If it does not, you may have created a tenancy, and if you have done that you will need to follow certain strict procedures in order to recover possession.

If you have any doubts, therefore, you should consult a solicitor, whether at the time when you are making the arrangement or seeking to bring it to an end.

If you wish to impose further obligations on the lodger than are contained in this form, we advise you to read the Office of Fair Trading's 'Guidance on unfair terms in tenancy agreements' which is available online.

Lost Credit Card Notice   Form OLF24

Date   _____

To   _____

        _____

        _____

Dear   _____

This is to confirm that the credit card described below has been lost or stolen. Please put a stop on all credit in respect of the card. I last remember using the card myself on _____

at _____. I shall destroy the card if subsequently found, and I would be grateful if you could issue me with a replacement card.

Yours faithfully

_____

Cardholder

Address _____

        _____

        _____

_____

Credit Card Number

Lost Credit Card Notice   Form OLF24

Note: You must notify the card issuer by telephone immediately you are aware of the loss of the card.

Magazine Article Commissioning Contract   Form OLF25

THIS AGREEMENT IS MADE the _____ day of _____ year_____

BETWEEN:

(1) _____ (the 'Author'); and

(2) _____ (the 'Publisher').

NOW IT IS HEREBY AGREED as follows:

1.   The Author agrees to deliver an original and one copy of the manuscript which is tentatively titled

_____(the 'Work'),

to the Publisher on or before _____.

The Work is described as:

_____

_____

If the Author fails to deliver the Work within _____ days of the Work due date, the Publisher may terminate this contract. The Article shall be submitted by email/on disk and shall be _____ words in length.

2.   Within _____ days of receipt of the Work, the Publisher agrees to notify the Author if the Publisher finds the work unsatisfactory in form or content. The Publisher also agrees to provide the Author with a list of necessary changes unless in the Publisher's reasonable opinion the Work is incapable of remedy. The Author agrees to make the changes within _____ days of receipt of the list. If the Publisher still reasonably rejects the Work as unsatisfactory, the Publisher may terminate this contract. If the Publisher does not reject the Work within ___ days of the receipt of any changes from the Author, the Work will be deemed to have been accepted.

3.   The Author grants the Publisher the exclusive licence to publish the Work for the period of _____ following the initial publication of the Work. Any rights not specifically granted to the Publisher shall remain with the Author. The Author agrees not to exercise any retained rights in such a manner as to adversely affect the value of the rights granted to the Publisher.

4.   The Publisher shall pay to the Author upon acceptance of the Work the amount of £_____.

5.   The style, format, design, layout, and any required editorial changes of the published work shall be in the sole discretion of the Publisher.

6.   The Author warrants that:

(a)   the Work is the sole creation of the Author;

(b)   the Author is the sole owner of the rights granted under this contract;

(c)   the Work does not infringe the copyright of any other work;

(d)   the Work is original and has not been published before;

(e)   the Work is not in the public domain;

(f)   the Work is not obscene, libellous, and does not invade the privacy of any person;

(g)   all statements of fact in the Work are [true and] based upon reasonable research.

The Author will indemnify the Publisher for any breach of these warranties and for any legal costs which the Publisher may incur by reason of the same.

Continued on next page

Magazine Article Commissioning Contract (cont) Form OLF25

7. The Publisher acknowledges that the Author retains worldwide copyright in the Work.

8. The Publisher agrees that, within [six] months from the receipt of a satisfactory manuscript of the Work, the Work will be published at the Publisher's sole expense. [If the Publisher fails to do so, unless prevented by conditions beyond the Publisher's control, the Author may terminate this Contract.] [If the Publisher fails to publish the Work within one year from receipt, the licence shall cease to be exclusive and the Author will be at liberty to publish the Work as he sees fit.] Notwithstanding any prior acceptance by the Publisher of the Work, the Publisher shall be under no obligation to publish the same if the Publisher reasonably believes that any of the warranties contained in Clause 6 hereof are breached. If any of the said warranties are actually breached, the Publisher may reject the Work and terminate the contract, whereupon all sums paid by the Publisher to the Author shall be returned.

9. This contract is the complete agreement between the Author and Publisher. No modification or waiver of any terms will be valid unless in writing and signed by both parties.

10. Nothing in this Agreement is intended to confer any benefit on a third party whether under the Contracts (Rights of Third Parties) Act or otherwise.

IN WITNESS OF WHICH the parties have signed this agreement the day and year first above written

_____

Signed by the Author

_____

in the presence of (witness)

Name _____

Address _____

_____

Occupation_____

_____

Signed for and on behalf of the Publisher

_____

in the presence of (witness)

Name _____

Address _____

_____

Occupation_____

Mailing List Name Removal Request   Form OLF26

Date _____

The Mailing Preference Service (MPS)

DMA House

70 Margaret Street

London

W1W 8SS

Dear Sirs

I regularly receive unsolicited, 'junk' mail from companies advertising their products. I understand that I can ask you to have my name and this household removed from the mailing lists of companies which send out unsolicited mail, and that this service is free of charge.

[I wish to register my address details so it can be removed from mailing lists].*

[I wish to register a previous occupier at my current address, he/she being _____].*

[I wish to register my previous address, this being _____].*

[I wish to register details of _____, who has died]*

[Although other members of the household wish to register, I would like to continue to receive mail]*

Please put this into action with immediate effect.

Yours faithfully.

_____

Name

_____

Address

*Delete as appropriate

Mileage Reimbursement Report   Form E45

Employee Name: _____

Driving Licence No. _____ Car Reg No. _____

Make/Model of Vehicle _____

Department _____ Month _____

Date	Beginning Reading	Ending Reading	Total Mileage	Reason for Travel

Total mileage this month: _____ @ £ _____ Per Mile = £ _____

Approved by _____ Date _____

Title _____

Minutes of Annual General Meeting — Form B15

_____ LIMITED

MINUTES of the annual general meeting of the Company held at

_____ on._____ at _____ a.m./p.m.

PRESENT _____ (in the chair)

_____

IN ATTENDANCE _____

_____

1. The Chairman announced that consents to the meeting being held at short notice had been received from all of the members of the Company having a right to attend and vote at the meeting.

2. The Chairman declared that a quorum was present.

3. It was unanimously agreed that the notice convening the meeting should be taken as read.

4. The Chairman submitted the Company's profit and loss account for the period ended _____ , together with the balance sheet as at that date and it was resolved that the accounts as submitted to the meeting be and are approved.[1]

5. It was resolved that a final dividend of _____ p per share in respect of the year ended _____ be declared on the ordinary shares of _____ each in the capital of the company, payable on _____ to the holders of ordinary shares registered at the close of business on _____ .

6. It was resolved that _____ be re-appointed auditors of the Company until the next general meeting at which accounts are laid before the company, at a fee to be agreed with the board of directors.

7. It was resolved that _____ , the director(s) retiring by rotation, be re-elected a director(s) of the Company.[2]

8. It was resolved that the appointment of _____ to the board on _____ be confirmed.[3]

9. The meeting then ended.

_____

Chairman

Note: From 1 October 2007 it will no longer be a statutory requirement for a private company to hold an AGM. This form is, however, retained because many companies will continue to find this a convenient course.

[1] There is no requirement for the accounts to be approved by the shareholders; they need only be laid before them in general meeting.

[2] In a private company, it is possible to vote on the re-election of directors en bloc although best practice is to vote on each individually.

[3] The reappointment of directors appointed during the year should not be confused with the re-election of directors.

Minutes of Directors' Meeting Changing Objects of Company

Form B16

Minutes of a meeting of the directors held on the _____ day of _____ year __

Present: _____ (Chairman)

               _____ (Managing Director)

               _____ (Director)

In attendance: _____(Company Secretary)

1.   On opening the meeting the Chairman declared that a quorum was in attendance.

2.   The board considered the future activities of the Company. Having determined that the objects of the Company were too restrictive and should be altered, it was decided that the memorandum of association of the Company should be altered by deleting subclause (__) of clause ___ of the memorandum of association and substituting therefor: 'To carry on business as a general commercial company.'

3.   It was resolved that an extraordinary general meeting of the Company be held on _____ the _____ day of _____ year ____ at _____ o'clock for the purpose of considering and, if thought fit, passing as a special resolution the following:

     'That the memorandum of association of the Company should be altered by deleting subclause (__) of clause ___ of the memorandum of association and substituting therefor:

     'To carry on business as a general commercial company.'

     Furthermore, the secretary was instructed to give notice to all shareholders of the extraordinary general meeting and to obtain their consent to the meeting being held on short notice.

4.   There being no further business the meeting was closed.

_____

Chairman

Note: All companies formed after the Companies Act 2006 Section 31 comes into force will have unlimited objects, unless these are specifically restricted in the company's Articles.

Minutes of Extraordinary General Meeting   Form B17

_____ LIMITED

MINUTES of an extraordinary general meeting of the Company held at

_____ on _____ at _____ a.m./p.m.

PRESENT _____ (in the chair)

_____

IN ATTENDANCE _____

_____

1.   The Chairman [confirmed that notice of the meeting had been given to all the members of the company having a right to attend and vote at the meeting] / [announced that consents to the meeting being held at short notice had been received from all of the members of the Company having a right to attend and vote at the meeting] .

2.   The Chairman declared that a quorum was present.

3.   It was unanimously agreed that the notice convening the meeting should be taken as read.

4.   The Chairman proposed the following resolution as an ordinary/special resolution: _____

     _____

     _____

5.   The Chairman put the resolution to the meeting, took the vote on a show of hands[1] and declared the resolution passed as an ordinary/special resolution of the Company.[2]

6.   There being no further business the meeting then closed.

_____

Chairman

Note: If it is intended to pass a resolution removing a director or the auditor from office before the expiry of their term of appointment, then special notice (which is 28 days' notice) of the meeting is required.

From 1 October 2007 private companies will no longer be required to hold an AGM; all meetings will therefore be ordinary and none will be extraordinary. This form may continue to be used. Note that the law requiring 28 days' notice of a meeting, where a resolution requiring special notice is to be considered, remains unchanged.

[1]   If a poll is validly demanded, the resolution may not be passed or blocked on a show of hands. The circumstances in which a poll may be demanded and the way in which it should be conducted are set out in the articles (in Table A, the relevant provisions are articles 46-52). The fact that a poll has been demanded, by whom and the result of the poll should be recorded in the minutes.

[2]   Repeat points 4 and 5 for each resolution.

Minutes of Extraordinary General Meeting Changing Objects of Company

Form B18

Minutes of an extraordinary general meeting of the members of _____ _____

_____ Limited held at _____ at _____

o'clock on _____ the _____day of _____ year _____

Present: _____ (Chairman)

                  _____ (Managing Director)

                  _____ (Members)

In attendance: _____ (Company Secretary)

1.   The chairman declared that a quorum was present.

2.   The notice convening the meeting was read.

3.   It was proposed as a special resolution:

      'That the memorandum of association of the Company be altered by deleting subclause (___) of

      clause ___ and substituting therefor the following subclause:

      'To carry on business as a general commercial company.'

      The resolution was carried unanimously.

4.   There being no further business the meeting was closed.

_____

Chairman

Note: All companies formed after the Companies Act 2006 Section 31 comes into force will have unlimited objects, unless these are specifically restricted in the company's articles.

From 1 October 2007 it will no longer be a statutory requirement for a private company to hold an AGM. This form is, however, retained because many companies will continue to find this a convenient course. The notice post 1 October 2007 for a resolution to alter the objects of the company is 14 days.

Minutes of First General Meeting of a Private Company   Form B21

_____ LIMITED

Minutes of the general meeting of the Company held at

_____on _____ at _____am/pm

PRESENT   _____(in the chair)

_____

IN ATTENDANCE _____

1. The Chairman announced that consents to the meeting being held at short notice[1] had been received from all of the members[2] of the Company having a right to attend and vote at the meeting.

2. The Chairman declared that a quorum was present.

3. The meeting resolved by a vote of _____ to _____ that _____should be appointed a director of the Company.[3]

4. The meeting resolved by a vote of _____ to _____ that _____ should be appointed a director of the Company.

5. It was agreed by a majority of _____ per cent that the Company's name should be changed from _____ Ltd. to _____ Ltd.

6. It was agreed that the following amendment should be made to the Company's Articles of Association:[4]

7. The meeting then ended.

_____

Chairman

[1] Under the Companies Act 1985, 14 days' notice is required for meetings of a private company, except for the annual general meeting, which requires 21 days' notice. A resolution that needs to be passed as a special resolution (e.g. a resolution to alter the articles or to change the name of the company), can only be passed if 21 days' notice has been given. Certain other resolutions require special notice of 28 days, but these resolutions, by the nature of their subject matter, would not arise at a first meeting. Normally, a first meeting would be intended to serve as the AGM, and therefore 21 days' notice will be required. The Companies Act 2006 abolishes, in the case of private companies, the requirements for annual general meetings and for 21 days' notice for special resolutions. When it comes into effect, 14 days' notice will be sufficient.

[2] Under the Companies Act 1985, the holders of 95 per cent of the shares conferring the power to vote may consent to short notice, except in the case of the AGM where unanimity is required. From 1 October 2007, that the holders of 90 per cent of the shares conferring the right to vote or such higher percentage as the articles may specify (not being more than 95 per cent) can consent to short notice.

[3] A simple majority will suffice.

[4] A 75 per cent majority is required.

Mutual Termination of Contract   Form OLF27

THIS DEED IS MADE the _____ day of _____ year _____

BETWEEN:

(1) _____ of _____(the 'First Party'); and

(2) _____ of _____ (the 'Second Party').

WHEREAS:

(A) The parties entered into a Contract dated _____ (the 'Contract').

(B) The parties wish mutually to terminate the Contract and all their obligations and rights thereunder.

NOW IT IS HEREBY AGREED as follows:

1.   The parties hereby agree to terminate the Contract.

2.   The parties further agree that the termination shall be without further recourse by either party against

     the other and this document shall constitute mutual releases of any further obligations under the

     Contract, to the same extent as if the Contract had not been entered into in the first instance,

     [provided that the parties shall hereby undertake to perform the act or acts, if any, described below,

     which obligations, shall remain binding, notwithstanding this agreement to terminate.

     _____

     _____]

IN WITNESS OF WHICH the parties have signed this agreement as a Deed the day and year first above

written

_____   _____

Signed as a Deed by or on behalf of the First Party   Signed as a Deed by or on behalf of the Second
                                                           Party

_____   _____

in the presence of (witness)   _____

Name _____   in the presence of (witness)

Address _____   Name _____

_____   Address _____

Occupation _____   _____

                                        Occupation _____

Mutual Releases   Form OLF28

THIS DEED IS MADE the _____ day of _____ year _____

BETWEEN:

(1) _____ of _____ (the 'First Party'); and

(2) _____ of _____ (the 'Second Party').

NOW IT IS HEREBY AGREED as follows:

1. The First Party and the Second Party do hereby completely, mutually and reciprocally release, discharge, acquit and forgive each other from all claims, contracts, actions, demands, agreements, liabilities, and proceedings of every nature and description that either party has or may have against the other, arising from the beginning of time to the date of this agreement, including but not limited to an incident or claim described as:

    _____

    _____

    _____

2. This release shall be binding upon and inure to the benefit of the parties, their successors and assigns.

IN WITNESS OF WHICH the parties have signed this agreement as a Deed the day and year first above written

_____   _____
Signed by or on behalf of the First Party   Signed by or on behalf of the Second Party

_____   _____
in the presence of (witness)   in the presence of (witness)

Name _____   Name _____

Address _____   Address _____

_____   _____

Occupation _____   Occupation _____

National Lottery Syndicate Agreement   Form OLF29

SYNDICATE NAME: _____

MANAGER	DATE OF APPOINTMENT	SIGNATURE

MEMBER	INDIVIDUAL STAKE (to be paid IN ADVANCE of of each Draw by the agreed deadline)	DATE JOINED SYNDICATE	MANAGER'S SIGNATURE	MEMBER'S SIGNATURE	DATE LEFT SYNDICATE	MANAGER'S SIGNATURE

The Syndicate will participate in Draws on: Wednesdays only*   (*delete as appropriate)

Saturdays only*

Wednesdays and Saturdays*

Agreed deadline for payment of Individual Stakes: Day (each week): _____

Time: _____

(Syndicate Rules on next page)

National Lottery Syndicate Rules

1. Definitions

   'Draw' means a draw of the Camelot National Lottery in which the Syndicate has agreed to participate;

   'Individual Stake' means the stake payable by each Member as set out in this Agreement and received by the Manager in advance of each Draw by the agreed deadline;

   'Manager' means the Manager of the Syndicate, who shall be appointed and may be replaced at any time without notice by a majority of the Members;

   'Members' means all those persons who have joined and not left the Syndicate;

   'Syndicate Stake' means the total of the Members' Individual Stakes in respect of any Draw.

2. Manager's Responsibilities

   2.1 The Manager will:

       (a) establish a procedure for agreeing the combinations of numbers to be entered by the Syndicate for each Draw;

       (b) buy tickets bearing the agreed numbers for the amount of the Syndicate Stake for each Draw. However, if the Syndicate Stake is not sufficient to buy tickets bearing all agreed combinations of numbers in any Draw, the Manager shall have absolute discretion as to which of the agreed combinations to enter;

       (c) keep a current record of each Member's payment, of each payment which he has made on behalf of any Member, of each reimbursement which such Member may have paid and of each ticket purchased;

       (d) collect any prize money and account to the Members for it in proportion to their Individual Stakes, holding it in trust for the Members in the meantime.

   2.2 If any Member fails to pay his Individual Stake to the Manager in advance of any Draw by the agreed deadline, the Manager may (but shall not be obliged to) pay that Individual Stake on the Member's behalf and, if the Manager does so, the Member will reimburse the Manager forthwith upon demand.

   2.3 The Manager shall not be liable to any Member for any loss or damage arising out of any failing of the Manager under this Agreement, provided that the Manager has acted honestly.

3. Members' Responsibilities

   The Members will each pay their Individual Stake to the Manager in advance of each Draw by the agreed deadline.

4. Ceasing to be a Member

   A Member shall be removed from the Group:

   4.1 if the Member wishes to leave; or

   4.2 at the discretion of the Manager, if the Member fails to pay his Individual Stake in accordance with Rule 3 in respect of any 3 weeks (whether consecutive or non-consecutive); or

   4.3 at the discretion of the Manager, if the Member fails to reimburse the Manager in accordance with Rule 2.2.

5. This Agreement

   5.1 It shall be the responsibility of the Manager to update and amend this Agreement in accordance with any amendment which may be passed by a simple majority of the Members. [Rule 4 may be amended only by the vote of 75 per cent of the members.]

   5.2 The list of Members in this Agreement shall be conclusive as to the membership of the Syndicate at any point in time, provided that a person whose application for membership has been accepted by the Manager and who has duly paid an agreed Individual Stake shall not be excluded from a share of prize money under Rule 2.1(c) merely because the Agreement has not been updated to record that person as a Member.

   5.3 If any person is removed from the list of Members, the Manager shall forthwith notify the member of that fact, but the Manager shall incur no liability to such Member for any loss incurred by reason of any such failure to inform the Member of such removal.

   5.3 The appointment or replacement of the Manager shall take effect whether or not this Agreement has been amended to that effect.

   5.4 This Agreement is subject to English law and the parties submit to the exclusive jurisdiction of the English courts in connection with any dispute hereunder.

Nominee Shareholder's Declaration of Trust   Form B19

I, _____, of _____,

hereby acknowledge and declare that I hold _____ fully paid ordinary shares in _____

_____ Ltd ('the Share') registered in my name as nominee of and Trustee for

_____ ('the Owner') and I undertake and agree not to transfer, deal with or dispose

of the Share save as the Owner may from time to time direct and further to give full effect to the trust

hereby declared I hereby deposit with the Owner the Certificate for the Share together with a transfer

thereof executed by me in blank and I hereby expressly authorise and empower the Owner at any time to

complete such transfer by inserting therein the name or names of any transferee or transferees and the date

of the transfer and to complete the same in any other necessary particular and I expressly declare that this

authority is irrevocable by me. Furthermore I irrevocably assign to the Owner the right to receive any

dividends which may be declared on the Share together with all profits and other monies which may be

paid or payable to me from time to time upon the Share or in respect thereof, and I further agree and

undertake to exercise my voting power as Holder of the Share in such manner and for such purpose as the

Owner may from time to time direct or determine.

Dated this _____ day of _____ year _____.

_____

Signature

_____

Signature of Witness

Address _____

_____

_____

_____

Occupation

Note. The Nominee's power to make a disposition of the shares on behalf of the registered owner will cease if the owner becomes mentally incapable. For this reason, an Enduring Power of Attorney (or a Lasting Power of Attorney after the Mental Capacity Act 2005 comes into force) should also be executed.

Notice for Regulated Hire Purchase or Credit Sale Agreements

Form BS32

NOTE: This form is prescribed by the Consumer Credit (Cancellation Notices and Copies of Documents) Regulations 1983 (S.I. 1983 No. 1557) as amended.

YOUR RIGHT TO CANCEL. You have a right to cancel this agreement. You can do this by sending or taking a WRITTEN notice of cancellation to _____ .

You have FIVE days starting with the day after you receive this copy in which to cancel the agreement. You can use the form provided. If you cancel this agreement, any money you have paid, goods given in part-exchange (or their value) and property given as security must be returned to you. You will not have to make any further payment. If you already have goods under the agreement, you should keep them safe (legal action may be taken against you if you do not take proper care of them). You can wait for them to be collected from you and you need not hand them over unless you receive a written request. If you wish, however, you may return the goods yourself.

NOTE: Complete and return this form only if you wish to cancel the agreement

Date _____

To _____

_____

_____

(Name and address of seller)

I/We hereby give notice that I/we wish to cancel agreement number _____ .

_____

Signature

_____

Signature

Note: We repeat our suggestion that if you enter into contracts which are regulated by the Consumer Credit Act 1974 in the course of your business, you should ask your solicitor to review your documents and contractual procedures.

Notice of Acceptance of Goods   Form BS33

Date   _____

Ref   _____

To   _____

_____

_____

Dear   _____

Re: Acceptance of Order

Please note that we have received the following goods, with thanks, as per our

order no. _____ dated _____:

_____

_____

_____

The goods are further identified by invoice no. _____ and consignment note/

packing slip no. _____

Please be advised that we have inspected the goods and they have been received in good condition, and in

conformity with our order.

Yours sincerely

_____

Notice of Annual General Meeting Form B20

_____ LIMITED

Company Number _____

NOTICE IS HEREBY GIVEN that the ANNUAL GENERAL MEETING of the

above-named Company will be held at _____

on _____ at _____ am/pm for the following purposes.

1. To consider and adopt the company's accounts and reports of the directors and auditors for the period

   _____

   to _____ .

2. To declare a dividend.

3. To re-appoint _____

   as auditors of the Company until the next general meeting at which accounts are laid before the

   company, at a fee to be agreed with the board of directors.

4. To elect directors in place of those retiring (see the directors report)[1].

5. To confirm appointments to the board.

Dated

_____

By order of the board

_____

Secretary

Registered office: _____

_____

A member entitled to attend and vote at the meeting convened by this Notice is entitled to appoint a proxy

to attend and vote on a poll[2] in his/her place. A proxy need not be a member of the Company.

[1] 21 days' notice is required - ie 21 days from the date when the member would receive the notice by ordinary post and the date of the meeting. Where a resolution requiring special notice is to be passed, 28 days' notice is required.

After Part 13 Chapter 3 of the Companies Act 2006 comes into force on 1 October 2007, there will no longer be any requirement on a private company to hold an annual general meeting. From that date, the notice requirement for meetings will be 14 days, unless a resolution requiring special notice is to be passed in which case it will still be 28 days. The Companies Act 2006 will provide, from 1 October 2007, that the holders of 90 per cent or such higher percentage as the articles may specify (not being more than 95 per cent) can consent to short notice.

[2] Unless the Articles provide otherwise, a proxy may only vote on a poll. At meetings of a private limited company, a proxy has the same right as a member to speak on a matter. He also has the right to demand a poll or to join in a demand that there be a poll. Once section 285 of the Companies Act 2006 comes into force on 1 October 2007, a proxy will be entitled to vote on a show of hands as well as on a poll. Once sections 324 and 325 of that Act come into force on 1 October 2007, the passage in square brackets above should be replaced by the following, 'A member entitled to attend and vote at the meeting convened by this Notice is entitled to appoint a person as his proxy to exercise all or any of his rights to attend and speak as proxy, or more the meeting. A member so entitled can appoint more than one proxy provided that each proxy is appointed to exercise the rights attached to a different share or shares held by him or (as the case may be) to a different £10, or multiple of £10, of stock held by him.

Notice of Assignment   Form TA09

Date   _____

To   _____

          _____

          _____

Dear   _____

I attach a copy of an assignment dated _____ by which I assigned my interest in the contract referred to therein to   _____of _____ (the 'Assignee') Please hold all sums of money affected by such assignment, now or hereafter in your possession, that otherwise are payable to me under the terms of our original agreement, for the benefit of the Assignee, in accordance with the provisions of the assignment.

Yours sincerely

_____

Notice of Cancellation of Purchase Order and Demand for Refund

Form BS34

Date _____

To _____

_____

_____

Dear _____

Re: Cancellation of Purchase Order

On _____, as per our order no. _____, a copy of which is enclosed, we ordered the following goods from you:

_____

_____

_____

We paid for these goods by our cheque no. _____, dated _____ in the amount of £ _____.

On _____, we demanded immediate delivery of the goods. To date, the goods have not been delivered to us.

By this notice we therefore cancel this order, because of late delivery, and demand immediate reimbursement. Unless we receive a refund within 10 days of the date of this letter, we will take immediate legal action. Please be advised that we reserve all our legal rights.

Yours sincerely

_____

Note: If you have paid for the goods and have not received them in the time specified by the contract, you can use this form without difficulty. If you have not paid for the goods, however, be very careful before cancelling your order. You do not have the right to cancel an order because of lateness unless: (1) time is expressed in the contract to be 'of the essence' and the deadline has expired; or (2) the time for delivery has passed, you have given reasonable notice that if the goods are not delivered by a specific date the order will be cancelled, and the new date has passed. If you cancel when you do not have a right to do so, the seller could treat you as being in breach. Therefore, do not cancel unless situation (1) or situation (2) applies. Do not send this notice without first obtaining legal advice.

Even if you have paid for the goods and sent this notice, you should be cautious if the goods are subsequently sent to you. Do not send them back without obtaining legal advice unless the contract says that time for delivery is 'of the essence' or unless a substantial further period has elapsed since you sent this notice of cancellation.

| **Notice of Claim for Indemnity From** | Form OLF30 |
| **Joint-Venturer (Non-Partner)** | |

Date _____

To _____

_____

_____

Dear _____

Re _____

A claim has been made by_____

to the effect that _____.

Under the terms of our joint venture we agreed to share the relevant expenses [equally] [in the proportions

of _____]. We are therefore entitled to ask you to indemnify us accordingly.

Please confirm that you accept liability for this matter (if there is any valid claim) and that you will hold us

indemnified to the extent of _____ per cent against the claim and the costs of defending it.

I should be pleased to hear from you as a matter of urgency.

Yours sincerely

_____

Note: This form is appropriate if your agreement was a cooperation agreement between two or more separate businesses, rather than a partnership where you are sharing or where you were sharing profits and losses generally. See form B10. If you are seeking an indemnity from a former partner what you really need is for an account to be taken in order to work out who is entitled to what in such a case this form is not appropriate and you should consult the firm's solicitor or accountant.

Notice of Conditional Acceptance of Faulty Goods — Form BS35

Date _____

To _____

_____

_____

Dear _____

Re: Order Number _____

On _____, we received a delivery from you as per our order no. _____,
dated _____. The goods delivered at that time were faulty for the following reason(s):

_____

_____

_____

Although these goods are defective and we are not obliged to accept them, we would be prepared to do so
on the condition that you credit our account with you for £ _____.

This credit will make the total amount payable under this order £ _____.

If you do not accept this proposal within 10 days from the date of this letter, we will reject these goods as
faulty and they will be returned to you. In the meantime, they are being kept in their original packing in
anticipation of their return. Please be advised that we reserve all our legal rights.

Thank you for your immediate attention to this matter.

Yours sincerely

_____

Note: There is a risk that if you use this form, you may be treated as having 'accepted' the goods because it contains what is in reality an
attempt to renegotiate the price. Once goods are accepted, they cannot as a rule be rejected. Therefore do not use this form unless you
are prepared to risk having to keep the goods and claim damages for the defects. If you wish not to take the risk, you should reject the
goods outright. See form BS39 or 40.

Notice of Conditional Acceptance of Non-Conforming Goods

Form BS36

Date _____

Ref _____

To _____

_____

_____

Dear _____

Re: Order Number _____

On _____, we received delivery from you as per our order no. _____,

dated _____. The goods delivered at that time do not conform to the specifications

that were provided with our order for the following reasons:

_____

_____

Although these goods are non-conforming and we are not obliged to accept them, we would be prepared

to accept these goods on the condition that you credit our account with you for £ _____. This credit will

make the total amount payable under this order £ _____.

If you do not accept this proposal within 10 days from the date of this letter, we will reject these goods as

non-conforming and they will be returned to you. In the meantime, they are being kept in their original

packing in anticipation of their return. Please be advised that we reserve all our legal rights.

Thank you for your immediate attention to this matter.

Yours sincerely

_____

Note: There is a risk that if you use this form, you may be treated as having 'accepted' the goods because it contains what is in reality an attempt to renegotiate the price. Once goods are accepted, they cannot as a rule be rejected. Therefore, do not use this form unless you are prepared to risk having to keep the goods and claim damages for the defects. If you do not wish to take the risk, you should reject the goods outright. See form BS39 or 40.

Notice of Default in Payment   Form LB09

Date _____

To   _____

        _____

        _____

Dear   _____

You are hereby notified that your payment of _____ pounds

(£_____) due on or before _____, has not been received by us. If payment is

not made by _____, we shall seek the remedies under the agreement between us

dated _____, together with such other remedies as we may have, and this matter

shall be referred to our solicitors.

Yours sincerely

_____

Notice of Demand for Delivery of Goods   Form BS37

Date   _____

Ref   _____

To   _____

       _____

       _____

Dear   _____

Re: Order Number _____

On _____, as per our order no. _____, a copy of which is enclosed, we ordered the following goods from you:

_____

_____

_____

We paid for these goods by cheque no. _____, dated _____in the amount of £ _____.

To date, the goods have not been delivered to us. We therefore demand the immediate delivery of these goods. Unless the goods are delivered to us within 10 days of the date of this letter, we will cancel this purchase order and demand return of our money. Please be advised that we reserve all our legal rights.

Thank you for your immediate attention to this matter.

Yours sincerely

_____

Note. Specify a longer period than 10 days if you consider it reasonable to do so in the light of your own requirements and the difficulties which the seller may be experiencing. The more reasonable you are, the more likely it is that you will be held to be entitled to cancel your order after the expiry of the period which you specify. If your contract says that time for delivery is 'of the essence', however, you can specify any period that you like, if the date specified for delivery in the order has already passed.

Notice of Dismissal Letter (Capability)   Form E46

Date   _____

To   _____

   _____

   _____

Dear   _____

I refer to our meeting on   _____.

As I explained at the meeting, you have been unable to carry out your duties to the standards required by the Company. Therefore, we have no alternative but to terminate your employment with the Company with effect from _____.

As you are aware, we have provided you with training and assistance to enable you to improve your performance but without success. In addition, we have attempted to find suitable alternative employment within the Company but regret that nothing is available.

You are entitled to be paid in full, including any accrued holiday pay, during your notice period.

I take this opportunity of reminding you that you are entitled to appeal against this decision through the Company's dismissal and disciplinary procedure. If you wish to exercise this right you must let me know within two working days of receipt of this letter.

It is with regret that we have had to take this action. We should like to thank you for your past efforts for the Company and wish you every success for the future.

Yours sincerely

_____

Personnel Manager

Note: Before any decision to dismiss is made the statutory dismissal and disciplinary procedure and any contractual procedures may be followed to avoid legal repercussions.

Notice of Dismissal Letter (Sickness)   Form E47

Date   _____

To   _____

_____

_____

Dear   _____

I refer to our meeting at your home on   _____.

I was very sorry to hear that your condition has not improved and that it is unlikely that you will be able to resume working.

As we discussed, there is little we can do to assist your return to work and our medical adviser has reported that you are not likely to be well enough to return to to your current job for some time, if at all. We have tried to find some alternative suitable work for you but, as you know, all of the work in this Company is fairly heavy work and there is nothing we can offer you.

I regret that I have no alternative other than to give you notice to terminate your employment with the Company with effect from   _____.

You are entitled to full pay for the period of your notice plus accrued holiday pay. I shall arrange for these sums to be paid to you, and for your P45 to be sent to you as soon as possible.

If your health does improve in the future and you are able to resume working, I would be pleased to discuss re-employing you.

Yours sincerely

_____

Personnel Manager

Note: Before any decision to dismiss is made the statutory dismissal and disciplinary procedure and any contractual procedures may be followed to avoid legal repercussions.

This letter is an example of dismissal due to a terminal illness. Such a letter would have to be reworded if the employee was likely to be able to resume work at some future date.

Notice of Disputed Account   Form CDC27

Date _____

Ref _____

To _____

_____

_____

Dear _____

We refer to your invoice/order/statement no. _____, dated _____, in the amount of £_____.

We dispute the balance you claim to be owed for the following reason(s):

☐   Items invoiced for have not been received.

☐   Prices are in excess of the agreed amount. A credit of £ _____ is claimed.

☐   Our payment of £ _____ made on _____, has not been credited.

☐   Goods delivered to us were not ordered and are available for return on delivery instructions.

☐   Goods were defective as per prior letter.

☐   Goods are available for return and credit as per your sales terms.

☐   Other: _____

Please credit our account promptly in the amount of £_____ so it may be satisfactorily cleared.

Yours sincerely

_____

Notice of Extraordinary General Meeting   Form B23

_____ LIMITED

Company Registered Number _____

NOTICE is hereby given that an extraordinary general meeting of the above-named Company will be held at _____ on _____ the _____day of _____ year _____ at _____ o'clock for the purpose of considering and, if thought fit, passing the following ordinary/special/elective/extraordinary resolutions:

_____

_____

_____

_____

_____

[A member entitled to attend and vote at the meeting convened by this Notice is entitled to appoint a proxy to attend and vote on a poll[1] in his/her place. A proxy need not be a member of the Company.]

Dated this _____ day of _____ year _____.

BY ORDER OF THE BOARD

_____

Company Secretary

Registered office:

_____

_____

_____

_____

Note: Any member entitled to attend and vote at the meeting is entitled to appoint a proxy to attend and vote in his place. A proxy need not be a member of the company. Unless the articles provide otherwise, proxies may vote only on a poll. However, proxies may demand a poll or join in a demand for a poll.

The notice of the meeting must generally be given in line with the requirements contained in the articles. Under statute the minimum period of notice is 14 days for an extraordinary general meeting where no special resolution is to be considered, and 21 days where there is a special resolution. Special notice of 28 days is required for meetings considering resolutions under which the auditors or the directors are to be changed before the end of their terms of office. From 1 October 2007, that the holders of 90 per cent of the shares conferring the right to vote or such higher percentage as the articles may specify (not being more than 95 per cent) can consent to short notice. Where special notice is required, there is no power to consent to short notice. Unless the articles provide otherwise, a proxy may only vote on a poll. At meetings of a private limited company, a proxy has the same right as a member to speak on a matter. He also has the right to demand a poll or to join in a demand that there be a poll. Once section 285 of the Companies Act 2006 comes into force, a proxy will be entitled to vote on a show of hands as well as on a poll.

Once sections 324 and 325 of that Act come into force on 1 October 2007, the passage in square brackets above should be replaced by the following, 'A member entitled to attend and vote at the meeting convened by this Notice is entitled to appoint a person as his proxy to exercise all or any of his rights to attend and speak as proxy. A member so entitled can appoint more than one proxy provided that each proxy is appointed to exercise the rights attached to a different share or shares held by him or (as the case may be) to a different £10, or multiple of £10, of stock held by him.

Notice of Extraordinary General Meeting to Change Objects of Company

Form B24

_____ LIMITED

Company Registered Number _____

NOTICE is hereby given that an extraordinary general meeting of the above named Company will be held at

_____ on _____ the _____day

of _____ year _____ at _____ o'clock for the purpose of considering and, if thought

fit, passing the following special resolution:

'That the memorandum of association of the Company be altered by deleting subclause (__) of clause ___

and substituting therefor the following subclause:

(__) _____To carry on business as a general commercial company.'

[A member entitled to attend and vote at the meeting convened by this Notice is entitled to appoint a

proxy to attend and vote on a poll[1] in his/her place. A proxy need not be a member of the Company.]

Dated this _____ day of _____ year _____.

BY ORDER OF THE BOARD

_____

Company Secretary

Registered office:

_____

_____

_____

Note: Any member entitled to attend and vote at the meeting is entitled to appoint a proxy to attend and vote in his place. A proxy need not be a member of the company.

[1] Where a change in the objects clause is desired, it is necessary to give the period of notice which the Articles require in the case of meetings which are to consider special resolutions. The minimum period which the Articles can authorise under the Companies Act 1985 is 21 days. This requirement can be waived with the unanimous consent of the shareholders, or with a slightly lesser majority in some cases. Take advice if unanimity is not available. Unless the Articles provide otherwise, a proxy may only vote on a poll. At meetings of a private limited company, a proxy has the same right as a member to speak on a matter. He also has the right to demand a poll or to join in a demand that there be a poll. Once section 285 of the Companies Act 2006 comes into force on 1 October 2007, a proxy will be entitled to vote on a show of hands as well as on a poll.

After 1 October 2007 the period of notice is 14 days for all resolutions except those where special notice is required (which does not include resolutions to change the company's objects). From 1 October 2007, that the holders of 90 per cent of the shares conferring the right to vote or such higher percentage as the articles may specify (not being more than 95 per cent) can consent to short notice.

Once sections 324 and 325 of that Act come into force on 1 October 2007, the passage in square brackets above should be replaced by the following, 'A member entitled to attend and vote at the meeting convened by this Notice is entitled to appoint a person as his proxy to exercise all or any of his rights to attend and speak as proxy. A member so entitled can appoint more than one proxy provided that each proxy is appointed to exercise the rights attached to a different share or shares held by him or (as the case may be) to a different £10, or multiple of £10, of stock held by him.

Notice of Goods Sold on Approval — Form BS38

Date _____

Ref _____

To _____

_____

_____

Dear _____

Re: Goods Sold on Approval

Please be advised that the following goods are being delivered to you on approval:

_____

_____

_____

If these goods do not meet your requirements, you may return all or a part of them at our expense within _____ days of your receipt of them.

Any goods sold on approval that are not returned to us by that time will be considered accepted by you and you will be invoiced for them accordingly.

We trust that you will find our goods satisfactory and thank you for your custom.

Yours sincerely

_____

Note. This form should only be used where the customer has actually agreed to take goods on approval. It must on no account be used where the goods are being sent unsolicited. There is a separate form for that. See BS22.

Notice of Intention to Recover Payment in Default   Form CDC28

Date _____

To _____

_____

_____

Dear _____

Re: Agreement Reference: _____

We refer to the default notice which we issued on _____ in connection with the above agreement. We note that you have failed to make payment of the arrears by _____, as requested in the default notice.

In the circumstances, this letter is our formal demand for payment of the outstanding balance, as detailed below:

Outstanding Balance: £ _____
Less Rebate Allowable *:   £ _____
Amount to be paid: £ _____

* This rebate has been calculated on the assumption that payment of the amount demanded reaches us by _____. If it does not, we shall bring proceedings against you for the outstanding balance claimed and, if this results in our obtaining payment before the sum would have become due under the agreement, we shall allow any appropriate rebate or change once we have received the payment in full.

Your sincerely

_____

Signature of Authorised Signatory on
behalf of the Finance Company

Note: This form must not be used to recover monies owing under any agreement which is regulated by the Consumer Credit Act 1974.

Notice of Particulars of Ownership

As required by the Business Names Act 1985[1]

Insert name of business

Proprietor

Insert full name of business proprietor [2]

Address within Great Britain at which documents relating to the
business may be effectively served on the proprietor

Insert full address

Note: This document should be displayed prominently at your principal place of business. Your obligations to disclose your name and address in business correspondence do not end here. You must also disclose the above information on all business letters, written orders for goods or services to be supplied to the business, invoices and receipts issued in the course of the business and written demands for payment of debts arising in the course of the business.

[1] When Part 41 of the Companies Act 2006 comes into force these words should be replaced by Companies Act 2006.

[2] You should insert here the individual, partners, company or limited partnership which owns or own the business.

Notice of Rejection of Non-conforming Goods   Form BS39

Date _____

Ref _____

To _____

_____

_____

Dear _____

Re: Rejection of Non-Conforming Goods

On _____, we received delivery from you as per our order no. _____,
dated _____. The goods delivered at that time do not conform to the specifications
that were provided with our order for the following reasons:

_____

_____

_____

We paid for these goods by our cheque no. _____, dated _____, in the amount of
£ _____. This cheque has been cashed by you.

By this notice, we reject the delivery of these goods and request reimbursement. Unless we receive a refund
of our money within 10 days of the date of this letter, we will take immediate legal action for its recovery.
Please further advise us as to your wishes for the return of the rejected goods at your expense. Unless we
receive instructions within 10 days of this letter, we accept no responsibility for their safe storage. Please be
advised that we reserve all our legal rights.

Thank you for your immediate attention to this matter.

Yours sincerely

_____

Note. If you reject the goods, you must still take some care of them before they are returned, because you can be held liable for gross
negligence. If substantial time elapses and the goods have not been taken back, you should obtain legal advice.

Notice of Rejection of Goods   Form BS40

Date _____

Ref _____

To _____

_____

_____

Dear _____

Re: Order no. _____

On _____, we received delivery from you as per our order no. _____,
dated _____. We reject these goods for the following reasons:

_____

_____

We paid for these goods by our cheque no. _____, dated _____, in the amount of
£_____.

By this notice, we reject the delivery of these goods and request reimbursement. Unless we receive a refund
of our money within 10 days of the date of this letter, we will take immediate legal action for its recovery.
Please further advise us as to your wishes for the return of the rejected goods at your expense. Unless we
receive instructions for their return within 10 days of this letter, we accept no responsibility for their safe
storage. Please be advised that we reserve all our legal rights.

Thank you for your immediate attention to this matter.

Yours sincerely

_____

Note: You should exercise the right of rejection with caution. In non-consumer sales, the buyer may not reject the goods if the breach is
so minor that it would be unreasonable for him to reject.

Be careful in stating the reason for rejecting the goods. Although you will be able later to justify a rejection for reasons other than
those which you have previously stated, as long as the reasons existed at the time of rejection, the seller may succeed if he shows that
the goods could have been remedied if you had brought the reasons to his attention at the time.

If you reject the goods, you must still take some care of them before they are returned, because you can be held liable for gross
negligence. If substantial time elapses and the goods have not been taken back, you should obtain legal advice.

Notice of Replacement of Rejected Goods   Form BS41

Date _____

Ref _____

To _____

_____

_____

Dear _____

Re: Order no. _____

On _____, we delivered the following goods to you as per your

order no._____ , dated_____:

_____

_____

_____

On _____, we received notice that you had rejected delivery of these goods.

Please return the rejected goods to us at our expense using the same carrier that delivered the goods.

[In addition, please be advised that we are shipping replacement goods to you at our expense. If replacement of the rejected goods is not satisfactory, please contact us immediately. We apologise for any inconvenience this may have caused you] / [what we propose to do with your consent is to ship replacement goods to you at our expense by _____. If this is acceptable to you, please let us know immediately. Whatever you decide, we apologise for any inconvenience which this may have caused you].[1]

Yours sincerely

_____

---

[1] If there was no specified date for delivery or if you are unable to deliver replacement goods by the specified date, you should delete the wording in the first set of square brackets.

Notice of Result of Grievance Investigation   Form E48

Date   _____

Ref   _____

To   _____

         _____

         _____

Dear   _____

I am writing to let you know that your grievance relating to _____

_____has been fully investigated in accordance with the company's

grievance procedures.

Having considered your complaint and having heard all that has been said by you, and on your behalf, and

having taken full account of all that has been said by your trade union representative, it has been decided

_____

_____

_____

You have a right of appeal against this decision and if you wish to exercise this right, please notify me in

writing within [_____] working days.

Yours sincerely

_____

Notice of Return of Goods Sold on Approval   Form BS42

Date   _____

Ref   _____

To   _____

_____

_____

Dear   _____

Re: Order no.   _____

On _____, as per our order no. _____, a copy of which is enclosed, we received the following goods from you on approval:

_____

_____

_____

_____

_____

Please be advised that we have decided to return these goods to you.

Thank you very much for the opportunity to examine the goods.

Yours sincerely

_____

Notice of Trade Term Violations   Form BS43

Date _____

Ref _____

To _____

_____

_____

Dear _____

We routinely review all our accounts. We have found a record of irregular payments on your account, which frequently leaves balances unpaid beyond our credit terms.

Whilst we value your continued custom, we would also appreciate payment within our agreed credit terms. We look forward to your future co-operation in this matter.

Yours sincerely

_____

Notice of Withheld Delivery   Form BS44

Date _____

Ref _____

To _____

_____

_____

Dear _____

Thank you for your order dated _____. It is now ready for delivery.

However, we find that the following invoices remain unpaid beyond our agreed credit terms:

Invoice no.	Amount	Due date
_____	£ _____	_____
_____	£ _____	_____
_____	£ _____	_____
_____	£ _____	_____

Please send us your cheque promptly in the amount of £ _____ to clear these invoices.

We shall then deliver your order immediately.

Yours sincerely

_____

Note. Only use this Form if: (a) you have not already promised the goods, or (b) if you have promised the goods, you have done so with reference to conditions which entitle you to refuse delivery if the account is in arrears.

Notice of Wrongful Refusal to Accept Delivery | Form BS45

Date _____

Ref _____

To _____

_____

_____

Dear _____

We refer to your order dated _____, a copy of which is enclosed.

We delivered the goods in accordance with the agreed terms but you have refused to accept them. We now consider the purchase contract to have been wrongfully breached by you.

[Accordingly, we shall not attempt further delivery and shall hold you liable for all damages arising from your failure to fulfil your obligations under the order.]

[Accordingly, we shall hold the goods for you to arrange collection and we shall claim the price and cost of storage if payment of the contract price is not received in accordance with your obligations under the agreement.]

Should you wish to rectify the situation by now accepting shipment you must call us immediately and we shall arrange re-shipment at your expense.

Please contact us immediately should you have any questions on this matter.

Yours sincerely

_____

Note. If property in the goods has passed to the buyer who has wrongly rejected them, you will be entitled to claim the price of the goods instead of damages. Damages are likely to consist of compensation for wasted expenditure in a sale that has gone off, and of loss of profits that you would have made on the sale. There may be more argument about this than there would be about a simple claim for the price. By sending this letter, you might lose the right to claim for the price. You may therefore think it worthwhile to ask your solicitor whether: (a) you can succeed in a claim for the price; and (b) a claim for the price is better from your point of view than a claim for damages.

Notice Requiring Possession: Assured Shorthold Tenancy Form RT21

ENGLAND & WALES
HOUSING ACT 1988
SECTION 21
Assured Shorthold Tenancy: Notice Requiring Possession

TO
_____

of _____

FROM _____

of _____

I/We* give you notice that, by virtue of Section 21 of the Housing Act 1988, I/we* require possession of the dwelling house known as

_____

after _____

or, if the alternative date mentioned below is different, after the alternative date. The alternative date is the first date after this notice was given to you which is:

- at least two months after service upon you of this notice, and

- (if your tenancy is for a fixed term which has not ended when this notice is given to you) which is a date not earlier than the end of the fixed term, or

- (if your tenancy is a periodic tenancy when this notice is given to you) which is the last day of a period of your tenancy and not earlier than the earliest date on which your tenancy could (apart from the landlord's inability, under s.5(1) of the Housing Act 1988, to terminate an assured tenancy by notice to quit) lawfully be ended by a notice to quit given to you on the same date as this notice.

DATED _____

SIGNED _____
Landlord/Landlord's agent*

_____

_____

Tenant's acknowledgment of service

I/We acknowledge the service of the notice of which the above is a true copy.

Signed_____ (Tenant(s))   Date_____

Note: This notice may be validly served even if this box has not been signed by the tenant. Make a note as to when, how and by whom it was served, so that you can refer to it later if necessary.

Notice to Cancel Delayed Goods   Form BS46

Date   _____

Ref   _____

To   _____

_____

_____

Dear   _____

We refer to our purchase order or contract dated _____,
a copy of which is enclosed.

Under the terms of the order, the goods were to be delivered by _____.
Due to your failure to deliver the goods within the required time, we hereby cancel this order, reserving such
further rights as we may have.

If the above goods are in transit, they shall be refused or returned at your expense.

Yours sincerely

_____

Note: This form should be used with caution. A delay in the delivery of goods does not justify a cancellation of the order unless it was
agreed in the contract that time should be 'of the essence' or unless after the time for delivery has expired, a further and reasonable
period has been given for performance which is expressed to be 'of the essence' and which has elapsed or unless it was apparent from
the facts as known to both parties, that delay would deprive the buyer of much of the benefit of the contract. Speak to a solicitor if you
are in doubt.

Notice to Dissolve a Two-Party Partnership   Form B25

Date _____

Ref _____

To _____

_____

_____

Dear _____

I hereby give you notice to dissolve the partnership between us on _____.

I request that final accounts of the partnership be drawn up to enable its assets to be distributed in accordance with the partnership agreement.

Yours sincerely

_____

Note: If the partnership provides for a period of notice to be given for dissolution, the period should be given unless an event has occurred which entitles the partner giving notice to give notice which is effective immediately. This would be when the party to whom the notice is addressed has acted in such a way that the breach of his duties is so serious as to make it necessary to terminate the partnership immediately. If no period of notice is provided for, the termination may be effective at once.

Notice to Employee Being Laid Off and Giving Guarantee Payments

Form E49

Date _____

To _____

_____

_____

Dear _____

I refer to our meeting on _____.

As I explained at that meeting, we regret that because of economic pressure we have no option but to lay you off from work.

The period of lay off shall take effect from _____and shall continue until _____. You shall receive guarantee payments of [_____] per day for the first five days of this period.

I very much regret that we have been forced to take this action, but I should like to assure you that we are working hard to ensure that the period of lay off is kept to a minimum.

Yours sincerely

_____

Personnel Managers

The current daily rate is £19.60 but this can be verified by contacting the Department of Work and Pensions or ACAS.

Notice to Employer of Intention to Take Maternity Leave   Form E50

Date _____

To _____

_____

_____

Dear _____

This is to inform you that I am pregnant and wish to take Maternity Leave. I enclose a medical/ maternity certificate dated _____ from Dr _____.

The expected week of childbirth is _____ and I intend to start taking my Maternity Leave on _____.

Please also let me know if I am entitled to receive Statutory Maternity Pay during my Maternity Leave.

Your sincerely

_____

Note: Notification must be given by the beginning of the 14th week before the expected week of childbirth or, if that is not possible, as soon as is reasonably practicable thereafter.

Notice to Stop Goods In Transit   Form BS47

Date _____

Ref _____

To _____ (Carrier)

_____

_____

Dear _____

You currently have goods of ours in transit under consignment note no. _____

for delivery to:

_____

_____

_____

This is to confirm our previous instruction by telephone to stop delivery of these goods and return them to us; we shall pay return freight charges.

[No negotiable bill of lading or document of title has been delivered to our customer (the consignee).]

A copy of our delivery documents for these goods is enclosed for your reference.

Yours sincerely

_____

Copy to [Customer]: _____

Note: The right to stop goods in transit arises if the seller has not been paid and the buyer has become insolvent. If the goods are stopped and it turns out that the buyer is solvent after all, then the buyer can sue the seller for damages. If a bill of lading or other document of title has been delivered to the buyer, that does not itself defeat the seller's right to stop the goods. However, if the buyer, having received a document of title, then sells the goods on, the seller's rights will be ineffective against the onward purchaser. If the right to stop is exercised, the carrier has a lien against the seller over the goods for the cost of carriage.

Notice to Terminate given by owner – House/Flat Share Licence Agreement – Resident Owner

Form RT14

TO

_____

_____

_____

(name(s) of Sharer)

THE OWNER

_____

_____

_____

(name(s) and address of Owner)

REQUIRES POSSESSION

OF THE PROPERTY

KNOWN AS

_____

_____

_____

(address of the Property)

ON THE

_____

(date for Possession)[1]

SIGNED BY

_____

(the Owner or his/her agent)

(if signed by the agent then the Agent's name and address must also be written here)

_____

_____

DATE OF NOTICE

_____

IMPORTANT NOTICE TO OWNERS/SHARERS:

1. This Notice is not suitable for a Protected or Statutory Tenancy under the Rent Act 1977 or for an Assured Tenancy, or for an Assured Shorthold Tenancy. Do not use this form without taking legal advice if the licensee is in occupation because of his employment.

2. A Licensee or Sharer who does not know if he has any right to remain in possession after the Notice to Terminate runs out can obtain advice from a solicitor. Help with all or part of the cost of legal advice and assistance may be available under the Legal Aid Scheme. The Licensee or Sharer should also be able to obtain information from a Citizens Advice Bureau, a Housing Aid Centre or a Rent Officer.

[1] The date specified should not be a date which is earlier than any expiry date previously agreed. If no such date has been agreed, a reasonable amount of time should be specified given to enable the licensee/sharer to expire one week or one month (as the case may be) after the next rent day.

Notice to Terminate given by sharer – House/Flat Share Licence Agreement – Resident Owner

Form RT14

TO

_____

_____

_____

(name(s) and address of Owner)

I/WE

_____

_____

_____

(name(s) of Sharer)

GIVE YOU NOTICE
THAT OUR
AGREEMENT IN
RESPECT OF

_____

_____

_____

(address of the Property)

IS HEREBY
TERMINATED
WITH EFFECT
FROM THE

_____

(date for Possession)

SIGNED BY

_____

(the Sharer)

DATE OF NOTICE

_____

IMPORTANT NOTICE TO OWNERS/SHARERS:

1. This Notice is not suitable for an Assured Shorthold Tenancy.

2. A Sharer who does not know if he has any right to remain in possession after the Notice to Terminate runs out can obtain advice from a solicitor. Help with all or part of the cost of legal advice and assistance may be available under the Legal Aid Scheme. The Sharer should also be able to obtain information from a Citizens Advice Bureau, a Housing Aid Centre or Rent Officer.

Notification of Business Transfer   Form E53

Date _____

Ref _____

To Trade Union Representative/Employee Representative

_____

_____

Dear _____

I am writing to you in accordance with Regulation 10 of the Transfer of Undertakings (Protection of Employment) Regulations 1981 ('the Regulations') to inform you of a proposal to transfer the business of _____.

It is proposed that the transfer of the Company will take place on or about _____. The reason for the transfer is that:

_____

_____

_____.

The proposed transfer will affect the following employees:

_____

_____

_____

By law, the affected employees will, by virtue of the operation of the Regulations, transfer on their existing terms and conditions of employment and with continuity of employment for statutory and contractual purposes. *[State whether there will be any social or economic implications of the transfer – economic would include loss of pension rights.]*

It [is]/[is not] envisaged that the Company or [_____][1] will be taking [any] measures in connection with the transfer in relation to those employees who will be affected by the transfer.[2]

Yours sincerely

[1] Name of transferee.

[2] If measures are envisaged state these – if this is the case there is a duty to consult.

Offer of Employment to Avoid Redundancy   Form E54

Date   _____

Ref   _____

To   _____

_____

_____

Dear   _____

After consultation with our employees and representatives of _____
_____ Union, we regret that we must close the _____
_____ section of the company. This will mean redundancy for some employees.

However, I am pleased to advise you that _____ can offer you suitable,
alternative employment as a _____. The salary and terms of
employment will approximate to what you are currently receiving from us.

Please confirm to me whether you accept this employment offer by [_____]. [If you do not accept
this offer your employment will terminate and you will not be entitled to a redundancy payment.] If you
have any questions about this offer please do not hesitate to contact me.

Yours sincerely

_____

Offer to Settle by Arbitration

Form OLF31

Date _____

To _____

_____

_____

Dear _____

I refer to our dispute regarding _____.

I am sorry that we seem to be unable to reconcile our differing points of view. I am sure that neither of us wishes to resort to the courts and I therefore suggest that we refer the dispute between us to arbitration. I propose:

1.   The dispute be referred to arbitration.

2.   The arbitrator shall be Mr. _____, who is an expert in these matters. If you cannot agree to him, the arbitrator shall be appointed by the President or Vice-President of the Chartered Institute of Arbitrators.

3.   [The Chartered Institute of Arbitrators Arbitration Rules]/[The IDRS Rules of Controlled Cost Arbitration] shall apply.[1]

4.   The costs of the arbitration shall be left at the discretion of the arbitrator. Any costs payable in advance shall be borne by the parties equally in the first instance, but the arbitrator may alter the incidence of those costs in his award

5.   Only one expert witness shall be allowed for each side.

6.   The arbitration shall take place at _____ and the dispute shall be decided in accordance with English law.

7.   The making of an award by the arbitrator shall be a condition precedent to any right of action by either of us against the other in respect of the matter in dispute.

If you agree to this suggestion, please sign and return the enclosed copy of this letter.

Yours sincerely

_____

Offer to Settle by Arbitration

Form OLF31

---

[1] The rules are available on the IDRS website at http://www.idrs.ltd.uk/business/adhoc_arbitration.asp.

One-Off Agency Agreement

THIS AGREEMENT is made the _____ day of _____ year _____

BETWEEN:

(1) _____ (the 'Consignor'); and

(2) _____ (the 'Agent').

NOW IT IS HEREBY AGREED that the terms of consignment are the following:

1. The Agent acknowledges receipt of goods from the Consignor as described on the attached schedule (the 'Goods'). The Goods shall remain the property of the Consignor until sold.

2. The Agent, at its own cost and expense, agrees to keep and display the goods only in its place of business and to keep the same in good order and condition, and agrees to return the same on demand in good order and condition to the Consignor.

3. The Agent agrees to use its best efforts to sell the Goods on behalf of the Consignor for the Consignor's account on cash terms and at such prices as shall from time to time be designated by the Consignor.

4. The Agent agrees, upon sale of the Goods, to keep the sale proceeds due to the Consignor separate and apart from its own funds, and to deliver such proceeds, less commission, to the Consignor, together with an account, within _____ days of sale.

5. The Agent agrees to accept as full payment for its obligations hereunder a commission equal to _____% of the gross sales price exclusive of any VAT, [but the Agent shall also be entitled to receive, in addition to his commission, the VAT which is chargeable to him thereon].

6. The Agent agrees to permit the Consignor to enter its premises during business hours to examine and inspect the Goods.

7. The Agent agrees to issue such accounts for public filing as may reasonably be required by Consignor for the purpose of enabling the Consignor to comply with his legal obligations.

8. The Agent will indemnify the Consignor for any liability which the Consignor may incur as a result of any breach by the Agent of this agreement or as a result of any misrepresentation or warranty given in respect of the Goods which misrepresentation or warranty has not been authorised by the Consignor.

9. Save that the Agent may disclose the identity of the Consignor as the seller of the goods, the Agent must not give any undertaking on behalf of the Consignor or purport to pledge his credit or represent himself as having any association with the Consignor or as being in partnership with him.

IN WITNESS OF WHICH the parties have signed the agreement the day and year first above written

Continued on next page

One-Off Agency Agreement (continued)   Form OLF05

_____   _____
Signed for and on behalf of the Consignor   Signed for and on behalf of the Agent

_____   _____
in the presence of (witness)   in the presence of (witness)

Name _____   Name _____

Address _____   Address _____

_____   _____
Occupation _____   Occupation _____

Note: This form is appropriate where there is a one-off arrangement under which a dealer receives a consignment of goods from someone else for the purpose of selling those goods on behalf of the Consignor. It is not appropriate where there is a series of such arrangements and where the parties have in mind that repeat business for the Consignor's goods is to be created. If that is what you have in mind, you should take advice on the effect of the Commercial Agents (Council Directive) Regulations 1993 which confers various rights on commercial agents.

Option to Buy Land   Form BS48

This Deed is made the _____ day of _____ year _____

BETWEEN:

(1) _____ of _____(the 'Buyer'); and

(2) _____ of _____(the 'Seller').

WHEREAS:

The Seller now owns the following land and/or property (the 'Property'):

_____

_____

NOW IT IS HEREBY AGREED as follows:

1.   In consideration of the sum of £ _____ , receipt of which is hereby acknowledged by the Seller, the Seller grants to the Buyer an exclusive option to buy the Property for the following price and on the following terms (the 'Option'):

      _____

      _____

      _____

      _____

.   _____

      [on the terms set out in the draft contract stapled hereto]

2.   The amount received by the Seller from the Buyer referred to in paragraph 1. above will be credited against the purchase price of the Property if the Option is exercised by the Buyer. If the Option is not exercised, the Seller will retain this payment.

3.   The option period will be from the date of this Agreement until _____ at which time the Option will expire unless exercised.

4.   During this period, the Buyer has the option and exclusive right to buy the Property on the terms set out herein. The Buyer must notify the Seller in writing of the decision to exercise the Option. A notice may be sent by [first class post to the Seller at _____] / [through a document exchange to the Seller at _____] / [by fax _____] / [by email at _____]. A notice sent by these respective means is deemed to have been received as follows: (a) by first class post at 12 noon on the second working day after posting; (b) through a document exchange at 12 noon on the first day after the date on which it would normally be available for collection by the addressee; (c) by fax: at 12:00 noon on the first working day after despatch; (d) by e-mail: at 12:00 noon on the first working day after despatch.

5.   No modification of this agreement will be effective unless it is in writing and is signed by both the Buyer and Seller. This agreement binds and benefits both the Buyer and Seller and any successors. Time is of the essence of this agreement. This document, including any attachments, is the entire agreement between the Buyer and Seller.

Continued on next page

Option to Buy Land (continued)   Form BS48

IN WITNESS OF WHICH the parties have signed this Deed the day and year first above written

_____   _____

Signed as a Deed by or on behalf of the Buyer   Signed as a Deed by or on behalf of the Seller

_____   _____

in the presence of (witness)   in the presence of (witness)

Name _____   Name _____

Address _____   Address _____

_____   _____

Occupation _____   Occupation _____

Important note:

The option is not valid unless signed by both parties or unless each signs a copy and the copies are then exchanged.

The greatest care must be taken in setting out the terms on which the property is to be bought and sold if the option is exercised. See paragraph one. Remember, there is more to the purchase of a property than merely agreeing the price. In all but the most straightforward cases, a solicitor should be consulted. If you have decided not to consult a solicitor, make certain that at the very least the terms are clear on what the property is, the identity of the parties who will buy and sell, what the price is, when possession is to be given and whether an absolute or qualified covenant to title is to be given. The Buyer must also register a notice of his interest at the Land Registry in order to prevent the seller from selling the land to a third party, to defeat the Buyer's interest.

Option to Purchase Goods   Form BS49

This Deed is made the _____ day of _____ year _____

BETWEEN:

(1) _____ of _____(the 'Buyer'); and

(2) _____ of _____ (the 'Seller').

NOW IT IS HEREBY AGREED as follows:

1.   In consideration for the sum of £ _____, receipt of which is hereby acknowledged by the Seller, the Seller grants to the Buyer an option to buy the following goods (the 'Goods') on the terms set out herein.

_____

_____

_____

_____

_____

_____

_____

2.   The Buyer has the option and right to buy the Property within the option period for the full price of £ _____.

3.   This option period shall be from the date of this agreement until _____ _____, at which time the option will expire unless exercised.

4.   During the option period the Buyer has the option and exclusive right to buy the Property on the terms set out herein. The Buyer must notify the Seller in writing of the decision to exercise the Option. A notice may be sent by [first class post to the Seller at _____] / [through a document exchange to the Seller at _____] / [by fax _____] / [by email at _____]. A notice sent by these respective means is deemed to have been received as follows: (a) by first class post at 12 noon on the second working day after posting; (b) through a document exchange at 12 noon on the first day after the date on which it would normally be available for collection by the addressee; (c) by fax: at 12:00 noon on the first working day after despatch; (d) by e-mail: at 12:00 noon on the first working day after despatch.

5.   This Deed shall be binding upon and inure to the benefit of the parties, their successors and assigns.

Continued on next page

Option to Purchase Goods (continued)   Form BS49

IN WITNESS OF WHICH the parties have signed this Deed the day and year first above written

_____	_____
Signed as a Deed by or on behalf of the Buyer	Signed as a Deed by or on behalf of the Seller
_____	_____
in the presence of (witness)	in the presence of (witness)

Name _____   Name _____

Address _____   Address _____

_____   _____

Occupation _____   Occupation _____

Note: Great care must be given in drafting the terms on which the goods will be sold if the option is exercised (see clause 1). You must consider all of the matters which you would consider in a contract for the sale of goods, because if the option is exercised that is what you will have.

Order to Stop a Cheque   Form OLF32

Date _____

To _____

_____

_____

Dear _____

Please stop the payment of the following cheque:

Name of Payee: _____

Date of Cheque: _____

Cheque No.:   _____

Amount: _____

If this cheque has already been honoured, please advise me of the date of payment.

Thank you for your co-operation.

Yours sincerely

_____

_____

Name of Account

_____

Account No.

Note: You should use this form if you have reason to believe that the cheque has been lost or stolen. If this is not the case and if the payee is in possession of the cheque, you must only stop it if the payment was a gift or if you have been defrauded or if the payee has committed a breach of your agreement which is so serious as to deny you any benefit of the agreement at all. Anything short of the above will entitle the payee to obtain 'summary judgment' against you within a matter of weeks.

Organ Donation

Form PF14

Organ Donation

of

_____(Full name)

In the hope that I may help others, I hereby make this gift, if medically acceptable, to take effect upon my death.

The words and marks below indicate my wishes:

I give:

a) ☐ any needed organs for transplantation or other therapeutic purposes [or anatomical study or medical research].

b) ☐ only the following organs _____

_____

_____

[which may be used for purposes of transplantation or other therapeutic purposes only] / [which may be used for transplantation or other therapeutic purposes or for anatomical or medical study].

c) ☐ my entire body, for anatomical or medical study, if needed [save to the extent that any organs may be required for transplantation or other therapeutic purposes].

[I request that after the removal from my body of any organs which may be required my body should be [cremated] / [buried] / [in such manner as_____may direct].

Limitations or special wishes:

_____

_____

Signed by the donor and the following two witnesses, in the presence of each other.

_____   _____
Signature of Donor   Witness, who hereby attests the Donor's signature

_____   _____
Date Signed   Address

_____   _____
Date of Birth   Occupation

_____
Address

Note: Written consent is only required in law if a person wishes his body to be used after his death for public display or anatomical examination. Persons in a 'qualifying relationship' (by which is meant spouses, civil partners, children, parents, siblings, half siblings and friends of long standing) can give consent for the use of organs for therapeutic purposes.

Given the need for speed if an organ is to be used for therapeutic purposes, however, a would-be donor should always give a written direction, tell his family and friends that he has done so, and carry a donor card of the type issued by the Department of Health.

Once you have chosen the paragraph that accords with your wishes, delete the other two paragraphs before you print the form. If there are any passages in square brackets that you wish to delete within the paragraph that you have chosen, make sure that you delete these passages as well before printing.

Overdue Account Reminder   Form CDC29

Date _____

Ref _____

To _____

_____

_____

Dear _____

We sent you a statement a recently. Please note that your account is overdue in the amount of £_____.

Please remit payment to us as soon as possible.

Yours sincerely

_____

Partial Delivery Request   Form BS50

Date _____

Ref _____

To _____

_____

_____

Dear _____

Thank you for your order dated _____. The value of the order is approximately £ _____. We regret that we cannot extend to credit to you for the entire amount.

Accordingly, we suggest that we deliver to you a partial delivery on our standard credit terms reducing the quantities ordered by _____ per cent. Upon payment, we shall deliver the balance of the order.

Please let us know immediately whether you are prepared to accept this proposal, as we will be unable to fulfil any part of your order without such acceptance.

We should be happy to consider an application by you to increase your credit limit.

Yours sincerely

_____

Partnership Agreement
Form B27

This Partnership agreement is made the _____ day of _____ year ____

BETWEEN

(1)_____ of_____

_____(the 'First Partner');

and

(2)_____ of_____

_____ (the 'Second Partner');

hereinafter together called the 'Partners'.

NOW IT IS HEREBY AGREED as follows:

1. THE BUSINESS

   The Partners shall carry on business in Partnership as _____ under the name of

   _____ at _____

   _____ as from _____ year _____.

2. DURATION OF THE PARTNERSHIP

   The Partnership shall continue until terminated under the terms of this Agreement or until the death

   or bankruptcy of either Partner.

3. CAPITAL

   The Capital of the Partnership shall consist of the sum of £_____which belongs to each Partner

   respectively as follows

   _____

   _____

   Unless otherwise agreed, the capital of the Partnership shall belong to the Partners equally and any

   increase in capital shall be made in equal shares.

4. PROFITS AND LOSSES

   The Partners will share all profits and losses (including capital losses)[equally] [in the following

   proportions

   _____

   _____]

   No partner shall make any drawings on account of his share of the profits without the agreement of

   the other partners. If upon the taking of an account for any accounting period any partner shall have

   overdrawn his account, he shall forthwith restore such overdrawings to the account.

5. BANK

   The Partners shall open an account in the name of the Partnership at _____ Bank

   of _____

   and any money belonging to the Partnership shall be paid into the account and the signatures of

   _____ Partners shall be required on all cheques drawn and on all other instruments and instructions

   made in connection with the account.

Continued on next page

Partnership Agreement (continued)   Form B27

6.   ACCOUNTANTS

The accountants to the Partnership shall be _____

of _____

The Partners shall keep such accounting records as the accountants shall recommend, and each partner shall promptly make accurate entries concerning their activities in accordance with any practice which the accountants shall recommend. The accountants shall be instructed to prepare accounts in respect of each accounting period of the Partnership, such period to end on

_____ each year, and the Partners shall agree and sign the accounts.

7.   WORKING PRACTICE

Each Partner shall devote his best efforts and his whole time and attention to the business of the Partnership. He shall not act in competition with the Partnership and he shall conduct himself as regards the other Partners in utmost good faith. Each Partner shall be entitled to take____weeks' holiday in each calendar year at such times as the Partners shall agree. All decisions relating to the Partnership shall be made by unanimous agreement between the Partners unless otherwise agreed [No]/[Neither] Partner shall without the consent of the others _____

_____

_____

_____.

8.   INDEMNITY

Each Partner shall indemnify the other Partners or their estates for any loss which may be incurred by them and which may have been caused by any breach on such Partner's part of any of the terms of this agreement.

9.   RETIREMENT

Any Partner may retire from the Partnership by giving to the other partner or partners not less than

_____ months' notice in writing, in which case the other Partner or any of the other Partners shall have the right exercisable by counternotice before the expiry of such notice to purchase the share of the outgoing Partner at the net value of such share. If more than one Partner shall serve such Counternotice the share of the outgoing Partner shall be acquired by them equally. If such counternotice is not served before the expiry of the period of notice the Partnership shall be dissolved. If the share is to be acquired as aforesaid, the net value of the same shall be determined by the Partners and in default of agreement shall be decided by the accountants acting as experts not arbitrators. Goodwill shall be valued as the lower of the cost or the net realisable value of the same (as certified by the accountant). No partner may give notice as aforesaid within a period of ____ months of any other Partner having given such notice.

Any group of Partners holding between them more than [2/3rds] of the Capital may at any time and without specifying a reason require the other Partner or Partners to retire from the Partnership on not less than _____ notice. The Partners giving such notice or any of them shall have the right exercisable by a further notice served during the period of notice, to purchase the share or shares of the outgoing Partner or Partners at the net value of such share, whereupon such share shall be acquired equally by the Partners giving such further notice. If such further notice is not served before

Continued on next page

Partnership Agreement (continued)   Form B27

the expiry of the period of notice, the Partnership shall be dissolved. If the share or shares is or are to be acquired as aforesaid, the net value of the same shall be determined as if the Partners on whom the notice has been served had themselves given notice to retire.

10. DEATH OR INCAPACITY

   If any Partner should die, the surviving Partner or any of the surviving Partners as the case may be shall have the right, exercisable by notice within a period of _____ months of the date of the death, to purchase the share of the deceased Partner as if the deceased Partner had given a notice of retirement. If more than one surviving Partner shall serve such notice, the share of the deceased Partner shall be acquired by such surviving Partners equally. If such notice is not served as aforesaid, the Partnership shall be dissolved.

11. EXPULSION

   If any Partner commits a serious breach or consistent breaches of this Agreement or is guilty of any conduct which may have a serious and detrimental effect on the Partnership [the other Partner] or such other Partners as between them have [2/3rds] of the Capital ('the remaining Partners') may by notice in writing expel such Partner from the Partnership, whereupon the remaining Partners shall have the right, exercisable by notice given within ___ month(s) of the notice of expulsion, to buy out the share(s) of the expelled partner(s) by re-payment to him of his share of the capital only. In the absence of such notice, the Partnership shall be dissolved.

12. RESTRICTIONS

   If the firm shall be dissolved, each Partner shall be free to solicit the clients of the firm. If any Partner(s) shall acquire the shares of any other Partner(s), the persons whose shares have been acquired shall not for a period of _____ years[1] approach or solicit any customers of the firm [and shall not be engaged, whether as partner, director or employee in a business of _____[2] within a radius of one mile[3] of the said address of this firm.

IN WITNESS OF WHICH the parties hereto have signed this Agreement the day and year first above written.

SIGNED   _____ DATED _____

              Signed by the First Partner

SIGNED   _____ DATED _____

              Signed by the Second Partner

---

[1] The purpose of a restriction of this sort is to protect the business, rather than to punish an expelled partner. If the restriction is too broad, a court will refuse to enforce it. When deciding how long the restriction should operate, consider what the minimum period of time would be to enable the remaining partners to prevent a customer from following the expelled partner. A hairdresser, for example, often has a personal following which might last longer than that of a newsagent.

[2] Once again, the purpose of this restriction is to protect the business, not to punish the expelled partner. Make certain, therefore, that the activities which he is restricted from pursuing are the same as the activities of the business as actually conducted. For example, a business selling T-shirts should not forbid a former partner from working in a general clothing shop.

[3] Again, restrict only to the extent necessary. The less customers are likely to travel to a business of the type in question, the smaller the excluded area should be. For example, a hairdresser can be excluded from a wider area than can a greengrocer. The exclusion area in a sparsely populated district can be larger than such an area in central London.

Pay Advice   Form E55

_____ Ltd

Name: _____   Date: _____

Works/Dept No.: _____   Tax Code: _____

National Insurance: _____   Tax Week: _____

Payments	Hours	Rate			Total		
		£	p		£	p	
Basic	_____						
Overtime	_____						
Bonus, Holiday, Sick Pay	_____						

Gross Payable

Gross wages to date	
£	.	p

Deductions	£	p
Company Pension		
Income Tax		
National Insurance		
Standard rate at ____%		
Reduced rate at ____%		
Other deductions		
Total deductions		
Net Payable		

Tax deducted s to date	
£	.	p

Keep this record of your earnings

Permission to Use Photograph Form OLF33

The copyright owner (the 'Grantor') hereby grants to: _____ (the 'Grantee')
non-exclusive worldwide rights to the following photograph(s), copies of which are appended hereto, for
the following purposes:

_____

_____

_____

_____

This licence will expire on _____.

Use for any other purpose will require an additional licence and may require an additional fee.

The Grantor hereby asserts his/her moral rights as author of the photograph(s), and the following credit
should appear against every usage of the photograph(s) in acknowledgement of those rights:

_____

_____

_____

_____

The Grantor hereby warrants that he/she is the owner of the copyright of the said photograph(s), that
he/she has the right to grant this licence to the Grantee and that the publication of this photograph will not
be libellous and that, if it was taken on or after 1st August 1989, it was not taken for private or domestic
purposes.

In return for the grant of this permission, Grantee has paid the Grantor the sum of £_____ [plus VAT
thereon of £_____] receipt of which the Grantor hereby acknowledges.

Permission is granted on _____.

_____

Signature of Grantor

Permission to use Quotation or Personal Statement   Form OLF34

THIS LICENCE IS MADE the _____ day of _____ year_____

BETWEEN:

(1) _____ of _____(the 'Licensor'); and

(2) _____ of _____(the 'Licensee').

NOW IT IS HEREBY AGREED as follows:

1.   In consideration for the sum of £ _____, receipt of which the Licensor hereby acknowledges, the Licensor hereby grants a non-exclusive worldwide licence to the Licensee (the 'Licence') to use, publish or reprint in whole or in part, the following statement, picture, endorsement, quotation or other material ('the Material'):

        _____

        _____

        _____

2.   This Licence shall extend only to [a publication] / [publications] known as _____

        _____, but shall extend to all new editions, reprints, excerpts, advertisements, publicity and promotions for publication.

3.   This Licence shall expire on _____, after which date no further use shall be made of the Material without a further licence for which an additional fee will be chargeable. Without such further licence all use of the Material shall cease and all presentations of the Material in electronic or on-line format shall be deleted.

4.   This agreement shall be binding upon and inure to the benefit of the parties, their successors and assigns.

IN WITNESS OF WHICH the parties have signed this licence the day and year first above written

_____   _____
Signed by or on behalf of the Licensor   Signed by or on behalf of the Licensee

_____   _____
in the presence of (witness)   in the presence of (witness)

Name _____   Name _____

Address _____   Address _____

_____   _____

Occupation _____   Occupation _____

Personal Property Rental Agreement   Form PF15

THIS AGREEMENT IS MADE the _____ day of _____ year _____

BETWEEN:

(1) _____ of _____ (the 'Owner'); and

(2) _____ of _____ (the 'Hirer').

NOW IT IS HEREBY AGREED as follows:

1.   The Owner hereby rents to the Hirer the following personal property (the 'Property'):

      _____

      _____

2.   The Hirer shall pay to the Owner the sum of £ _____ as payment for the rental herein, payable as follows:

      _____

      _____

      _____

3.   The Hirer shall during the rental term keep and maintain the Property in good condition and repair and shall be responsible for any loss, damage or destruction to the Property notwithstanding how caused and the Hirer agrees to return the Property in its present condition, reasonable wear and tear excepted.

4.   The Hirer shall not during the rental period allow others use of the Property nor pawn or pledge the same nor permit the same to stand as security.

5.   The Hirer shall during the rental period [keep the Property at _____] / [shall not take the Property] [out of the United Kingdom] / [more than _____ miles from _____].

6.   The rental period shall commence on _____, and terminate on _____, at which date the Property shall be promptly returned to the Owner at _____or at such other location as the Owner shall reasonably specify.

Continued on next page

Personal Property Rental Agreement (continued) Form PF15

IN WITNESS OF WHICH the parties have signed this agreement the day and year first above written

_____   _____
Signed by or on behalf of the Owner   Signed by or on behalf of the Renter

_____   _____
in the presence of (witness)   in the presence of (witness)

Name _____   Name _____

Address _____   Address _____

_____   _____
Occupation _____   Occupation _____

Health warning: Do not use this form for a consumer hire agreement, within the meaning of the Consumer Credit Act 1974. A hire agreement is a 'consumer hire agreement' unless (1) it is a small agreement (requiring payments of less than £50) or (2) it is non-commercial (i.e not entered into by the owner in the course of a business) or (3) the hirer is a limited company. At present there is a further exclusion of agreements where the hirer is obliged to pay more than £25,000, but this exclusion will no longer apply once the Consumer Credit Act 2006 Section 1 is in force. There will, however, be two new exclusions. The first applies where the hirer is a partnership with more than three partners. The second applies where the goods are for use in the hirer's business and the payments to be made under the agreement exceed £25,000. Because this is a rapidly changing field, please check for recent developments.

Above all, note that if the hire agreement is a 'consumer hire agreement' it will have to be in a special statutory form and these are beyond the scope of this book.

Pools Syndicate Agreement Rules

Form OLF35

For the Football Pools competition run by: _____

and called: _____

SYNDICATE NAME: _____

MANAGER	DATE OF APPOINTMENT	SIGNATURE

MEMBER	INDIVIDUAL STAKE (to be paid IN ADVANCE of of each Match Day by the agreed deadline)	DATE JOINED SYNDICATE	MANAGER'S SIGNATURE	MEMBER'S SIGNATURE	DATE LEFT SYNDICATE	MANAGER'S SIGNATURE

Agreed deadline for payment of Individual Stakes: Time: _____

Day: _____ days before each Match Day

(Syndicate Rules on next page)

Pools Syndicate Agreement Rules (continued)   Form OLF35

1. Definitions
    'Coupon' means an appropriate coupon or coupons for the agreed pools competition;

    'Individual Stake' means the stake payable by each Member as set out in this Agreement and received by the Manager in advance of each Match Day before the agreed deadline;

    'Manager' means the Manager of the Syndicate, who shall be appointed and may be replaced at any time without notice by a majority of the Members;

    'Match Day' means a day or days of scheduled football matches for which a Coupon may be submitted under the agreed pools competition;

    'Members' means all those persons who have joined and not left the Syndicate;

    'Syndicate Stake' means the total of the Members' Individual Stakes in respect of any Match Day.

2. Manager's Responsibilities
    2.1   The Manager will:
    (a)   establish a procedure for agreeing the match selections to be entered by the Syndicate for each Match Day;
    (b)   complete and enter a Coupon bearing the agreed match selections for the amount of the Syndicate Stake for each Match Day. However, if the Syndicate Stake is not sufficient to buy a Coupon bearing all agreed match selections for any Match Day, the Manager shall have absolute discretion as to which of the match selections to enter;
    (c)   keep a current record of each Member's individual stake, of each individual stake which he, the Manager, may make on behalf of any Member, of each reimbursement of each such stake as any Member may make to the Manager and of each Coupon purchased;
    (d)   collect any prize money and account to the Members for it in proportion to their Individual Stakes, holding it in trust for the Members in the meantime.

2.2   If any Member fails to pay his or her Individual Stake to the Manager in advance of any Match Day by the agreed deadline, the Manager may (but shall not be obliged to) pay that Individual Stake on the Member's behalf and, if the Manager does so, the Member will reimburse the Manager forthwith upon demand.

2.3   The Manager shall not be liable to any Member for any loss or damage arising out of any failing of the Manager under this Agreement, provided that the Manager has acted honestly.

3. Member's Responsibilities
    The Members will each pay their Individual Stake to the Manager in advance of each Match Day by the agreed deadline.

4. Ceasing to be a Member
    A Member shall be removed from the Group:

    4.1   if the Member wishes to leave; or

    4.2   at the discretion of the Manager, if the Member fails to pay his or her Individual Stake in accordance with Rule 3 in respect of any 3 weeks within a calendar year (whether consecutive or non-consecutive); or

    4.3   at the discretion of the Manager, if the Member fails to reimburse the Manager in accordance with Rule 2.2.

5. This Agreement

    5.1   It shall be the responsibility of the Manager to update and amend this Agreement in accordance with any amendment which the Members may pass. Any such amendment, other than the removal of a Member in accordance with Rule 4, must have been authorised by majority vote of the Members. [Rule 4 may be amended only by the vote of 75 per cent of he Members.]

    5.2   The record of Members shall be conclusive as to membership of the Syndicate at any point in time, provided that a person whose application for membership has been accepted by the Manager and who

Continued on next page

has duly paid an agreed Individual Stake shall not be excluded from a share of prize money under Rule 2.1(c) merely because the Record has not been updated to record that person as a Member. The Record shall be evidence of each Member's individual Stake and shall only be challenged on the basis of any proven failure by the manager to record a payment which has actually been made. If the Record is successfully challenged the same shall be altered and any prize money shall be paid out in accordance with the Record as altered.

5.3   If any person is removed from the list of Members, the Manager shall forthwith notify the Member of that fact, but the Manager shall incur no liability to such Member for any loss incurred by reason of any failure to inform the Member of such removal. If any Member shall be removed, the Manager shall have the power to reinstate the Member, but the Member shall not be entitled to receive any share of any prize money which may accrue to the syndicate on any Match Day falling between his removal and his reinstatement.

5.4   The appointment or replacement of the Manager shall take effect whether or not this Agreement has been amended to that effect.

5.5   This Agreement is subject to English law and the parties submit to the exclusive jurisdiction of the English courts in connection with any dispute hereunder.

Premarital Agreement

Form PF16

THIS AGREEMENT IS MADE the _____ day of _____ year_____

BETWEEN:

(1) _____ of _____ (the 'First Party'); and

(2) _____ of _____(the 'Second Party').

WHEREAS:

The parties contemplate legal marriage, and it is their mutual desire to enter into this agreement so that they will continue to own and control their own property, and are getting married because of their love for each other but do not desire that their present respective financial interests be changed by their marriage.

NOW IT IS HEREBY AGREED as follows:

1.   All property which belongs to each of the above parties shall be, and shall remain, their personal estate, including all interest, rents, and profits which may accrue from said property, and said property shall remain free of claim by the other.

2.   The parties shall have at all times the full right and authority, in all respects as if the parties had not married, to use, sell, enjoy, manage, give and convey all property as may presently belong to him or her.

3.   In the event of a separation or divorce, the parties shall have no right against each other by way of claims for support, alimony, maintenance, compensation or division of property existing as of this date.

4.   In the event of separation or divorce, marital property acquired after marriage shall nevertheless remain subject to division, either by agreement or judicial determination.

5.   This agreement shall be binding upon and inure to the benefit of the parties, their successors and assigns.

IN WITNESS OF WHICH the parties have signed this agreement the day and year first above written

_____   _____
Signed by or on behalf of the First Party   Signed by or on behalf of the Second Party

_____   _____
in the presence of (witness)   in the presence of (witness)

Name _____   Name _____

Address _____   Address _____

_____   _____
Occupation _____   Occupation _____

Important Note: Premarital agreements are not binding under English law. The distribution of assets is at the discretion of the court. The court may give some weight to an agreement which both parties have made freely and with full knowledge of the meaning of the agreement and of the relevant facts. It can therefore be worthwhile to enter into such an agreement, even though it may not be clear to what extent the court will be influenced by it.

In order for the agreement to have any influence at all, however, both parties should be independently advised by solicitors. An agreement, such as the one above, should merely be used as a draft when seeking such advice. It can assist you to concentrate on the questions that you will have to think about, and may enable you to take up less of your solicitor's time. When going through it you should ask yourselves whether, in the event of a divorce, you ought to provide (contrary to what this form says) that one of you ought to pay maintenance or a lump sum by instalments to the other for a given period (the amount and the time perhaps increasing according to the time which elapses before separation.

Product Defect Notice   Form BS51

Date _____

Ref _____

To _____

_____

_____

Dear _____

Recently I purchased a product manufactured, distributed or sold by you and described as:

_____

This is to inform you that the product is defective; details as follows:

1. Date of purchase _____

2. Nature of defect _____

_____

3. Injuries or damage _____

4. Item purchased from _____

This information is provided to give you the earliest possible notice of the claim. Please inform me as to what course of action you intend to take to repair or replace the product and make good any damage.

Yours sincerely

_____

Name

_____

Address

_____

Tel

Note: If you are provided with defective goods, you must make a choice as to whether to reject them and ask for your money back, or accept them and claim money to make up the loss caused by the defect. By sending a Note in the terms in this form you may be regarded as having elected to give up your claim to have your money back. If you think it appropriate to reject the goods, other forms in this book can be used.

Promissory Note   Form CDC30

Principal Amount £ _____ Date _____

I, the undersigned, hereby promise to pay on demand to the order of _____

_____ the sum of _____pounds (£ _____) together with

interest thereon from the date hereof until paid at the rate of ___% per annum.

_____

Signed

_____

Name

_____

Witness

Important Note: Do not use this form for a consumer credit agreement, within the meaning of the Consumer Credit Act 1974. An agreement is a consumer credit agreement unless (1) it is a small agreement (requiring payments of less than £50) or (2) it is non-commercial (i.e. not entered into by the owner in the course of a business) or (3) the borrower is a limited company. At present there is a further exclusion of agreements where the loan is for less than £25,000, but this exclusion will no longer apply once the Consumer Credit Act 2006 Section 1 is in force. There will, however, be two new exclusions. The first applies where the borrower is a partnership with more than three partners. The second applies where the loan is for the purposes of the borrower's business and the loan exceeds £25,000. Because this is a rapidly changing field, please check for recent developments.

Above all, note that if the loan agreement is a consumer credit agreement it will have to be in a special statutory form and these are beyond the scope of this book.

Promissory Note for Repayment by Instalments | Form LB10

1. I hereby promise to pay to _____or to his order for value received the sum of _____

_____Pounds (£ _____), with interest thereon at the rate of _____ % per annum on

the unpaid balance in the following manner:

£_____ on _____ date_____

£_____ on _____ date_____

£_____ on _____ date_____

If I should default on any of the above payments, the entire unpaid balance of principal and interest

shall be paid on demand.

_____
Signed by or on behalf of the Borrower

_____
in the presence of (witness)

Name _____

Address _____

_____

Occupation _____

_____
Signed by or on behalf of the Guarantor

_____
in the presence of (witness)

Name _____

Address _____

_____

Occupation _____

Important Note: It is essential that the dates for payment are specified. Do not say 'by' a given date, or 'on or before' the date. Use 'on.'

Do not use this form for a consumer credit agreement, within the meaning of the Consumer Credit Act 1974. An agreement is a consumer credit agreement unless (1) it is a small agreement (requiring payments of less than £50) or (2) it is non-commercial (i.e. not entered into by the owner in the course of a business) or (3) the borrower is a limited company. At present there is a further exclusion of agreements where the loan is for less than £25,000, but this exclusion will no longer apply once the Consumer Credit Act 2006 Section 1 is in force. There will, however, be two new exclusions. The first applies where the borrower is a partnership with more than three partners. The second applies where the loan is for the purposes of the borrower's business and the loan exceeds £25,000. Because this is a rapidly changing field, please check for recent developments. Above all, note that if the loan agreement is a consumer credit agreement it will have to be in a special statutory form and these are beyond the scope of this book.

Guarantee to Support a Promissory Note   Form LB13

If you_____will discount the promissory note dated _____ of _____ , I will in consideration of your so doing, in the event of the said promissory note being dishonoured, pay you the balance owing (including interest) of such dishonoured note.

_____

Signed

_____

Name of Guarantor

_____

Witness,

Solicitor of _____who certifies as follows:

The above named _____has instructed me to advise him/her as to the meaning and effect of this guarantee. I have explained its meaning and effect to him/her and have further explained that the reason why I have been asked to witness this document is to enable you to enforce the guarantee contained therein against him/her should you wish to do so. I am satisfied that he/she understands the obligations contained in the guarantee and that he/she is entering into the same of his/her own free will.

Important note: Do not use this form for a consumer credit agreement, within the meaning of the Consumer Credit Act 1974. An agreement is a consumer credit agreement unless (1) it is a small agreement (requiring payments of less than £50) or (2) it is non-commercial (i.e not entered into by the owner in the course of a business) or (3) the borrower is a limited company. At present there is a further exclusion of agreements where the loan is for less than £25,000, but this exclusion will no longer apply once the Consumer Credit Act 2006 Section 1 is in force. There will, however, be two new exclusions. The first applies where the borrower is a partnership with more than three partners. The second applies where the loan is for the purposes of a borrower's business and the loan exceeds £25,000. Because this is a rapidly changing field, please check for recent developments. Above all, note that if the loan agreement is a consumer credit agreement it will have to be in a special statutory form and these are beyond the scope of this book.

If the guarantor is a friend or relative of the borrower, you should insist that the guarantor get independent legal advice, as otherwise it may be very difficult to enforce the guarantee.

Property Inventory — Form PF17

Property Inventory

OF

_____(NAME)

ITEM	ESTIMATED VALUE	LOCATION
_____	_____	_____
_____	_____	_____
_____	_____	_____
_____	_____	_____
_____	_____	_____
_____	_____	_____
_____	_____	_____
_____	_____	_____
_____	_____	_____
_____	_____	_____
_____	_____	_____
_____	_____	_____
_____	_____	_____
_____	_____	_____
_____	_____	_____
_____	_____	_____
_____	_____	_____
_____	_____	_____
_____	_____	_____
_____	_____	_____
_____	_____	_____
_____	_____	_____
_____	_____	_____
_____	_____	_____
_____	_____	_____
_____	_____	_____
_____	_____	_____
_____	_____	_____
_____	_____	_____
_____	_____	_____

Purchase Order — Form BS52

_____ Ltd

Address: _____

Contact Details: _____

Order to:		Order date:
		Order no.:
Deliver to:		Our ref no.:
		Account no.:
Delivery date:		

Product no	Description	Quantity	Unit price	Net
			Total Goods	
			Total VAT	
			Total £	

Please quote our order number on all correspondence.

Issued subject to our Conditions of Purchase a copy of which is enclosed.

Signed_____

For & on behalf of _____Limited

[_____] Limited registered in England Reg. No _____

Quotation   Form BS53

_____ Ltd

Address: _____

Contact Details: _____

To: _____ Date: _____

_____ Contact: _____

We have pleasure in providing our quotation as follows:

Your Ref.	Spec No.	Description	Quantity	Unit cost £
			VAT	
			Total	

Delivery time from order:
Payment terms:
Samples available:
SUBJECT TO OUR CONDITIONS OF SALE ENCLOSED

[_____] Limited registered in England Reg. No _____

Receipt Appropriated to a Particular Debt　　　　　　Form BS54

Date　　_____

Ref　　_____

To　　_____

　　　_____

　　　_____

The undersigned hereby acknowledges receipt of the sum of £　_____

paid by _____. It is appropriated to the following debt:

_____

_____

_____

_____

The remaining unpaid balance of this debt is now £ _____.

Signed this _____ day of _____ year _____.

_____

Receipt for Company Property   Form E56

Employee: _____

Identification No: _____

Department/Section: _____

I hereby acknowledge receipt of the company property listed below. I agree to keep the property in good condition and to return it when I leave the company, or earlier on request. I agree to report immediately any loss or damage to the property. In addition, I agree to use the property only for work-related purposes.

1. Item _____   Received From _____   Date_____
    Serial No _____   Returned To   _____   Date_____

2. Item _____   Received From _____   Date_____
    Serial No _____   Returned To   _____   Date_____

3. Item _____   Received From _____   Date_____
    Serial No _____   Returned To _____   Date_____

4. Item _____   Received From _____   Date_____
    Serial No _____   Returned To _____   Date_____

5. Item _____   Received From_____   Date_____
    Serial No _____   Returned To   _____   Date_____

6. Item_____ Received From _____   Date_____
    Serial No _____   Returned To   _____   Date_____

_____

Employee

_____

Date

Receipt in Full   Form BS55

Date _____

Ref _____

To _____

_____

_____

The undersigned acknowledges receipt of the sum of £ _____ in full payment of all demands.

_____

Signed

[For and on behalf of _____ Ltd]

Receipt Credited to a Particular Account   Form CDC31

Date   _____

Ref   _____

To   _____
         _____
         _____

The undersigned acknowledges receipt of the sum of £ _____ paid by _____

_____. This payment will be applied and credited to the following account:

_____

_____

_____

_____

This leaves a balance on that account outstanding of £_____ as at the date hereof.

_____

Signed

[For and on behalf of _____ Ltd]

Receipt for non-cash consideration upon Allotment of Shares

Form B28

of

_____Limited

On this date, _____ has purchased _____ shares of common stock

in this company, represented by share certificate number _____. The shareholder has

transferred to the company the following assets, with an agreed fair value of £ _____, in consideration

for the receipt of the shares:

_____

_____

_____

Payment in full has been received for these shares and the share certificate representing the shares has

been issued by the company to the shareholder. Record of this transaction has been recorded in the share

transfer book of this company.

_____

Date

_____

Secretary of the company

_____

Shareholder

Important note: For as long as the Companies Act 1985 section 88 (2) (b) remains in force the company is required to provide Companies House with a copy of any contract under which a shareholder is to acquire shares from a company in exchange for consideration other than cash. If there is no written contract, details of any oral contract must be supplied. The details must include as a minimum, the name of the shareholder, the name of the company, a description of the property which forms the consideration and the agreed price of the property.

This requirement will be abolished when the relevant provision of the 2006 Companies Act comes into force.

Remember that there is a legal requirement to file a 'Return of Allotment' in statutory form whenever shares are allotted. You should consult Companies House immediately after the allotment to obtain the appropriate form. Remember also that it is not permitted to issue shares at a discount. The value attached to the non-cash consideration paid for the shares must therefore be a genuine estimate of its worth.

Redundancy with Ex Gratia Payment   Form E57

Date   _____

To   _____
_____
_____

Dear   _____

Further to our meeting on _____, I write to confirm that with regret
you will be made redundant with effect from _____ , due to:

_____

_____

At the meeting we discussed the reasons for reaching this decision and the method in which you had been
selected. We have made every effort to find alternative employment for you but I regret that there are no
suitable positions available at present.

The redundancy benefits that you are entitled to are:

1.   Statutory redundancy pay   £ _____
2.   Pay in lieu of notice (if less than the full notice is given)   £ _____
3.   Other _____   £ _____
4.   TOTAL   £ _____

In addition, in recognition of your years of good service to the company, you will be paid an ex gratia sum of
£ _____ . We will be writing to you separately about your pension entitlement.

Thank you for your past efforts on behalf of the company and I hope that you will soon find other suitable
employment. You may submit our name as a reference in the confidence that the reference will be
favourable.

If you wish to discuss any aspect of this letter, please do not hesitate to contact me.

Yours sincerely

_____

Note: Before any decision to dismiss is made the statutory dismissal and disciplinary procedure and any contractual procedures must
be followed to avoid legal repercussions.

Reference Letter on Employee   Form E58

Private and Confidential

Date _____

Ref _____

To _____

_____

_____

Dear _____

Re _____

In reply to your request for a reference for the above job application, I report to you as follows:

_____

_____

_____

I confirm that the individual was employed by this firm between the dates of

_____ and _____ in the capacity of

_____. My additional comments are as follows:

_____

_____

_____

This reference is given to be of help to you and in fairness to your proposed employee. It is given on the basis that we accept no legal liability and that you must rely upon your own judgment whether or not to proceed with your proposed employment of this individual. We trust you shall hold this reference in strict confidence.

Yours sincerely

_____

Rejected Goods Notice   Form BS56

Date _____

Ref _____

To _____

_____

_____

Dear _____

Please note that on _____, we received goods from you under our order or contract

dated _____.

We hereby notify you of our intent to reject and return the goods for the reason(s) indicated below:

☐   Goods were not delivered within the time specified.

☐   Goods were defective or damaged as described overleaf.

☐   Goods did not conform to sample, advertisement, specifications, or price, as stated overleaf.

☐   An order acknowledgment has not been received, and we therefore ordered these goods from other

sources.

☐   Goods represent only a partial shipment.

Please credit our account or issue a refund if prepaid, and provide instructions for the return of these goods

at your expense. Return of these goods however shall not be a waiver of any legal claim we may have.

Yours sincerely

_____

Note: A buyer should be careful not to reject goods unless he is confident that he has the right to reject them. If he rejects them when he is not entitled to do so, he will himself be in breach of contract and liable to be sued. Note also that, except in sales to consumers, the buyer does not have the right to reject the goods for defects if the defects are so minor as to make rejection unreasonable.

Reminder of Unpaid Account   Form CDC32

Date   _____

Ref   _____

To   _____

_____

_____

Dear   _____

Re: Date   Invoice No.   Invoice Amount

      _____   _____   £ _____

Our records indicate that the above account remains outstanding. We would be grateful for an early remittance.

If you have paid the amount within the past seven days, please ignore this letter.

Yours sincerely

_____

Remittance Advice   Form CDC33

Date _____

Ref _____

To _____

_____

_____

Dear _____

We enclose our cheque no._____ in the amount of £ _____. This cheque is only to be credited to the following charges/invoices/orders:

Invoice	Amount
_____	£_____
_____	£_____
_____	£_____
_____	£_____
_____	£_____

Please note that this payment shall only be applied to the items listed and shall not be applied, in whole or in part, to any other, charge, order or invoice that may be outstanding.

Yours sincerely

_____

Rent Review Memorandum   Form RT16

The PROPERTY   _____

Name(s) of   _____

LANDLORD(S)   _____

Name(s) of   _____

TENANT(S)   _____

DATE OF TENANCY   _____

RENT REVIEW DATE   _____

NEW RENT   _____

The Landlord(s) and the Tenant(s) hereby record their agreement that with effect from the rent review date stated above (and subject to any provisions in the tenancy for any further review in the future) the rent payable under the tenancy shall be the figure stated as the new rent above.

SIGNED   _____   _____

            _____   _____

                 (The Landlord(s))   (The Tenant(s))

Note: Do not use this form for a tenancy protected under the Rent Act 1977. It may, however, be used for Business Tenancies or for assured and assured shorthold tenancies (as to which see Housing Act 1988 Section 13 (5)).

Rent Statement   Form RT17

Property _____

Name of Landlord/Owner _____

Address of Landlord/Owner _____

_____

Name of Tenant/Sharer _____

_____

Date Due	Amount Due	Date of Payment	Amount Paid	Cumulative Arrears	Signature of Landlord/Owner

IMPORTANT NOTICE:

This Rent Statement, or a Rent Book, must be supplied to the Tenant/Sharer if the rent/payment is paid weekly.

continued on next page

Rent Statement (continued) Form RT17

> **IMPORTANT - PLEASE READ THIS:**
> If the rent for the premises you occupy as your residence is payable weekly, the landlord must provide you with a Rent Book or similar document. If you have an Assured Tenancy, including an Assured Shorthold Tenancy (see paragraph 7 below), or a protected or statutory tenancy, the rent book or similar document must contain the notices and information which are appropriate to your type of tenancy properly filled in.

1. Address of premises _____

2. Name and address of Landlord[1] _____
   _____
   _____

3. Name and address of agent (if any)[1] _____
   _____
   _____

4. The rent payable[1] including/excluding council tax[2] is £ _____ per week.

5. Details of accommodation (if any) which the occupier has the right to share with other persons _____
   _____
   _____
   _____

6. The other terms and conditions of the tenancy are _
   _____
   _____
   _____
   _____
   _____
   _____
   _____

7. If you have an Assured Tenancy or an Assured Agricultural Occupancy you have certain rights under the Housing Act 1988. These include the right not to be evicted from your home unless your Landlord gets a possession order from the courts. Unless the property is let under an Assured *Shorthold* Tenancy, the courts can only grant an order on a limited number of grounds. Further details regarding Assured Tenancies are set out in the Department for Communities and Local Government and the Welsh Assembly Government booklet 'Assured and Assured Shorthold Tenancies - a

Guide for Tenants' no. 97HC228C in the series of the housing booklets. These booklets are available from the rent officers, council offices and housing aid centres, some of which also give advice.

8. You may be entitled to get help to pay your rent through the housing benefit scheme. Apply to your local council for details.

9. It is a criminal offence for your Landlord to evict you without an order from the court or to harass you or interfere with your possessions or use of facilities in order to force you to leave.

10. If you are in any doubt about your legal rights or obligations, particularly if your Landlord has asked you to leave, you should go to a Citizens Advice Bureau, housing aid centre, law centre or solicitor. Help with all or part of the cost of legal advice from a solicitor may be available under the Legal Aid Scheme (now the Community Legal Service).

THE HOUSING ACT 1985

Summary of Part X of the Housing Act 1985, to be inserted in a Rent Book or similar document.

1. An occupier who causes or permits his dwelling to be overcrowded is liable to prosecution for an offence under the Housing Act 1985, and, if convicted, to a fine of up to level 2 of the standard scale, and a further fine of up to one-tenth of that level in respect of every day on which the offence continues after conviction. Any part of a house which is occupied by a separate household is a 'dwelling'.

2. A dwelling is overcrowded if the number of persons sleeping in it is more than the 'permitted number', or is such that two or more of those persons, being ten years old or over, of opposite sexes (not being persons living together as husband and wife), must sleep in the same room.

3. The 'permitted number' for the dwelling to which this Rent Statement relates is _____ persons. In counting the number of persons each child under ten counts as half a person, and a child of less than a year is not counted at all.

4. The name and address of the Local Health Officer is:
   _____
   _____
   Tel:_____

5. The name and address of the landlord or other person responsible for repairs is:
   _____
   _____
   Tel:_____

---

[1] These entries must be kept up-to-date.

[2] Cross out if council tax is not payable to the landlord.

Note: use this form for an assured or assured shorthold tenancy. Do not use it for a protected or statutory tenancy governed by the Rent Act 1977, where a different form is prescribed. If in doubt, you should consult a solicitor.

Rejection of Claim for Credit Note

Form CDC34

Date _____

Ref _____

To _____

_____

_____

Dear _____

We have investigated your claim that we should credit your account for the following ticked reason(s) which you have given:

☐   Prices are above the agreed amount.

☐   Non-credited payments in the amount of £_____.

☐   Goods invoiced for have not been received.

☐   Goods were not ordered.

☐   Goods were defective or wrongly delivered.

☐   Goods are available for return.

☐   Other: _____.

We regret we must reject your claim for a credit for the following reason:

_____

_____

_____

We now request payment in the amount of £ _____ without further delay. Please contact us if you have any further questions.

Yours sincerely

_____

Request for Advance Payment   Form CDC35

Date _____

Ref _____

To _____

_____

_____

Dear _____

Upon reviewing your past credit record with us, we are compelled to say that we cannot continue to offer credit terms to you. Consequently, future orders can only be delivered with payment in advance.

We regret any inconvenience this may cause, but remind you that this arrangement will allow you to take advantage of the discounts we offer for early payment.

We hope this will be only a temporary arrangement, and that in the near future we can again extend credit terms to you.

Yours sincerely

_____

Request for Bank Credit Reference   Form CDC36

Date _____

Ref _____

To _____
_____
_____

Dear _____

Re _____

The above account holder has requested the we obtain a banking reference from you. In order that we may evaluate trade terms for this account. He has requested that we [grant him credit in the amount of £_____] / [that we permit him to run up a bill of £_____ on terms of payment within 30 days of invoicing.] We would appreciate the following information:

1. How long has the account holder had an account with you?
2. What has the average balance on the account been during the last quarter?
3. Is the account holder permitted to overdraw? If yes, what is his permitted overdraft?
4. Does the account holder have any term loans?
5. If the account holder has any term loans, please advise:
    i) present balance on loans;
    ii) terms of repayment;
    iii) is repayment satisfactory;
6. Has the borrower exceeded his overdraft limit within the last 6 months? If yes, please provide details.
7. Is the level of credit which the borrower has requested from us in line with what you would regard as normal, bearing in mind the nature and size of his business?
8. Is the overall banking relationship satisfactory?

Any additional comments or information you provide would be greatly appreciated and, of course, we would equally appreciate any future information involving a change in the account holder's financial situation or their banking relationship with you.

All information will be held in the strictest confidence.

Yours sincerely

_____

I hereby consent to the Bank furnishing to _____ the information requested above.
Signed
_____ Account holder

Request for Credit Reference   Form CDC37

Date _____

Ref _____

To _____
_____
_____

Dear _____

Re _____

The above named has recently applied to us for credit terms and has cited you as a credit reference. He has requested that we [grant him credit in the amount of £_____] / [that we permit him to run up a bill of £_____ on terms of payment within 30 days of invoicing].

We would be grateful if you could provide us with the following information:

i)   Credit limit.

ii)   Terms.

iii) How long the credit account has been open.

iv)   Present amount owed.

v)   Payment history.

vi)   Is the level of credit which the borrower has requested from us in line with what you would regard as normal, bearing in mind the nature and size of his business?

vii) Have you found his dealings with you to be satisfactory?

Any other information you believe to be helpful is welcome. All information will be held in the strictest confidence. We accept your reference without liability on your part.

A pre-paid envelope is enclosed for your convenience. Thank you for your help.

Yours sincerely

_____

I hereby consent to the bank furnishing to _____ the information requested above.
Signed

_____ Applicant for credit

Request for Guarantee   Form CDC38

Date   _____

To   _____

          _____

          _____

Dear   _____

We often find that we do not have sufficient credit information to allow us to offer trade credit to newly established businesses applying for credit.

We should be happy to offer you our normal trade credit terms if you provide us with the personal guarantee of the directors of your company and we find their credit satisfactory. Accordingly, we enclose our standard guarantee and guarantor's credit application.

Thank you for your interest in our firm and we sincerely hope you will accept our suggestion in order that we may both enjoy a mutually beneficial business relationship.

Yours sincerely

_____

Request for Information on Disputed Charge   Form CDC39

Date _____

Ref _____

To _____

_____

_____

Dear _____

We refer to your letter dated _____ disputing your account balance.

To help us resolve this matter, we ask you to provide us with the following:

☐   Copies of statements dated _____, annotated by you to show disputed amounts.

☐   Copies of any bills containing disputed items, with those items indicated and reasons given.

☐   List of all payments made since _____ with dates of payments and cheque numbers or other details of payment.

☐   Copies of returned goods authorisations.

☐   Credit notes outstanding.

☐   List of goods claimed as not received.

☐   List of goods claimed to be damaged.

☐   List of goods claimed to be non-conforming.

☐   Other:_____.

Upon receipt of the above information, we shall consider your claim at the earliest opportunity and attempt to resolve the issue.

Thank you for your prompt attention to this matter.

Yours sincerely

_____

Request for Quotation   Form BS57

Date _____

Ref _____

To _____
    _____
    _____

Dear Sirs

Re: Request for Quotation

We are interested in purchasing the following goods:

_____

_____

_____

Please provide us with a firm quotation for these goods. Please also provide us with your discount structure for volume purchases and the following information:

i)   Standard terms for payment.

ii)   Availability of an open credit account with your firm. If available, please provide us with the appropriate credit application form.

iii) Delivery costs for orders.

iv) VAT applicability.

v)   Delivery time for orders from the date of your receipt of a purchase order to our receipt of the goods.

vi) Length of the validity of the quotation.

Yours faithfully

_____

Request for Replacement Share Certificate   Form B29

To: The Secretary

_____ Limited (the 'Company').

_____

_____

I, _____ do hereby request that the Company (or its registrars) issue

to me a duplicate certificate no _____ for _____ shares in the capital of the Company, and

I solemnly and sincerely declare that I am the registered holder of those shares and that I believe the

original certificate to have been mislaid, destroyed or lost. In consideration of the Company so doing, I

hereby indemnify the Company against all claims and demands, monies, losses, damages, costs and expense

which may be brought against or be paid, incurred or sustained by the Company by reason or in

consequence of the issuing to me of the duplicate certificate, or otherwise howsoever in relation thereto. I

further undertake and agree, if the original certificate shall hereafter be found, forthwith to deliver up the

same or cause the same to be delivered up to the Company, its registrars or their successors and assigns

without cost, fee or reward.

[I make this solemn declaration conscientiously believing the same to be true, and by virtue of the

provisions of the Statutory Declarations Act 1835][1]

Dated this _____ day of _____ year ____

_____

Member's signature

Before me

_____

_____

a solicitor/commissioner for oaths

_____

Note: Depending on the size of the shareholding and the possible future value of the same, some companies may also require a bank
or insurance company to be party to the indemnity.

[1] If the company wishes to require the request to have the force of a statutory declaration, the wording in square brackets should be
added and the signature should be witnessed by a solicitor or commissioner for oaths.

Resignation

Form E59

Date _____

Ref _____

To _____

_____

_____

Dear _____

This is to inform you that I hereby tender my resignation from the Company with effect from

_____.

Please acknowledge receipt and acceptance of this resignation by signing below and returning to me a copy of this letter.

Yours sincerely

Name _____

Address _____

_____

_____

The foregoing resignation is hereby accepted and is effective as of this _____ day of _____

_____ year _____.

Name _____

Company _____

Resignation

Form E59

Note: Resignation without giving the required contractual or statutory minimum notice may have legal consequences.

Resignation of Director Relinquishing All Claims

Form B30

Date _____

To: Board of Directors

_____ Limited

Dear Sirs

I hereby resign my office of director of the company with immediate effect and confirm that I have no outstanding claims whatsoever against the company.

Yours faithfully

_____

Note: If the Director is receiving a payment or other consideration for loss of office, there are requirements for the members to be informed and for their approval to be obtained and these must be observed, even if the resignation takes this form.

Response to Employee's Complaint | Form E60

Date   _____

Ref   _____

To   _____

_____

_____

Dear   _____

We acknowledge receipt of your letter dated _____ regarding your complaint about:

_____

_____

_____

_____

As you are aware, the company follows a standard complaints procedure in these circumstances. I should be grateful if you would complete the attached form and return it to the Personnel Manager as quickly as possible so that we may follow that procedure. An investigation will then be made into the matter.

Yours sincerely

_____

Restaurant Food Poisoning Claim Form GS27

Date _____

To _____
_____
_____

Ref _____

Dear _____

On _____my party of _____ came to have _____ at your restaurant. Shortly afterwards _____ members of the group came down with food poisoning. The effects on the members of my immediate family were as follows:

Name	Time of first onset of symptoms	Description of Symptoms	Duration of symptoms, time off school or work

My GP has concluded that our illnesses were directly caused by the consumption of food served at your restaurant. As I am sure you are aware, your conduct in selling food which is damaging to health renders you civilly liable for breach of contract and negligence, as well as criminally liable under the Food Safety Act 1990 Section 8. I therefore hold you responsible to compensate each of us for the suffering we have endured, time off work and other expenses. The figure I have arrived at as reasonable compensation for each of us is £_____ being made up as follows:

Name	Amount

I look forward to receiving your payment.

Yours sincerely

_____
Name _____
Address _____
Tel. _____

Note: If the symptoms are severe or if all of the members of your party have not yet fully recovered, or if the financial loss is substantial, you should consult a solicitor before sending this letter. You should also consider reporting the matter to the health department of the local authority where the restaurant is located in order to ensure that the evidence is recorded and that repetitions are prevented.

Restaurant Food Quality Complaint ⟶ Form BS58

Date _____

To _____
_____
_____

Ref _____

Dear _____

We came for _____ at your restaurant on _____. I was disappointed to find that upon tasting the _____ that had been ordered it was not satisfactory for the following reason: _____.

I expressed my disappointment immediately and requested that the price of the dish be deducted from the bill. But upon receiving the bill for £_____ I discovered nothing had been done to adjust for the uneaten dish. I was given no alternative but to pay the bill in full, which I did under protest, making it clear that I would seek proper compensation from your establishment at a later date.

[You will be aware that the Food Safety Act 1990 makes it a criminal offence to supply food which is not of the 'nature, substance or quality demanded'. As the dish you served [was contaminated]/[did not contain the ingredients which it was described as containing][1] you are liable for a breach of that Act.]

Furthermore, because the purpose of a meal in a restaurant is to obtain enjoyment and because the quality of the dish referred to above was such that no reasonable person could have been expected to consume it, I am entitled to compensation on behalf of myself and the members of the party who accompanied me]/ [to receive compensation for the annoyance and disappointment which you have caused, in addition to a refund for the dish itself.

I shall expect to receive a cheque for £_____ within 10 days. Otherwise, I shall have no alternative but to issue you a county court claim for recovery of the amount owed to me without further notice.

Yours sincerely

_____

Name _____
Address _____
Tel. _____

---

[1] Do not include the words in square brackets unless the food was uncooked to an extent which was dangerous or unless it was contaminated or did not contain the ingredients which it was said to contain. If there has been such an offence, you should also consider informing the local authority where the restaurant is located. On the other hand, merely serving badly-prepared food is not a criminal offence in itself, although it can give rise to civil liability for breach of contract, as the following letter states.

Restaurant Lost Reservation Claim   Form GS28

Date   _____

To   _____

_____

_____

Ref   _____

Dear   _____

On _____ I called your restaurant and made a reservation for _____ at _____ [am] / [pm] for ___ people on_____. [In order to secure the booking I was requested to supply, and did supply, my credit card details.]

Upon our prompt arrival at your restaurant I was told that no booking existed in my name. I was forced to improvise other arrangements which caused me considerable embarrassment and disappointment.

Your failure to keep the reservation I had made constitutes your breach of contract and I am entitled to compensation from you as a result. Considering the travel expenses incurred in getting to your restaurant and the inconvenience suffered I consider £_____ to be a reasonable sum.

Failure to pay me compensation within 10 days shall result in a claim being issued against you in your local small claims court for recovery of the money.

Yours sincerely

_____

Name _____

Address _____

Tel. _____

Revocation of Power of Attorney   Form PF18

THIS DEED OF REVOCATION is made on the _____ day of _____, year____

by me _____ of _____

WITNESSES as follows:

1.   I revoke the instrument dated _____, year___ (the 'Instrument') in which I appointed

     _____ of _____

     to be my attorney for the purpose of the [Power of Attorney Act 1971 (Section 10)] / [the Enduring

     Powers of Attorney Act 1985 (Section 2)] / [the Mental Capacity Act 2005 (Section 9)].

2.   I declare that all power and authority conferred by the Instrument is now revoked and withdrawn by me.

3.   I verify everything done by my attorney under the Instrument.

4.   This deed of resolution is a deed and has been executed by me as a deed.

IN WITNESS OF WHICH the said _____ has executed this deed the day

and year first above written.

_____

Signature

_____

Signed by Witness

Name _____

Address _____

_____

_____

Occupation_____

Important Note:

Although you can always claim against an agent who misuses his powers under a power of attorney, you can only make a claim based solely on the agent using the power of attorney after revocation, if you have informed him of the revocation.

If your agent has been dealing with people on your behalf, and if they know that he has been acting under a power of attorney, those other people will be entitled to hold you to anything done on your behalf by the agent, until they know about the revocation. Therefore, once you have revoked the power of attorney you must be sure to inform anyone with whom your agent has been dealing on your behalf that the power has been revoked. You must also demand that the agent return the power of attorney to you. If he does not do so, you must immediately see a solicitor in order to get an order compelling him to return it and to forbid him from acting upon it.

Sale Agreement of Moveable Property Subject to Debt   Form BS59

THIS AGREEMENT is made the _____ day of _____ year_____

BETWEEN:

(1)_____(the 'Buyer'); and

(2) _____ (the 'Seller').

NOW IT IS HEREBY AGREED as follows:

1.   In consideration of the sum of £ _____, receipt of which the Seller hereby acknowledges, the Seller hereby transfers and sells the following property to the Buyer (the 'Property'):

_____

_____

_____

2.   The Seller warrants that he/she owns the Property and that he/she has the authority to sell the Property to the Buyer. The Seller also states that the Property is sold subject to the following debt, but that it is otherwise free from encumbrances:

_____

_____

_____

3.   The Buyer and the Seller agree that in respect of the debt they shall apply to the creditor for the substitution of the Buyer in place of the Seller and that they shall execute any instrument which may be necessary to achieve such substitution. Until such substitution is achieved, the Buyer warrants that he/she will pay all instalments due under the debt and that he/she will indemnify and hold the Seller harmless from any claim arising from any failure by the Buyer to pay off this debt.

4.   The Seller also warrants that the Property is in good working condition and otherwise of satisfactory quality as of this date.

IN WITNESS OF WHICH the parties have signed this agreement the day and year first above written

_____   _____

Signed by or on behalf of the Buyer   Signed by or on behalf of the Seller

_____   _____

in the presence of (witness)   in the presence of (witness)

Name _____   Name _____

Address _____   Address _____

_____   _____

Occupation _____   Occupation _____

Note: This agreement should be used for moveable property and not for land or buildings. Because of the legal complexities involved, you should consult a solicitor in relation to land or buildings. You should also be careful not to use this agreement for property which is subject to a hire-purchase agreement, because a sale of such property without the hire purchase company's prior consent will usually entitle the hire purchase company to bring the agreement to an end and repossess the property. Before parting with money, the Buyer should ask the creditor to confirm the amount of the debt and the permission which has been given for the property to be sold subject to the debt.

Sales Representative Agreement Form E61

THIS AGREEMENT is made the _____ day of _____ year____

BETWEEN:

(1) _____ of _____ (the 'Principal'); and

(2) _____ of _____ (the 'Representative').

PARTICULARS

This appointment commences on the _____ day of _____ year____ [for a period of ____ years]

Sales Territory:_____ [in which the Representative

shall have the exclusive right to represent the Principal in respect of the Products below-mentioned.]

Products/Services: _____

Commission Rates:

(a)   (subject to (c) below), _____ per cent of the price charged to the customer on all prepaid sales, net of

freight, insurance and duties;

(b)   (subject to (c) below), _____ per cent of the price charged to the customer on all credit sales, net of

freight, insurance and duties;

(c)   a commission percentage to be negotiated between the Principal and the Representative in advance

of sale on all orders on which the Principal allows a quantity discount or other trade concession.

Run Off Period: _____ months from the termination of this Agreement.

[Target: A gross turnover of sale of £_____ a month]

NOW IT IS HEREBY AGREED as follows:

1.   The Representative hereby agrees:

1.1   To act in good faith towards the Principal.

1.2   To represent and sell the Principal's Products/Services in the Sales Territory.

1.3   To represent and state accurately the Principal's policies and terms of trading to all potential

and present customers and to make or give no other representations or warranties other

than those contained in any standard terms of trading of the Principal.

1.4   To notify promptly to the Principal all contacts and orders within the Sales Territory, and all

enquiries and leads from outside the Sales Territory, to the Principal.

1.5   Not to solicit orders outside the Sales Territory.

1.6   To inform the Principal or the Principal's sales manager of any problems concerning

customers of the Principal within the Sales Territory.

1.7   During the period of this Agreement to inform the Principal or the Principal's sales manager

if the Representative is representing, or plans to represent, any other trader within the Sales

Continued on next page

Sales Representative Agreement (continued)   Form E61

Territory. In no event shall the Representative be involved directly or indirectly with a competing company or product line within the Sales Territory.

1.8   During the period of this Agreement in no event shall the Representative directly or indirectly sell or solicit orders on behalf of any person other than the Principal in respect of any product which competes with those of the Principal's Products that are the subject of this Agreement.

1.9   For a period of [2 years] after the termination of this Agreement, in no event shall the Representative directly or indirectly sell or solicit orders within the Sales Territory for any product which competes with those of the Principal's Products that are the subject of this Agreement.

1.10   To achieve the Target.

1.11   To provide the Principal upon request with sales reports detailing sales progress within the Sales Territory.

1.12   To return promptly at its expense all materials and samples provided by the Principal to the Representative after the termination of this Agreement.

1.13   Not to pledge the credit of the Principal.

1.14   To indemnify the Principal against any and all loss suffered by the Principal resulting from any breach of this Agreement by the Representative.

2. The Principal agrees:.

2.1   Not later than the last day of the month following the quarter in which the Principal receives payment in respect of a sale made [as a result of or mainly attributable to the actions or efforts of the Representative] [to any customer within the Territory]', to provide the Representative with a statement of commission due, and to pay commission to the Representative at the appropriate Commission Rate for that sale. The Principal shall, upon request, allow the Representative any records which the Representative may reasonably require in order to enable him/her to check the accuracy of the statement of commission.

2.2   All sales concluded after the termination of the Agreement but prior to the end of the Run-Off Period which are a result of, or attributable to, the actions or efforts of the Representative during the period of this Agreement shall attract commission at the appropriate Commission Rate and shall be apportioned, as the Principal shall consider to be reasonable, between the Representative and any person who may be appointed to the Sales Territory in replacement of the Representative

2.3.   To provide the Representative with reasonable quantities of business cards, brochures, catalogues, and product samples required for sales purposes.

2.4.   To provide to the Representative details of any enquiries or leads which it may receive from outside the Sales Territory in respect of those of its products which are subject to this Agreement.

Continued on next page

Sales Representative Agreement (continued) Form E61

3. It is further agreed that:

3.1 Should refunds be made to any customer of the Principal, a proportion of the commission already paid to the Representative on that transaction, commensurate with the sums refunded, shall be deducted from future commissions to be paid to the Representative by the Principal provided that the refund to the customer shall not have been made necessary through the fault of the Principal.

3.2 Either Party may terminate this Agreement by giving written notice to the other Party. If the Agreement has run for one year or less when notice is served, one month's notice must be given. If it has run for between one and two years, two months' notice must be given. Otherwise, three months' notice must be given unless one Party has committed a material breach of the terms of this Agreement in which case the other can terminate without notice.

3.3 Upon termination of the Agreement the Representative shall have the right to be indemnified as provided in the Commercial Agents (Council Directive) Regulations 1993, but the Representative shall have no right to compensation under those Regulations[2].

3.4 This constitutes the entire Agreement between the Parties. Any amendments to this Agreement shall only be valid if both parties confirm such amendments in writing.

3.5 This Agreement shall be binding upon the Parties and their successors and assigns.

3.6 The Parties are not partners or joint venturers, nor is the Representative an employee of the Principal, nor is the Representative able to act as the agent of the Principal except as authorised by this Agreement. Further, the Representative shall not enter into any contract with any customer on the Principal's behalf [without the Principal's prior authority].

3.7 This Agreement is governed by and shall be construed in accordance with English law.

IN WITNESS OF WHICH the Parties have signed this Agreement the day and year above written

_____   _____

Signed by the Representative   Signed for and on behalf of the Principal

[1] Choose this if the Representative has the exclusive right to represent the Principal within the Territory.

[2] The Regulations permit the parties to choose between the Representative having the right to an 'indemnity' or to 'compensation' on termination of the Agreement. If neither is specified, the Representative is entitled to compensation. The two remedies can lead to different results. You should take advice from a solicitor as to which is the more appropriate in your case.

Samples and Documents Receipt   Form E62

_____ Ltd

I, _____, employed in the position

of _____, confirm that I have received from the

company the following samples:

No. Rec'd	Serial No.	Description	Value Each	Total Value
_____	_____	_____	_____	_____
_____	_____	_____	_____	_____
_____	_____	_____	_____	_____
_____	_____	_____	_____	_____
_____	_____	_____	_____	_____
_____	_____	_____	_____	_____

In addition I confirm that I have received the following documents:

_____

_____

_____

_____

_____

_____

I accept responsibility to safeguard these materials, to prevent the disclosure of confidential material otherwise than as may be necessary in discharge of my duties as an employee and to return these (except those authorised for and delivered to customers) to the company on demand and, in any event, upon termination of employment

_____

Employee

_____

Date

Second Notice of Overdue Account   Form CDC40

Date _____

Ref _____

To _____

_____

_____

Dear _____

Payment of your account is now unacceptably overdue. Your account balance currently stands as follows.

PAST DUE DATE

Over 30 days   £_____

Over 60 days   £_____

Over 90 days   £_____

Total   £_____

May we please now have your immediate payment without further delay.

[Under the terms of our conditions of trading, interest is payable at the rate of _____ per cent per annum][1]

[Under the Late Payment of Commercial Debts (Interest) Act 1998 statutory interest is payable.][1]

Yours sincerely

_____

[1] Add this in non-consumer credit sales.

Second Warning For Lateness   Form E63

Date _____

To _____
_____
_____

Dear _____

Further to our meeting, I write to confirm the outcome of our discussion about your bad time-keeping, for which you have already been warned on _____.

Despite these verbal and written warnings, you continue to be late for work, in breach of your employment terms. Your hours of work are stated in the Statement of Terms and Conditions of Employment previously given to you. A further copy of the terms and conditions is enclosed.

Since you have ignored the previous warnings, I have no alternative but to issue this second formal warning. If you fail to improve your time-keeping, we may have no option but to consider your dismissal.

This second written warning is being recorded on your personnel file. If you wish to exercise your right of appeal against this warning, please notify me in writing within ____ working days.

Yours sincerely

_____

Security Agreement   Form LB11

THIS DEED IS MADE the _____ day of _____ year _____

BETWEEN:

(1) _____ of _____ (the 'Debtor'); and

(2) _____ of _____ (the 'Secured Party').

WHEREAS:

(A)   The Debtor is indebted to the Secured Party in the Sum of £ _____ (the 'Debt').

(B)   The Secured Party wishes to obtain from the Debtor security for the Debt.

NOW THIS DEED WITNESSES as follows:

1.   The Debtor hereby undertakes to repay all indebtedness and to discharge all obligations which it may owe to the Secured Party whether now or hereafter. WIthout prejudice to the generality of the foregoing, these indebtednesses and obligations include the following:

   _____

   _____

2.   The Debtor grants to Secured Party of and its successors and assigns a fixed charge over the following property (the 'Security'), which shall include all after-acquired property of a like nature and description and proceeds of sale thereof:

   _____

   _____

[3.   The Debtor hereby acknowledges to the Secured Party that the Security shall be kept at the Debtor's above address and not moved or relocated without written consent.]/[The Debtor shall not move the Security from the Debtor's above address without informing the Secured Party in advance.

4.   The Debtor warrants that the Debtor owns the Security and that it is free from any other lien, charge, encumbrance or other adverse interest and the Debtor has full power to grant this charge.

5.   The Debtor will keep the Security in good repair, and take all reasonable care to protect it from damage, and will not act in any way so as to prejudice or invalidate any warranty or insurance policy in respect of the Security. The Debtor further will preserve all documents of title and all maintenance records, and will provide copies of the same to the Secured Party forthwith upon demand.

6.   The Debtor will not assign or charge the Security. Should any lien attach to the Security, the Debtor will forthwith procure the discharge of the same. The Debtor will pay any charges or licence fees which may be imposed by any statutory body in respect of the Security.

7.   If the Security should become subject to any incumbrance, the Debtor shall forthwith inform the Secured Party of the same.

8.   The Debtor agrees to execute such assignments, assents or other documents as may reasonably be required by the Secured Party to perfect this Charge.

9.   Upon default in payment or performance of any obligation for which this security interest is granted, or upon breach of any term of this security agreement, or upon the presentation of a petition for the winding up of the Debtor, or upon the appointment of a Receiver or Administrator in respect of the

Continued on next page

Security Agreement (continued) Form LB11

Debtor or if the Secured Party's surveyor shall decide that there has been any material decrease in the value of the Security then in any such instance the Secured Party may declare all obligations immediately due and payable.

10. Upon the occurrence of any of the events in clause 8 hereof, the Secured Party's rights to enforce this Agreement under section 101 of the Law of Property Act 1925 shall become exercisable. The restrictions upon the exercise of that power contained in section 103 of the said Act shall not apply.

11 The Debtor agrees to to insure the Security against fire, theft, flood, storms, malicious damage and any other risks that the Secured Party, and upon request by the Secured Party forthwith to provide copies of all policies and receipts for premiums. The Secured Party shall be named the beneficiary of any insurance policy taken out for such purpose.

12. Upon default the Debtor shall indemnify the Secured Party for all solicitors' and other fees and costs incurred in the enforcement of this Agreement.

13. Nothing in this Agreement is intended to confer any benefit on a third party whether under the Contracts (Rights of Third Parties) Act or otherwise.

IN WITNESS WHEREOF the parties have signed this deed the day and year first above written.

_____   _____

Signed by or on behalf of the Debtor   Signed by or on behalf of the Secured Party

_____   _____

in the presence of (witness)   in the presence of (witness)

Name _____   Name _____

Address _____   Address _____

_____   _____

Occupation _____   Occupation _____

Important:

Use this form only if the Debtor is a company, rather than an individual. If the Debtor is an individual, a security over 'personal chattels' by which is meant most physical objects not attached to land, will be void unless (1) it is in the form prescribed by the Schedule to the Bills of Sale (1878) Amendment Act 1882; (2) it secures only the types of obligation permitted by the Bills of Exchange Acts; (3) it contains nothing which is inconsistent with the statutory form; (4) it is executed exactly as the Acts prescribe; and (5) it is registered within seven days by the Registry at the High Court having responsibility for bills of sale. In addition, you will have to comply with the formalities prescribed by the Consumer Credit Act 1974. In other words, do not attempt to take security from individuals without obtaining professional advice.

Make certain to register this Agreement at Companies House under Sections 395 – 396 of the Companies Act 1985, as otherwise the Agreement will be void against a liquidator of the Company.

This form is not appropriate for use in respect of the debtor's stock in trade or other items which the debtor is to be free to dispose of and replace from time to time. A security to cover such items must be in the form of a floating charge which is not including in this book.

Settlement Statement

Form CDC41

NOTE: This statement complies with the Consumer Credit (Settlement Information) Regulations 1983 (S.I. 1983 No. 1564).

To _____

_____

_____

_____

(Name and address of customer)

From: _____

_____

_____

_____

(Name and address of creditor)

This statement is given in respect of an agreement dated _____ which was made

between you and _____ in respect of the hire purchase

(credit sale) of _____ _____ and

has the reference number _____.

Settlement date _____ calculated in accordance with regulation 3 of the Consumer

Credit (Settlement Information) Regulations 1983.

Amount required to settle the agreement early without any rebate due: £ _____

[Note: Include one of the three alternatives below as appropriate; NB: if the customer is entitled to a rebate, the rebate must be the higher of (a) the customer's entitlement under the agreement, (b) the customer's entitlement under section 95 of the Consumer Credit Act 1974]* *Delete this note before sending*

The customer is not entitled to any rebate for settlement of the outstanding amount before the settlement date.

Rebate calculation made in regard to the Consumer Credit (Rebate on Early Settlement) Regulations 1983.

Rebate made in accordance with the agreement.

[Include the following if a rebate is due]

Amount due under agreement	£ _____
Less: rebate	_____
Amount required to settle:	£ _____

(General information about the operation of the Consumer Credit Act and Regulations made under it is made available by the Office of Fair Trading, www.oft.gov.uk, and advice may be obtained by contacting the local Trading Standards Department or nearest Citizens' Advice Bureau).

Note: Although we have included this form we repeat our suggestion that if you engage in transactions which are regulated by the Consumer Credit Act 1974 in the course of your business you should ask your solicitor to review your contractual forms and procedures.

Share Certificate Form B32

Certificate No. _____

Number of Shares _____

_____ LIMITED

This is to Certify that

of _____

is/are the Registered holder(s) of _____ [ordinary][1] _____ shares of £ _____ each [fully] _____ paid[2]

in the above-named Company, subject to the Memorandum and Articles of Association of the Company.

Delete one of the following two sentences.

This document is hereby executed by the company.

The Common Seal of the Company was hereto affixed in the presence of:

_____ Directors

_____ Secretary _____ year _____

[1] If the shares are not ordinary shares, substitute 'preference' or such other class of share as may be.

[2] In the unlikely event that the shares are not fully paid up, state the amount by which they have been paid up and record the share numbers, as well as the certificate number.

Share Subscription/Application　　　　　　　　　　　　　　Form B33

I/We offer to acquire _____ ordinary shares of_____

_____ (company) at the offer price of £_____ per share.

I/We attach a cheque or bankers draft for the amount of £_____.

I/We agree to take such shares subject to the Memorandum and Articles of Association of the Company and to be registered on the register of members.

Applicant's name　　　　_____

Applicant's full address　_____

　　　　　　　　　　　　_____

　　　　　　　　　　　　_____

Applicant's signature　　_____

Additional joint applicants:

Second Applicant's name　_____

Address　　_____

　　　　　　_____

　　　　　　_____

Signature　_____

Third Applicant's name　_____

Address　　_____

　　　　　　_____

　　　　　　_____

Signature　_____

Solicitor's Charges: Detailed Account Request   Form GS33

Date _____

To _____

_____

_____

Ref _____

Dear _____

I am in receipt of your bill dated _____ for the work on _____ but am unclear about the fees I have been charged.

To clarify the matter, please send me a detailed, itemised breakdown of the account of charges for the services you have performed, as I am legally entitled to under Section 64 of the Solicitors Act 1974. If you intend to charge me for this please let me know before proceeding.

I look forward to hearing from you shortly.

Yours sincerely

_____

Name _____
Address _____

_____
Tel. _____

Note: If the client is dissatisfied with the detailed bill, a solicitor's bill can be assessed by the court under the Solicitors Act 1974 Section 70. However, there are time limits for making an application. In particular, the court is entitled to impose conditions on the client or refuse to entertain the application altogether if the challenge is made more than one month after the bill has been delivered to the client. The court also has no power to consider the application except in certain special circumstances, if the client has paid the bill (sometimes even if he has paid under protest) and if more than a year has elapsed since the bill was paid. Note also that the client can be made to pay the costs of a court application, just as in any other litigation. You should therefore seek advice before embarking on this course of action.

You should also consider the alternative, set out in the next form, for requiring your solicitor to obtain a remuneration certificate (although it is only available for non-contentious work, such as conveyancing).

Solicitor's Charges: Remuneration Certificate Request   Form GS32

Date _____

To _____

_____

_____

Ref _____

Dear _____

I am in receipt of your letter dated _____ detailing the charges for the services you have provided

up to _____.

I feel these charges are unreasonably high and should be grateful if you would apply for a Remuneration

Certificate from the Law Society on my behalf. As I am sure you are aware I am entitled to such a Certificate

stating what should be a reasonable and fair charge for the work you have done.

Please confirm your acceptance of the above.

Yours sincerely

_____

Name _____

Address _____

_____

Tel. _____

Note: The procedure for obtaining a remuneration certificate is free of charge, but applies only if (a) the bill is for £50,000 or less; (b) it has not yet been paid; (c) no more than a month has elapsed from the solicitor informing the client of the right to obtain a certificate; and (d) the Court has not ordered the bill to be assessed. The procedure is as follows: the client requests that the solicitor obtain a certificate, the solicitor obtains a form from the Law Society's Consumer Complaints Service, the solicitor forwards the form to the client and the client fills it in and returns it to the solicitor who will in turn send it along with his file to the Remuneration Department of the Law Society. More information is available on the website of the Law Society at www.lawsociety.org.uk.

Special Notice for the Removal of Auditors Form B35

Date _____

Ref _____

To The Directors

_____ Limited

_____

_____

Dear Sirs

I hereby give notice pursuant to sections [379 and 391A of the Companies Act 1985]/[312, 510 and 511 of the Companies Act 2006][1] I hereby give special notice of my intention to propose the following ordinary resolution at a General Meeting of the company, to be held not earlier than 28 days from the date of this notice.

Ordinary Resolution

'That _____ be and are hereby removed from office as auditors of the company and that _____ be appointed as auditors of the company in their place to hold office until the conclusion of the next General Meeting at which accounts are laid before the company at a remuneration to be fixed by the directors.'[2]

Dated this _____ day of _____ year___.

Yours faithfully

_____

Note: Virtually the same provisions apply if there is a resolution not to reappoint an auditor whose term has expired. This notice must be given by a member and left at the company's registered office at least 28 days before the general meeting. On receipt of this notice the company must send a copy to the auditors. The company must give notice of this resolution to the members when it gives them notice of the meeting (or, if that is not practicable, either by advertisement in a newspaper having an appropriate circulation or in any other mode allowed by the articles, not less than 21 days before the meeting). The Companies Act give the auditor the right to make representations in writing and to the meeting at which the resolution to remove him is to be considered, as well as to have those representations circulated. 'Note that the Companies Acts give the auditor the right to make representations in writing and to the meeting at which the resolution to remove him is to be considered, as well as to have those representations circulated.'

[1] Delete according to whether or not the cited sections of the Companies Act 2006 are in force when you come to use this form. You may consult Companies House as to whether the sections are in force.

[2] Notice of the removal of an auditor must be given to Companies House on Form 391, to be submitted within 14 days of the resolution being passed.

Special Notice for the Removal of a Director — Form B34

_____ LIMITED

The Directors

_____

In accordance with sections [379 and 303(2) of the Companies Act 1985]/[312 and 168 of the Companies Act 2006], I hereby give special notice of my intention to move the following ordinary resolution at a general meeting of the company, to be held not earlier than 28 days from the date of this notice.

ORDINARY RESOLUTION

That _____ be and is hereby removed from office as a director of the company.

Dated

_____

_____

_____

Note: Use the references to the 2006 Act after 1 October 2007. The removal of a director or the appointment of a replacement must be notified to Companies House within 14 days.

Note also that the Companies Acts give the director the right to make representations in writing to the meeting at which the resolution to remove him is to be considered, as well as to have those representations circulated. You may consult Companies House about this.

This notice must be given by a member and left at the company's registered office at least 28 days before the general meeting. On receipt of this notice the company must send a copy to the director concerned. The company must give notice of this resolution to the members when it gives them notice of the meeting (or, if that is not practicable, either by advertisement in a newspaper having an appropriate circulation or in any other mode allowed by the articles, not less than 21days before the meeting). If the directors are not willing to call a meeting they can be compelled to do so under Section 368 of the Companies Act 1985 or 304 of the Companies Act 2006.

Standard Board Minutes   Form B36

_____ LIMITED

MINUTES of a Meeting of the Board of Directors held at _____

_____ on _____ at _____ a.m./p.m.

PRESENT:

_____(in the chair)

_____

_____

_____

_____

IN ATTENDANCE:

_____

_____

_____

_____

The Chairman confirmed that notice of the meeting had been given to all the directors of the Company and that a quorum of the board of directors was present at the meeting.

_____ declared his/their interest(s) in the following proposed transactions of the Company which were to be discussed at the meeting in accordance with Section [317 Companies Act 1985] / [177 of the Companies Act 2006]:

_____.

IT WAS RESOLVED THAT

_____

_____

_____

_____

There being no further business the meeting then ended.

Chairman: _____

Note: Sections 117 of the 2006 Act is in force from 1 October 2007. The company is required by law to keep copies of all board resolutions for 10 years.

Standard Contractual Terms for Sale of Services Online Form BS63
where the customer is a business – services and
price negotiated individually

SALE AGREEMENT
_____ [Limited][1]

Address[2] _____

Contact Details[3] _____

Publicly accessible register (if applicable)[4] _____

Relevant supervisory authority (if applicable)[5] _____

Professional body of which a member (if applicable)[6] _____

VAT Registration Number _____

Terms and Conditions

1. **Parties**: This Agreement is made between _____ Ltd. of _____ ('the Company'), of the one part and the person who is named in the Acceptance Form ('the Customer') of the other part.

2. **Agreement of Price and Formation of Contract:** The Company will submit a quote for acceptance by the Customer. Acceptance by the Customer shall be by way of e-mail ('the Acceptance Form') in such manner as may be prescribed on this internet site from time to time. [No contract will arise between the Customer and the Company, and the Company shall therefore not be under any obligation to undertake any work, until the Company shall have received payment of the price agreed for the work.]

3. **Choice of Law and Jurisdiction**: This contract will be governed by the laws of England. Any disputes of whatever nature arising out of or connected with this contract shall be subject to the exclusive jurisdiction of the English Courts.

4. **The Company's Services:** The Company will

_____[7] In particular

_____

_____

   4.1   The Company will _____[8]

   4.2   The Company will not _____[9]

5. If any work undertaken by the Company shall contain any error or omission caused by the Company, the Company shall correct the same or at its discretion refund to the Customer the sums which the Customer shall have paid in respect of the work in question. In all such cases of such error or omission, whether or not the same be caused by the Company's negligence, the Customer's remedies shall be limited to the correction of the work or to a refund as aforesaid. The Company will not be liable for any consequential loss including but not limited to loss of reputation or business or profits.

6. The Company reserves the right at any time to refuse to do any work which in the Company's opinion:

   •   is unlawful, whether in the United Kingdom or elsewhere;

   •   would involve the publication of offensive or obscene material;

Continued on next page

Standard Contractual Terms for Sale of Services Online   Form BS63
where the customer is a business – services and
price negotiated individually (continued)

- would involve the publication of material which is defamatory;
- would involve a breach of copyright to publish.

If during the course of any work, the Company shall decide to refuse to continue with the same for any of the above reasons, the Company will refund the sums paid by the Customer in respect of the same, less such proportion thereof as in the Company's opinion is appropriate to remunerate the Company for the work undertaken, but (whether or not the Company's refusal to continue the work was justified) the Customer's remedies shall be limited to such refund and the Customer shall not be entitled to damages or other remedy for any consequential loss which it may sustain whether by way of loss or reputation, or loss of business or profits or otherwise.

7. The time taken for performance of the Company's work will be specified in the Company's quote. Unless otherwise stated in the quote, the period will run from the receipt of payment. If the period expires without the work having been completed, the Customer may give to the Company notice by e-mail that the Customer will refuse to accept the work if the same shall not be substantially completed before the expiry of _____ working days. The Customer will be entitled to a refund of all sums paid in respect of the work in question upon the expiry of such notice if the work shall not by then have been substantially completed. The right to serve a notice as aforesaid will affect only the work mentioned in the quote in question. Work done or to be done in pursuance of other quotes will remain unaffected, as will the Company's entitlement to payment therefor. The Customer will not be entitled to any remedy other than a refund in respect of delayed performance or failure to perform, and the Customer shall not be entitled to any remedy for consequential loss, whether for loss of reputation or business or profits or otherwise.

8. The Customer will co-operate with the Company so as to facilitate the Company's performance of its work and will when requested provide such clarifications and instructions as the Company may reasonably require. If the Customer shall fail to provide clarification or instructions requested by the Company, any period for performance referred to in Clause 7 will cease to run until such instructions or clarifications are provided.

9. **Security:** The Company will presume, unless the Company receives an e-mail from the Customer to contrary effect, that information submitted by the Customer is not confidential and that there is no requirement for the encryption of communications between the Customer and the Company in respect of it. If the Customer instructs the Company that any communications are to be encrypted or treated as confidential, the Company will do its best to comply and will arrange encryption with the Customer at no extra charge.

10. **Copyright:** The copyright in the material produced for the Customer shall belong to the Customer, provided however, that the Company shall be entitled to retain a copy of such material for the purposes of enabling it to provide further services to the Customer and also, without the payment of royalties, for the purpose of using the same as precedents to enable it to prepare work for other Customers.

11. **Indemnity:** The Customer warrants that material supplied to the Company does not contain any

Continued on next page

Standard Contractual Terms for Sale of Services Online   Form BS63
where the customer is a business, services and
price negotiated individually (continued)

material which is defamatory, that its publication will not infringe the laws of the United Kingdom or of any country in which the Customer intends to publish or make use of the same and that its publication will not constitute a breach of the rights of any third party. The Customer will indemnify the Company for any claim or loss suffered by the Company arising out of any breach of this warranty.

12.   **Privacy**

12.1   The Company will not disclose any information about the Customer without the Customer's express permission to anyone other than a person whom the Company believes to be authorised by the Customer to receive such information, save where the Company, in its opinion, is obliged to do so by legal process or obligation.

12.2.   The Customer's remedy for any breach of confidentiality or security by the Company, whether occasioned by the Company's negligence or not, shall be limited to a refund of the monies paid for the work in respect of which the information, the subject of the breach, was supplied. The Customer shall not be entitled to damages or other remedy for any consequential loss which it may sustain whether by way of loss or reputation, or loss of business or profits or otherwise.

13.   **Statutory rights**

All restrictions of liability hereinbefore contained shall take effect to the full extent of the laws of England, but they shall not be construed so as to limit the Customer's statutory rights.

Note: This form must on no account be used for the sale of services to consumers (persons who are buying the service otherwise than for the purposes of their business), because the restrictions on liability which this form contains would be likely to infringe the requirements of the Unfair Terms in Consumer Contracts Regulations and the Distance Selling Regulations. Note also that any contract for the sale of services online (whether or not to consumers) will engage the E-Commerce Regulations and will therefore have to contain the information about the company which appears at the beginning of the form.

[1]   Business name.

[2]   Geographic address, not web address.

[3]   Include email address.

[4]   Any publicly accessible register (e.g. companies register) on which you appear (include registration number)

[5]   Authority to which you are subject.

[6]   With which professional body are you registered, what professional rules govern you and where can they be accessed.

[7]   Here provide brief description of the services to be provided.

[8]   Here insert a description of what the company will do.

[9]   Here insert a description of what the company will not do, and what it will rely upon the customer to do.

Summary of Employment Terms   Form E64

Date   _____

To   _____

         _____

         _____

Dear   _____

We are pleased that you have accepted a position with our company, and should like to take this opportunity to summarise your initial terms and conditions of employment.

1.   Commencement date of employment   _____

2.   Position/title _____

3.   Starting salary: _____

4.   Weeks holiday per year: _____

5.   Eligible for holiday starting: _____

6.   Health insurance: _____

     _____

7.   Pension/profit-sharing: _____

     _____

8.   Other benefits: _____

     _____

9.   Other terms/conditions: _____

     _____

If this is not in accordance with your understanding, please let me know immediately. We look forward to you joining us.

Yours sincerely

_____

Supplier Questionnaire   Form BS60

_____ Ltd

We are introducing a supplier rating system to meet the requirements of BS5750/ISO9000. We should be grateful if you would complete this questionnaire and return it to us.

Company name _____   Tel _____

Reg. Number _____   Fax _____

Address _____

_____

Post Code_____

Products/Services Provided_____

1)   Is your firm registered as a firm of assessed capability
     to BS5750/ISO9000?   Yes ☐   No ☐

2)   Does your firm hold any other nationally or internationally
     recognised approvals?   Yes ☐   No ☐

3)   Has your firm been approved by an accredited assessing body?   Yes ☐   No ☐
     Please give your certificate number and expiry date _____
     If you answered Yes to question 1) and 3) please move to question 7).

4)   Does your firm intend to apply for registration to BS5750/ISO9000?   Yes ☐   No ☐
     If Yes please state when you expect this _____

5)   Does your firm have a quality or procedures manual?   Yes ☐   No ☐

6)   Does your firm have a documented system to control the following?
     a) recording of changes to customers orders/contracts   Yes ☐   No ☐
     b) receipt and checking of purchased products/services   Yes ☐   No ☐
     c) identification of products during manufacture, storage & delivery   Yes ☐   No ☐
     d) calibration and maintenance of measuring and testing equipment   Yes ☐   No ☐
     e) inspection of products at each stage of manufacturing process   Yes ☐   No ☐
     f) identification, segregation and disposal of
         non-conforming products   Yes ☐   No ☐
     g) investigating and taking action against the cause of
         non-conforming products   Yes ☐   No ☐
     h) personnel training   Yes ☐   No ☐

Continued on next page

Supplier Questionnaire (continued)   Form BS60

7)   Does your firm implement internal quality audits?   Yes ☐   No ☐

8)   Does your firm provide Certificates of Conformity
     for your products?   Yes ☐   No ☐

9)   Does your firm have a Quality Control Officer or nominated
     quality representative?   Yes ☐   No ☐
     Name _____   Position _____

10) Would your firm object to a representative of our company
     visiting you and reviewing your quality system?   Yes ☐   No ☐

11) Additional supplier comments: _____
     _____
     _____
     _____

Questionnaire completed by

Name _____   Signature _____
Position _____   Date _____

Telecoms Bill Dispute   Form GS35

Date   _____

To   _____

_____

_____

Ref   _____

Dear   _____

I received your bill dated _____ for £_____the above account.

I am questioning the accuracy of the bill as it appears improbably high and not in line with my usage during the period in question. Please review and adjust the bill or, if necessary, test the line metering and security so we can determine its accuracy and settle the matter. In particular:

_____ [1]

I look forward to hearing from you within 14 days with the appropriate adjustment or the result of a technical investigation. Otherwise, I may refer this matter to the Office of Communications.

Yours sincerely

_____

Name _____

Address _____

_____

Tel. _____

Note: you can reach the Office of Communications at www.ofcom.org.uk.

[1] Supply details, for example, 'the usage shown is twice as great as my usage in any of the previous three months' or 'calls to Lithuania are recorded, and I know no one in that country', or as the case may be.

Tenant's Bank Standing Order Mandate   Form RT20

TO   _____   (Tenant's bank
         _____   name & address)

PLEASE PAY   _____   (Landlord's bank
         _____   name & address)
         _____ □□ □□ □□   (& sort code)

TO THE
CREDIT OF   _____   (Landlord's account
         _____   name & account
         number)

THE SUM OF   _____   (Amount in figures
         _____   & words)

COMMENCING   _____   (Date of first payment)

AND THEREAFTER

EVERY   _____   (Due date & frequency
         e.g. '13th monthly')

UNTIL   _____   (Date of last payment, you
         may write 'until further
         notice')

QUOTING THE
REFERENCE   _____   (The address of the
         _____   Property being let)

ACCOUNT NAME
TO BE DEBITED   _____   (Tenant's name)

ACCOUNT No.
TO BE DEBITED   _____   (Tenant's A/C No.)

SIGNED   _____   DATED _____

         _____

         (Tenant(s))

Trading Standards Officer Complaint   Form GS37

Date _____

To The Trading Standards Officer

_____ Local Authority

Dear Sir

I am writing to ask that you investigate _____ which I believe is acting in breach of trading standards for the reason briefly described below:

- Product safety: _____
- Consumer Credit: _____
- Counterfeiting: _____
- Misleading Prices or Promotions: _____
- Weights and Measures: _____
- Vehicle Safety: _____
- Overloaded Vehicles: _____
- False Descriptions: _____
- Under Age Sales: _____
- Estate Agents: _____

I am enclosing any documentary evidence I have to support this accusation. Please let me know if I can be of further help in your investigation. I look forward to hearing from you in due course.

Yours faithfully

_____

Name _____

Address _____

_____

Tel. _____

Unfurnished House/Flat Rental Agreement   Form F302

The PROPERTY   _____

_____

The LANDLORD   _____

of   _____

_____

The TENANT   _____

_____

The GUARANTOR   _____

of   _____

The TERM   _____ weeks/months* beginning on _____

The RENT   £ _____ per week/month* payable in advance on the _____ of each week/month*

The DEPOSIT   £ _____ which will be registered with one of the Government authorised tenancy

deposit schemes ("the Tenancy Deposit Scheme") in accordance with the Tenancy

Deposit Scheme Rules.

DATED   _____

Signed and executed as a Deed by the following parties

Landlord	**Tenant**	**Guarantor***
_____	_____	_____
Landlord(s)' name(s)	_____	_____
	_____	Guarantor's name
	Tenant(s)' name(s)	_____
_____	_____	_____
Landlord(s)' signature(s)	_____	_____
	Tenant(s)' signature(s)	Guarantor's signature

In the presence of:

Witness signature _____   Witness signature _____   Witness signature _____

Full name _____   Full name _____   Full name _____

Address_____   Address_____   Address_____

_____   _____   _____

(*delete as appropriate)

Continued on next page

Unfurnished House/Flat Rental Agreement (continued)   Form F302

THIS TENANCY AGREEMENT comprises the particulars detailed above and the terms and conditions printed overleaf whereby the Property is hereby let by the Landlord and taken by the Tenant for the Term at the Rent.

IMPORTANT NOTICE TO LANDLORDS:

1   The details of 'The LANDLORD' near the top of this Agreement must include an address for the Landlord in England or Wales as well as his/her name, or all names in the case of joint Landlords.

2   Always remember to give the written Notice Requiring Possession to the Tenant at least two clear months before the end of the Term if you want the tenant to vacate.

3   Before granting the tenancy agreement, you should check whether your chosen deposit scheme provider requires you to insert any additional terms concerning the deposit into the tenancy agreement or to alter or delete any of the terms appearing in the form below. Details of the websites of the scheme providers are set out in Note 4 for tenants below. Currently only The Tenancy Deposit Scheme has any such requirements.

IMPORTANT NOTICE TO TENANTS:

1   In general, if you currently occupy Property under a protected or statutory tenancy and you give it up to take a new tenancy of the same or other accommodation owned by the same Landlord, that tenancy cannot be an Assured Shorthold Tenancy and this Agreement is not appropriate.

2   If you currently occupy Property under an Assured Tenancy which is not an Assured Shorthold Tenancy your Landlord is not permitted to grant you an Assured Shorthold Tenancy of that Property or of alternative property and this Agreement is not appropriate.

3   If the total amount of rent exceeds £25,000 per annum, an Assured Shorthold Tenancy cannot be created and this Agreement is not appropriate. Seek legal advice.

4   Further information about the Government authorised Tenancy Deposit Schemes can be obtained from their websites: The Deposit Protection Service at www.depositprotection.com, Tenancy Deposit Solutions Ltd at www.mydeposits.co.uk and The Tenancy Deposit Scheme at www.tds.gb.com.

Terms and Conditions on next page

Unfurnished House/Flat Rental Agreement
Terms and Conditions (continued)

1. This Agreement is intended to create an Assured Shorthold Tenancy as defined in the Housing Act 1988, as amended by the Housing Act 1996, and the provisions for the recovery of possession by the Landlord in that Act apply accordingly. The Tenant understands that the Landlord will be entitled to recover possession of the Property at the end of the Term.

2. **The Tenant's obligations:**

   2.1 To pay the Rent at the times and in the manner set out above.

   2.2 To pay all charges in respect of any electric, gas, water, sewage and telephonic or televisual services used at or supplied to the Property and Council Tax or any property tax that might be charged in addition to or replacement of it during the Term.

   2.3 To keep the interior of the Property in a good and clean state and condition and not damage or injure the Property (fair wear and tear excepted).

   2.4 To yield up the Property at the end of the Term in the same clean state and condition it was in at the beginning of the Term (but the Tenant will not be responsible for fair wear and tear caused during normal use of the Property and the items listed on the Inventory (if any).

   2.5 Not to make any alteration or addition to the Property and not without the prior written consent of the Landlord (consent not to be withheld unreasonably) do any redecoration or painting of the Property.

   2.6 Not do anything on or at the Property which:

   (a) may be or become a nuisance or annoyance to any other occupiers of the Property or owners or occupiers of adjoining or nearby premises

   (b) is illegal or immoral

   (c) may in any way affect the validity of the insurance of the Property and the items listed on the Inventory (if any) or cause an increase in the premium payable by the Landlord

   (d) will cause any blockages in the drainage system and in the case of breach of this clause the Tenant to be responsible for the reasonable cost of such repair or other works which will be reasonably required.

   2.7 Not without the Landlord's prior consent (consent not to be withheld unreasonably) allow or keep any pet or any kind of animal at the Property.

   2.8 Not use or occupy the Property in any way whatsoever other than as a private residence.

   2.9 Not assign, sublet, charge or part with or share possession or occupation of the Property (but see clause 5.1 below).

   2.10 To allow the Landlord or anyone with the Landlord's written permission to enter the Property at reasonable times of the day to inspect its condition and state of repair, carry out any necessary repairs and gas inspections, and during the last month of the Term, show the Property to prospective new tenants, provided the Landlord has given at least 24 hours' prior written notice (except in emergency).

   2.11 To pay the Landlord's reasonable costs reasonably incurred as a result of any breaches by the Tenant of his obligations under this Agreement, and further to pay the Landlord's reasonable costs of responding to any request for a consent which the Tenant may make of the Landlord under this Agreement.

   2.12 To pay interest at the rate of 4% above the Bank of England base rate from time to time prevailing on any rent or other money lawfully due from the Tenant under this Agreement which remains unpaid for more than 14 days, interest to be paid from the date the payment fell due until payment.

   2.13 To provide the Landlord with a forwarding address

when the tenancy comes to an end and to remove all rubbish and all personal items (including the Tenant's own furniture and equipment) from the Property before leaving.

3. **The Landlord's obligations:**

   3.1 The Landlord agrees that the Tenant may live in the Property without unreasonable interruption from the Landlord or any person rightfully claiming under or in trust for the Landlord.

   3.2 To insure the Property and items listed on the Inventory (if any) and use all reasonable efforts to arrange for any damage caused by an insured risk to be remedied as soon as possible and to provide a copy of the insurance policy to the Tenant if requested.

   3.3 To keep in repair (where provided by the Landlord)

   3.3.1 the structure and exterior of the Property (including drains gutters and external pipes)

   3.3.2 the installations at the Property for the supply of water, sewage, gas and electricity and for sanitation (including basins, sinks, baths and sanitary conveniences)

   3.3.3 the installations at the Property for space heating and heating water

   3.4 But the Landlord will not be required to

   3.4.1 carry out works for which the Tenant is responsible by virtue of his duty to use the Property in a tenant-like manner

   3.4.2 reinstate the Property in the case of damage or destruction if the insurers refuse to pay out the insurance money due to anything the Tenant has done or failed to do

   3.4.3 rebuild or reinstate the Property in the case of destruction or damage of the Property by a risk not covered by the policy of insurance effected by the Landlord.

   3.5 If the property is a flat or maisonette within a larger building then the Landlord will be under similar obligations for the rest of the building but only in so far as any disrepair will affect the Tenant's and in so far as the Landlord is legally entitled to enter the relevant part of the larger building and carry out the required works or repairs.

   3.6 To arrange for the Tenant's Deposit to be protected by an authorised Tenancy Deposit Scheme in accordance with the provisions of the Housing Act 2004 within 14 days of receipt, and to comply with the rules of the Tenancy Deposit Scheme at all times.

4. **Guarantor**

   If there is a Guarantor, he guarantees that the Tenant will keep to his obligations in this Agreement. The Guarantor agrees to pay on demand to the Landlord any money lawfully due to the Landlord by the Tenant.

5. **Ending this Agreement**

   5.1 The Tenant cannot normally end this Agreement before the end of the Term. However after the first three months of the Term, if the Tenant can find a suitable alternative tenant, and provided this alternative tenant is acceptable to the Landlord (the Landlord's approval not to be unreasonably withheld) the Tenant may give notice to end the tenancy on a date at least one month from the date that such approval is given by the Landlord. On the expiry of such notice and upon (i) payment by the Tenant to the Landlord of the reasonable expenses reasonably incurred by the Landlord in granting the necessary approval and in granting any new tenancy to the alternative tenant, and (ii) the execution by the alternative tenant of a new tenancy agreement in the form of this Agreement for a period of 6 months or for a period not less than the unexpired portion of the

Continued on next page

Unfurnished House/Flat Rental Agreement

Terms and Conditions (continued)

term of this Agreement (if that be greater than 6 months), or for such other period as the Landlord shall approve this tenancy shall end

5.2 If the Tenant stays on after the end of the fixed term, a new tenancy will arise that will run from month to month or week to week (a 'periodic tenancy'). This periodic tenancy can be ended by the Tenant giving at least one month's written notice to the Landlord, the notice to expire at the end of the rental period.

5.3 If at any time

5.3.1 any part of the Rent is outstanding for 21 days after becoming due (whether formally demanded or not) and/or

5.3.2 there is any breach, non-observance or non-performance by the Tenant of any covenant and/or other term of this Agreement which has been notified in writing to the Tenant and the Tenant has failed within a reasonable period of time to remedy the breach and/or pay reasonable compensation to the Landlord for the breach and/or

5.3.3 any of the grounds set out as Grounds 2, 8 or Grounds 10-15 (inclusive) (which relate to breach of any obligation by a Tenant) contained in the Housing Act 1988 Schedule 2 apply

the Landlord may recover possession of the Property and this Agreement shall come to an end. The Landlord retains all his other rights in respect of the Tenant's obligations under this Agreement. Note that if possession of the Property has not been surrendered and anyone is living at the Property or if the tenancy is an Assured or Assured Shorthold Tenancy then the landlord must obtain a court order for possession before re-entering the Property. This clause does not affect the Tenant's rights under the Protection from Eviction Act 1977.

6. The Deposit

6.1 The Deposit will be held in accordance with the Tenancy Deposit Scheme Rules as issued by the relevant Tenancy Deposit Scheme.

6.2. No interest will be payable to the Tenant by the Landlord in respect of the Deposit save as provided by the Rules of the relevant Tenancy Deposit Scheme.

6.3. Subject to any relevant provisions of the Rules of the relevant Tenancy Deposit Scheme, the Landlord shall be entitled to claim from the Deposit the reasonable cost of any repairs or damage to the Property or its contents caused by the Tenant (including any damage caused by the Tenant's family and visitors) any rent in arrears and for any other financial losses suffered or expenditure incurred by the Landlord as a result of the Tenant's breach of these terms and conditions, provided the sum claimed by the Landlord is reasonably incurred and is reasonable in amount. The Landlord is not entitled to claim in respect of any damage to the Property or its contents which is due to 'fair wear and tear' i.e. which is as a result of the Tenant and his family (if any) living in the property and using it in a reasonable and lawful manner.

7. Other provisions

7.1 The Landlord hereby notifies the Tenant under Section 48 of the Landlord & Tenant Act 1987 that any notices (including notices in proceedings) should be served upon the Landlord at the address stated with the name of the Landlord overleaf.

7.2 The Landlord shall be entitled to have and retain keys for all the doors to the Property but shall not be entitled to use these to enter the Property without the consent of the Tenant (save in an emergency) or as otherwise provided in this Agreement.

7.3 Any notices or other documents (including any court claim forms in legal proceedings) shall be deemed served on the Tenant during the tenancy by either being left at the Property or by being sent to the Tenant at the Property by first-class post. Notices shall be deemed served the day after being left at the property or the day after posting.

7.4 Any person other than the Tenant who pays the rent due hereunder or any part thereof to the Landlord shall be deemed to have made such payment as agent for and on behalf of the Tenant which the Landlord shall be entitled to assume without enquiry.

7.5 Any personal items left behind at the end of the tenancy after the Tenant has vacated (which the Tenant has not removed in accordance with clause 2.13 above) shall be considered abandoned if they have not been removed within 14 days of written notice to the Tenant from the Landlord, or if the Landlord has been unable to trace the Tenant by taking reasonable steps to do so. After this period the Landlord may remove or dispose of the items as he thinks fit. The Tenant shall be liable for the reasonable disposal costs which may be deducted from the proceeds of sale (if any), and the Tenant shall remain liable for any balance. Any net proceeds of the sale to be returned to the Tenant at the forwarding address provided to the Landlord.

7.6 In the event of destruction to the Property or of damage to it which shall make the same or a substantial portion of the same uninhabitable, the Tenant shall be relieved from paying the rent by an amount proportional to the extent to which the Tenant's ability to live in the Property is thereby prevented, save where the destruction or damage has been caused by any act or default by the Tenant or where the Landlord's insurance cover has been adversely affected by any act or omission on the part of the Tenant.

7.7 Where the context so admits:

7.7.1 The 'Landlord' includes the persons from time to time entitled to receive the Rent.

7.7.2 The 'Tenant' includes any persons deriving title under the Tenant.

7.7.3 The 'Property' includes any part or parts of the Property and all of the Landlord's fixtures and fittings at or upon the Property.

7.7.4 All references to the singular shall include the plural and vice versa and any obligations or liabilities of more than one person shall be joint and several (this means that they will each be liable for all sums due under this Agreement, not just liable for a proportionate part) and an obligation on the part of a party shall include an obligation not to allow or permit the breach of that obligation.

7.7.5 All references to 'he', 'him' and 'his' shall be taken to include 'she', 'her' and 'hers'.

Unsolicited Idea Acknowledgement   Form B37

Date   _____

Ref   _____

To   _____

_____

_____

Dear   _____

We appreciate your interest in submitting material for our consideration. Because of complications which may arise if we examine such material before any agreement has been reached about the terms on which we conduct such examination, however, it is our practice to return the material without reading or examining it in any way, and to invite the sender, if he or she wishes, to resubmit the material under the cover of a letter (which must be signed by the sender and witnessed by a person not related to the sender) in the following terms:

'Dear   _____,

I would be grateful if you would consider our idea or proposal, the details of which are set out in the material herewith.

In consideration of your reviewing the material, which I have submitted to you unsolicited, I agree to the following terms:

1.   Samples, or written or other material (hereinafter 'material') will be returned only if a stamped addressed envelope is enclosed or carriage is prepaid.

2.   You are not responsible for damage or loss to samples or other submitted material no matter how such loss or damage may occur and whether or not such loss or damage has resulted from your negligence.

3.   You are not obliged to keep confidential any of the material. Without prejudice to the foregoing, you are expressly authorised to copy, lend or reveal the contents of the material to any person or body to whom you may in your absolute discretion consider it desirable to reveal, lend or copy the same for the purpose of facilitating the eventual exploitation of the material. For the avoidance of doubt, you will not in any way be liable for any use which such third party may make of the material without your authority.

Continued on next page

Unsolicited Idea Acknowledgement (continued)   Form B37

4. You will not be obliged to pay me any consideration or compensation in respect of the material unless you and I enter into a separate agreement in respect of the same, provided that this exclusion shall not apply if (a) you use the material or a substantial part thereof, (b) the material includes information which is not in the public domain, and (c) the material which is not in the public domain contributes significantly to the value of the material. If the proviso shall apply, I shall be entitled to compensation, but such compensation shall be no greater than that which a willing seller of the material might be deemed to receive from a willing buyer, and in particular no aggravated or exemplary damages shall be payable.

5. I warrant that I am the owner of all intellectual or other property rights which may subsist in relation to the material, and that I have full power to grant to you exclusive rights in respect of the same. I warrant further that I am not aware of any possible claim which any other person might make in respect of any ownership or entitlement to exploit such property in the material.

6. For the avoidance of doubt, I confirm that I shall have no claim for any compensation or consideration in respect of any part of the material if such material or information included therein has been submitted to you by any other person.

7. If any provision of this agreement shall be held to be invalid, such invalidity shall not affect any other provision of this agreement.

Yours sincerely

_____

Signature

Witness name, address and occupation

_____

_____

_____

Witness signature

Variation of Contract   Form OLF36

THIS DEED is made the_____ day of _____ year _____

BETWEEN

(1) _____ of _____(the 'First Party');and

(2) _____ of _____(the 'Second Party').

WHEREAS:

(A)   The two parties above have entered into an agreement dated_____ (the 'Agreement')

(B)   The two parties above now wish to vary the terms of the Agreement.

NOW THIS DEED WITNESSES as follows:

1.   The two parties agree that the following additions and amendments to the Agreement shall apply

_____

_____

2.   All other terms and conditions of the Agreement shall remain in full force and effect.

IN WITNESS OF WHICH the parties have executed this deed the day and year first above written

(Individual)   (Company)

                                                Signed for and on behalf of

_____   _____ Ltd

Signed by the First Party

_____   _____

in the presence of (witness)   Director

Name _____

Address _____   Director/Secretary

_____

Occupation _____

_____   Signed for and on behalf of:

Signed by the Second Party   _____Ltd

_____

in the presence of (witness)   _____

Name _____   Director

Address _____

_____   Director/Secretary

Occupation _____

Variation of Employment Agreement   Form E65

Date _____

Ref _____

To _____
_____
_____

Dear _____

This letter is to inform you that the terms or conditions of your contract have been amended as set out below. Please acknowledge receipt of this letter and your agreement to the terms set out in it by signing the attached copy and returning it to me. You should retain the top copy with your contract of employment.

Please contact me should you wish to discuss any of the changes or require any further information.

Date changes effective: _____

Details of changes are as follows: _____
_____
_____

Yours sincerely

_____

For the Company

I,_____, acknowledge that I have received a statement of alteration to the particulars of my employment, as required by the Employment Rights Act 1996 Section 1, and agree to the terms set out in that agreement.

_____

Signed

_____

Dated

Waiver of Liability and Assumption of Risk   Form OLF37

I, the undersigned, _____ (the 'Customer'), voluntarily make and grant this Waiver of Liability and Assumption of Risk in favour of _____ _____ (the 'Seller') as partial consideration (in addition to monies paid to the Seller) for the opportunity to use the facilities, equipment, materials and/or other assets of the Seller; and/or to receive assistance, training, guidance and/or instruction from the personnel of the Seller; and/or to engage in the activities, events, sports, festivities and/or gatherings sponsored by the Seller; I hereby waive and release any and all claims whether in contract or tort, for any loss or damage that may arise from my aforementioned use or receipt, save for death or personal injury which may be occasioned by your negligence.

I understand and recognise that there are certain risks, dangers and perils connected with such use and/or receipt, which I hereby acknowledge to have been fully explained to me and which I fully understand, and which I nevertheless accept as being acceptable to me. I further agree to use my best judgment in undertaking these activities, and to adhere strictly to all safety instructions and recommendations, which may be communicated to me whether oral or written. I hereby certify that I am a competent adult assuming these risks of my own free will, being under no compulsion or duress.

The facilities, equipment materials and other assets referred to above include, but are not limited to, the following: _____
_____

The assistance, training, guidance and instruction referred to above include but are not limited to the following _____
_____

I warrant that I have the following experience and agree that the Seller may have reliance upon this warranty in permitting me to use the facilities materials equipment and other assets and in furnishing me the guidance, training and instruction above-mentioned: _____
_____

I warrant that the risks about which I have been advised include but are not limited to _____
_____

I warrant that I do not have any medical condition which enhances any of the risks above referred to.

_____

Customer's signature

Name _____

Address _____

_____

Date _____

Age _____

Warranty Increasing Statutory Rights   Form BS61

1. This warranty is given in addition to your statutory rights and does not affect your statutory rights in any way.

2. We warrant that, in the event that any fault or defect is discovered with the goods within one year of the date of sale, we will, unless the fault or defect has been caused by a misuse of the goods by the purchaser or by the goods being used for a purpose for which they have not been designed, either repair or, at our option, replace the goods free of charge to the purchaser.

Note: These terms can be added, where desired, to any contract for the sale of goods. They can also be displayed in a shop. The wording about statutory rights are intended to make clear that the promises made are for the purpose of adding to statutory protection rather than attempting to restrict it (which is often unlawful). This wording is therefore necessary and should on no account be omitted.

Water Supply Interruption: OFWAT Investigation Request

Form GS39

Date _____

To OFWAT Customer Service Committee

_____

_____

Ref _____

Dear Sirs

This letter is in reference to my complaint with _____ which has still not yet been resolved.

Please refer to the enclosed correspondence relating to this case. I understand I am entitled to [£20 for failure to keep an appointment]/[£20 for failure to respond to a complaint]/[£20 for failure to respond to an account enquiry within 10 working days]/[£20 for failure to tell me in writing at least 48 hours before a planned interruption of water supply][1]/[£20 for failure to restore interrupted supply within the time stated plus £10 for each 24-hour period the supply remains unrestored]/[£20 plus a further £10 for each 24 hour period of unplanned interruption beyond 12 hours (or 48 hours in the case of a 'strategic' water main][2]/[a refund of sewerage charges by reason of flooding from sewers]/[£25 for low pressure lasting more than an hour on two occasions within 28 days]. In addition, the water company is responsible for the damages that occurred as a result of the shut-off.

I should be grateful if you would please look into my claim. It is my understanding that during your investigation my services will not be further interrupted.

Please keep me informed on the status of my case.

Yours faithfully

_____

Name _____

Address _____

_____

Tel. _____

Note: If you have a complaint, you should first take it up with your supplier. If your supplier has not handled your complaint satisfactorily, you should contact the Consumer Council for Water, which can be reached at www.ccwater.org.uk or on 0845 039 2837 or 0121 345 1000. You will be given details for the regional office which you should contact.

[1] £50 in the case of a non-household customer.

[2] In the case of non-household customers £50 for failure to restore on time and £25 for each 24-hour period.

Withheld Delivery Notice   Form BS62

Date   _____

Ref   _____

To   _____

_____

_____

Dear   _____

Reference is made to your order no._____ dated _____.

We are withholding delivery of the goods for the reason(s) ticked:

☐   Overdue balance of £_____ must first be paid.

☐   Required payment of £_____ has not been made.

☐   You previously cancelled the order.

☐   You have not provided us with delivery instructions.

☐   Certain goods are back ordered and delivery will be made in a single lot.

☐   Other:_____

Please respond to this notice so we may fulfil your order without further delay or inconvenience.

Yours sincerely

_____

Withheld Delivery Notice   Form BS62

Note: make certain if you are deliberately withholding delivery that you are not placing yourself in breach of contract.

Working Time Regulations Opt Out Agreement   Form E66

WORKING TIME REGULATIONS 1998 OPT-OUT

1. DEFINITIONS

1.1 In this Agreement the following definitions apply:

'Employee' means _____

'the Employer' means _____

'Working Week' means an average of 48 hours each week over a 17-week period

1.2 Unless the context requires otherwise, references to the singular include the plural and references to the masculine include the feminine and vice versa.

1.3 The headings contained in these Terms are for convenience only and do not affect their interpretation.

2. RESTRICTIONS

2.1 The Working Time Regulations 1998 provide that an Employee shall not work in excess of the Working Week unless he agrees in writing that this limit should not apply.

3. CONSENT

3.1 The Employee hereby agrees that the Working Week limit shall not apply to his contract of employment with the Employer.

4. WITHDRAWAL OF CONSENT

4.1 The Employee may end this Agreement by giving the Employer three months' notice in writing.

4.2 For the avoidance of doubt, any notice bringing this Agreement to an end shall not be construed as termination by the Employee of his contract of employment with the Employer.

4.3 Upon the expiry of the notice period set out in clause 4.1, the Working Week limit shall apply with immediate effect.

5. THE LAW

5.1 These Terms are governed by the law of England & Wales and are subject to the exclusive jurisdiction of the courts of England & Wales.[1]

_____

Signed by the Employee

_____

Date